**Pearson Education**

# Test Prep Series

For

# AP® CHEMISTRY

## MARIAN DeWANE
University of California–Irvine

## THOMAS GREENBOWE
Iowa State University

To accompany:

*CHEMISTRY: A MOLECULAR APPROACH*
THIRD EDITION
AP® EDITION

NIVALDO J. TRO

D1372030

**PEARSON**

Boston  Columbus  Indianapolis  New York  San Francisco  Upper Saddle River
Amsterdam  Cape Town  Dubai  London  Madrid  Milan  Munich  Paris  Montréal  Toronto
Delhi  Mexico City  São Paulo  Sydney  Hong Kong  Seoul  Singapore  Taipei  Tokyo

**Editor in Chief:** Adam Jaworski
**Senior Acquisitions Editor:** Terry Haugen
**Executive Marketing Manager:** Jonathan Cottrell
**Project Editor:** Jessica Moro
**Assistant Editor:** Lisa R. Pierce
**Associate Media Producer:** Jackie Jakob
**Editorial Assistant:** Lisa Tarabokija
**Senior Marketing Assistant:** Nicola Houston
**Managing Editor, Chemistry and Geosciences:** Gina M. Cheselka
**Project Manager, Production:** Wendy Perez
**Full Service/Composition:** PreMediaGlobal
**Full Service Project Manager:** Revathi Viswanathan
**Interior Design:** PreMediaGlobal
**Cover Designer:** Seventeenth Street Studios

**Operations Specialist:** Christy Hall
**Supplement Cover Designer:** Seventeenth Street Studios
**Parent Cover Designer:** Jana Anderson
**Parent Cover Illustration:** Quade Paul
**Parent Cover Image Credit: Nanotube sensor:** A carbon nanotube treated with a capture agent, in yellow, can bind with and delect the purple-colored target protein—this changes the electrical resistance of the nanotube and creates a sensing device.
**Artist:** Ethan Minot, in Nanotube technology leading to fast, lower-cost medical diagnostics, Oregon State University, @ 2012, 01 pp., http://www.flickr.com/photos/oregonstateuniversity/6816133738/

Credits and acknowledgments borrowed from other sources and reproduced, with permission, in this textbook appear on the appropriate page within the text.

6    16

www.Pearson School.com/Advanced

ISBN-10: 0-13-310159-2
ISBN-13: 978-0-13-310159-1

## About the Authors

Marian DeWane taught AP® Chemistry and AP® Environmental Science in Boise, Idaho until 2010. She is currently teaching for the University of California-Irvine. She has won numerous awards for her teaching including the Presidential Award for Science Teaching in 2009. She has been involved as an editor of the AP® Chemistry Special Focus Series for the College Board which included AP® Chemistry Focus: Chemical Equilibrium, AP® Chemistry Special Focus: Thermodynamics, AP® Chemistry Focus: Acids and Bases, and the *AP® Chemistry Guided Inquiry Activities for the Classroom* Curriculum Module. She authored two chapters and a lab in the new *AP® Chemistry Guided-Inquiry Experiments: Applying the Science Practices Laboratory Manual*. She has been a question writer of both the old and new AP® exams and has been involved at the AP® Chemistry Reading as a Reader, Table Leader, and Question Leader. She has worked as a consultant for the College Board giving workshops, institutes, seminars and lectures around the world on AP® Chemistry. She has also presented at ACS and NSTA meetings on the teaching of chemistry.

Thomas J. Greenbowe is a Professor of Chemistry at Iowa State University. He served as Chair of the Division of Chemical Education of the American Chemical Society, Chair of the 18th Biennial Conference on Chemical Education and Chair of the 2009 Gordon Research Conference on Chemical Education Research and Practice. He has served as Chair of the 1993 ACS General Chemistry Exam, Co-Chair of the 2014 ACS General Chemistry Conceptual Exam, and a member of the 2013 ACS Laboratory Practical Exam Committee. He served on the test development committee for AP® Chemistry seven years, and has been involved in the AP® Reading as a Reader, Table Leader, and Question Leader. He is also an AP® Chemistry Consultant. He is the co-editor and co-chapter author of the new AP® Chemistry Curriculum Module *Guided Inquiry Activities for the Classroom* for the College Board. His work with the Science Writing Heuristic and the Process Oriented Guided-Inquiry Learning (POGIL) Projects have contributed to our understanding of effective techniques for implementing guided-inquiry in the chemistry laboratory. For Pearson Education he has worked on a project developing a series of interactive computer simulations and computer visualizations depicting chemical processes at the particulate nature of matter level of representation with John Gelder, Oklahoma State University, and Michael Abraham, University of Oklahoma. A new version of the computer simulations and animations will be available through Pearson Education. Tom Greenbowe has received several teaching awards and most recently was appointed as a Morrill Professor and as a Fellow of the American Chemical Society. He has given presentations at Regional and National ACS meetings, and seminars and workshops around the world about methods of teaching and learning chemistry.

*To my amazing family for their understanding, patience, and acceptance of my nerdiness! To my father Willis who is still going strong at 95, I especially want to thank you for a strong work ethic. To J. Barry, Jean-Paul (J.P.), Jean-Patrick (Pat), Jacqueline-Kristina (Nikki) and husband Eric, and the amazing and energetic Willis and Leo! Your love and support give me the strength to live each day. I love you all!*

Marian DeWane

*Thank you to my family for all their patience and understanding during the time-frame of this project. My wife Lynette, children Ben and his wife Sue, Joel, Meagan, Kaitlyn and husband Eric, and my grandchildren Ephraim, Willem, Atticus, and Theodore who put up with their Dad and Grandfather working on the computer at odd hours and weekends.*

Thomas Greenbowe

# Contents

# The AP® Chemistry Course

**B**eginning with the 2013–2014 school year, the AP® Chemistry curriculum and AP® Chemistry Exam have been redesigned. The focus of teaching and learning is on six big ideas (concepts) and seven science practices. Each big idea is subdivided into essential understandings and points of knowledge. Under these, learning objectives identify what students should be able to know and be able to do to be successful on the exam. Each learning objective (LO) is also tied to one or more science practices. Specific guidelines, suggested pacing guides, and sample syllabi for AP® Chemistry are on the College Board website. The College Board now recommends a minimum of 25% of the AP® Chemistry course should be dedicated to laboratory activities. The AP® Chemistry Exam will include questions assessing students' ability to design a laboratory experiment to answer a research question, to analyze data collected in a laboratory activity, and to explain how errors will influence the results.

## The Six Big Ideas of AP® Chemistry

1. The chemical elements are fundamental building materials of matter, and all matter can be understood in terms of arrangements of atoms. These atoms retain their identity in chemical reactions.

2. Chemical and physical properties of materials can be explained by the structure and the arrangement of atoms, ions, molecules, and the forces between them.

3. Changes in matter involve the rearrangement and/or reorganization of atoms and/or transfer of electrons.

4. Rates of chemical reactions are determined by the details of molecular collisions.

5. The laws of thermodynamics describe the essential role of energy and explain and predict the direction of changes in matter.

6. Any bond or intermolecular attraction that can be formed can be broken. These two processes are in a dynamic competition, sensitive to initial conditions and external perturbations.

## The Seven Science Practices (SP) of AP® Chemistry

**SP1:** The student can use representations and models to communicate scientific phenomena and solve scientific problems.

    1.1 The student can *create representations and models* of natural or man-made phenomena and systems in the domain.

    1.2 The student can *describe representations and models* of natural or man-made phenomena and systems in the domain.

    1.3 The student can *refine representations and models* of natural or man-made phenomena and systems in the domain.

    1.4 The student can *use representations and models* to analyze situations or solve problems qualitatively and quantitatively.

    1.5 The student can *re-express key elements* of natural phenomena across multiple representations in the domain.

**SP 2:** The student can use mathematics appropriately.

    2.1 The student can *justify the selection of a mathematical routine* to solve problems.

    2.2 The student can *apply mathematical routines* to quantities that describe natural phenomena.

    2.3 The student can *estimate numerically* quantities that describe natural phenomena.

**SP 3:** The student can engage in scientific questioning to extend thinking or to guide investigations within the context of the AP course.

    3.1  The student can *pose scientific questions.*

    3.2  The student can *refine scientific questions.*

    3.3  The student can *evaluate scientific questions.*

**SP 4:** The student can plan and implement data collection strategies in relation to a particular scientific question. [Note: Data can be collected from many different sources, e.g., investigations, scientific observations, the findings of others, historic reconstruction, and/or archived data.]

    4.1  The student can *justify the selection of the kind of data* needed to answer a particular scientific question.

    4.2  The student can *design a plan* for collecting data to answer a particular scientific question.

    4.3  The student can *collect data* to answer a particular scientific question.

    4.4  The student can *evaluate sources of data* to answer a particular scientific question.

**SP 5:** The student can perform data analysis and evaluation of evidence.

    5.1  The student can *analyze data* to identify patterns or relationships.

    5.2  The student can *refine observations and measurements* based on data analysis.

    5.3  The student can *evaluate the evidence provided by data sets* in relation to a particular scientific question.

**SP 6:** The student can work with scientific explanations and theories.

    6.1  The student can *justify claims with evidence.*

    6.2  The student can *construct explanations of phenomena based on evidence* produced through scientific practices.

    6.3  The student can *articulate the reasons that scientific explanations and theories are refined or replaced.*

    6.4  The student can *make claims and predictions about natural phenomena* based on scientific theories and models.

    6.5  The student can *evaluate alternative scientific explanations.*

**SP 7:** The student is able to connect and relate knowledge across various scales, concepts, and representations in and across domains.

    7.1  The student can *connect phenomena and models* across spatial and temporal scales.

    7.2  The student can *connect concepts* in and across domain(s) to generalize or extrapolate in and/or across enduring understandings and/or big ideas.

## About this Correlation Guide for AP® Chemistry for Tro's "Chemistry: A Molecular Approach"

The correlation guide at the end of this section will list the Learning Objectives of each Big Idea, the Science Practice it is linked to. Practically, the correlation guide helps you find this information in the Tro textbook.

Core content, vocabulary, and the learning objectives in each chapter are reviewed. The essential content and vocabulary are identified per section as they correspond to the chapter. Misconceptions students have indicated on previous exams are identified in these sections as well. Refer to the text for more examples and sample problems of each concept. End of chapter questions for additional practice on the concepts are listed in Additional Practice. Sample AP® multiple-choice questions with answers associated with the material in the chapter are given at the end of the chapter. Two full sample AP® Exams with both multiple-choice and free response questions with answers are given for practice at the end of the book.

- Learning Objectives addressed in the chapter are identified
- Important concepts and vocabulary to know are reviewed
- Good additional practice problems from the text are identified
- Sample AP Problems for each chapter are given
- Two full AP sample exams are included

## AP® Chemistry Laboratory Experiments

The College Board believes the laboratory portion of the AP® Chemistry course will help students gain a better understanding of chemistry processes. At least six of the 16 recommended AP® Chemistry laboratory experiments must be in a guided-inquiry format. Most college general chemistry laboratory courses included 10–12 laboratory experiments each semester or 7–9 experiments each quarter for a total of 20–24 experiments. Colleges want to know students have a college level laboratory experience in their AP® Chemistry laboratory course. To earn laboratory credit, some institutions will have a chemistry professor review each student's AP® Chemistry laboratory notebook.

## The AP® Chemistry Exam Format

The AP® Chemistry Exam is a comprehensive assessment of the topics presented in a first year general chemistry college course for science and engineering majors. The exam starting in 2014 is divided into two parts: Multiple-Choice and Free Response. Each section will account for fifty percent of the total score on the exam. When the overall scores are tallied and cut scores are determined, students deemed to be extremely well qualified will receive a mark of 5, the highest mark. Marks range from a 1 to 5. A table of marks and the recommendation associated with the mark is below. Depending on the institution the student attends for college, the institution will determine if they will give credit for the mark the student earned. This can be researched on the College Board website at apcentral.collegeboard.com.

| AP Mark | Recommendation to Colleges |
|---------|----------------------------|
| 5 | Extremely well qualified |
| 4 | Well qualified |
| 3 | Qualified |
| 2 | Possibly qualified |
| 1 | No recommendation |

## An Overview of AP® Chemistry Exam

### Section I Multiple-Choice Questions

The multiple-choice section will have sixty questions to be done in ninety (90) minutes. This means students have, on average, one and a half minutes (1 min 30 seconds) per question. Some questions will take longer than others to answer. Each question assesses a learning objective or a combination of learning objective and essential knowledge. Each question will have four choices. Every learning objective combines a Science Practice with content knowledge. The exam is scored using Rights Scoring, where no points are deducted for a wrong answer. This means the student should answer every problem even if they have to guess. The multiple-choice section will include chemistry problems requiring calculations.

Calculators are not allowed on Section 1. The numerical values in the multiple-choice section are purposely selected to facilitate easy calculations. This skill of doing simple calculations without the aid of a calculator needs to be practiced. For example, students should be able to obtain the log of 1,000, the square root of 36, and multiply and divide using scientific notation. Often students make errors with the placement of decimal points or putting the numerator in the denominator. Students need to solve every problem showing all of their work, not skipping steps, and including units with all answers even though they will only choose a letter answer. Skipping steps often leads to errors and results in choosing the wrong answer.

Other multiple-choice questions will assess students' conceptual understanding of chemistry. Both types of multiple-choice questions will involve data and/or models to analyze. Many questions will be grouped to one set of data or model.

The questions will vary in difficulty and there is no pattern of spacing them within the exam. Students need to have a strategy to not end up getting stuck on a question. If the student does NOT know anything about the question, they should make their best guess. If the student knows something about the topic but is not sure or thinks it will take longer than a minute to do, the student should mark the question and come back to it later. If the student knows the topic, make sure they read the entire question and answer choices before answering. This way the student will make it through all the questions and will only go back to the ones they have a question on and CAN answer. The students will need to make sure they always put the answer to a question on the right question on the answer sheet. When working through the sample AP® Chemistry Exam style questions, the student needs to practice being on pace by placing a time limit for answering the multiple-choice questions in Section I.

## Strategies:

- Practice staying on a pace of 1 minute 30 seconds per question.
- Read the entire question.
- Practice mathematical routines without the use a calculator!
- If you do not know the answer, try to eliminate choices and then guess. If you need additional time, mark the question and come back to it but in the end answer every multiple-choice question.
- Make sure you put the answer to each question on the right line of the answer sheet.

The exam will include a Periodic Table, physical constants and important equations. These can be found on the AP® website apcentral.collegeboard.org in the course description. The tables, equations, and information may change from year to year so it is always good to check each year for the current version. A copy of the SAME Periodic Table and equation tables used on the AP® Chemistry Exam should be used all year long in the classroom and on class exams. This way the students are familiar with the values, arrangement of the equation pages, and the formulas. It is important for students to recognize different texts may use a slightly different formula than those used on the AP® Chemistry Equation tables. For instance, there are different ways to write the specific heat equation; $q = m\Delta T C_P$, $q = m\Delta T s$, and $q = m\Delta T c$. On the AP® Chemistry Exam Equation Pages $q = m\Delta T c$ is used.

## Strategy:

- Practice using the periodic table and equation pages used on the exam.

The multiple-choice section will include two types of questions; single questions and grouped questions. Grouped questions will be based on one set of data or diagrams and several questions asked relating to the data or the scenario. The grouped questions will not necessarily focus on one topic (i.e. stoichiometry, calorimetry) but will include questions from several different topics. Examples of both types of questions will be in the Sample Questions Section.

### An Overview of Section II: Free Response Questions

The Free Response portion of the exam is divided into long and short questions. The long questions will be the first three questions worth ten (10) points each and the short will be the last four questions worth four (4) points each. Students should plan to spend no more than approximately twenty (20) minutes per long question and no more than approximately seven and a half (7.5) minutes per short question. In this section of the exam, students are allowed to use the provided periodic table, equation pages, and a calculator. Most questions will involve more than one area of chemistry. Students will need to explain concepts to show an understanding of experimental design, to show how to apply mathematical concepts in the lab setting, and show how to apply one or more of the science practices.

There are restrictions on the type of calculator permitted to be used on Section II. Calculator restrictions can be checked on the College Board website apcentral.collegeboard. com by searching AP® Chemistry calculator policies but in general calculators with QWERTY keyboards and ones with printing capabilities are not allowed. Students should use an accepted AP® Chemistry approved calculator throughout the course and they should be familiar with the proper order of operations for their calculator. For example, students will need to know how to use their calculator to take a square root, how to do natural and common logs, antilogs, $e^x$, etc.

Overall within the Free Response section, there are five types of problems. There are two types of questions involving lab, two types of representation problems, and quantitative problems. Each type will be explained and examples given in the Sample Questions Section. During the AP® Chemistry Exam, students should first quickly scan the questions in Section II and then choose to answer the ones they feel they know the most about first. Students can then return to the other questions when the ones they know best are answered. In other words, students do not need to answer each question in the order provided.

Regardless of the type of question, answers are expected to be in clear concise writing and in mathematical computations show clear work with units included. Students should not erase mistakes. Simply put a SINGLE line (~~SINGLE~~) through what they do not want the Reader to score. This should be emphasized in the classroom by the AP® Chemistry teacher all year. It is helpful for the person who reads your exam if the final answers to mathematical problems are circled or boxed, but it is not required. It is also helpful if you identify what part of the question in multipart questions you are answering such as "c)". You do not need to rewrite or paraphrase the question as this wastes valuable time.

## Strategies:

- Read all the questions quickly and then answer the ones you know best first.
- Do not erase but put a ~~SINGLE~~ line through incorrect information.
- Practice explaining concepts in clear concise writing.
- Practice providing evidence for each concept in three sentences or less.
- In mathematical problems include units and show all work. Box or circle final answers.
- Keep track of time spending no more than 20 minutes on each questions 1–3 and 7.5 minutes on each questions 3–7.

### Summary

| Section | Percentage | Time | Structure | Allowed to Use |
|---|---|---|---|---|
| Multiple-Choice | 50% | 90 minutes | 60 Questions all with 4 choices; up to half grouped questions | Periodic Table and equation pages |
| Free Response | 50% | 90 minutes | 7 Questions; 3 long and 4 short; 5 types | Periodic Table, Equation Pages, and Calculator |

### How to Study

Begin studying for the AP® Chemistry Exam at the very beginning of the school year. If you take the time each week to study and review, you will not need to cram at the end. This takes discipline and practice. Set aside the same time each week such as Monday night from

8 – 10 P.M. Have a space where you can focus and not do anything else. Turn off your phone and other devices. Make a review sheet of the major concepts or add to one in progress if you are in the same unit, make new vocabulary flash cards if needed, and include the evidence to support concepts. Review previous concepts, go through all your vocabulary flash cards, work through the section in this book corresponding to the topics being presented by your AP® Chemistry teacher in class and do the sample AP® questions on the topics being covered in class. Only attempt the AP® Chemistry Practice Test about three weeks prior to taking the AP® Chemistry Exam.

## General Hints

- All year long
  - Have a set aside time to study
  - Make vocabulary flash cards—there are apps you can put on your phone to study vocabulary.
  - Make concept maps linking learning objectives to the big ideas.
  - Use data and models to practice explaining the concepts
  - Do practice AP® problems
- The Night before the exam
  - Review your concept maps
  - Get a good nights rest
- Test Day
  - Have a good breakfast
  - Be early and have your proper identification
  - Take pencils for multiple-choice with number 2 lead (mechanical pencils are fine)
  - Take good erasers for multiple-choice so no stray marks are left
  - Take ball point pens (never felt tip—they will bleed through the paper)
  - Take a calculator with extra batteries or an extra calculator you know how to use

## AP® Chemistry Exam Style Sample Questions with Answers

The AP® Chemistry Exams are secure examinations. Students do not have access to the exact questions on the exam until they take the exam. The questions on each of the AP® Chemistry Exams vary from year to year. Few, if any questions are repeated. The questions in Section II, the "Free Response" or "Constructed Response" questions are posted online approximately two days after the exams is administered. The questions in Section I, the multiple-choice questions are posted every fourth or fifth year. Because only members of the AP® Chemistry Development Committee have knowledge of the exact questions on the AP® Chemistry Exam, it is not possible to write sample AP® Chemistry Exam questions exactly matching the AP® Chem Exam questions. However, an AP® Chemistry practice exam was released in May 2013. From this practice exam one can see the changes in the new format and make several inferences about the style of questions. Due to testing time limitations, the AP® Chemistry Exam will not asses students understanding on every topic presented in class. Students should be prepared to answer questions on all topics corresponding to the information described in Essential Knowledge and Learning Objectives for the AP® Chemistry course.

The multiple-choice questions are all linked to one learning objective or a combination of learning objectives and essential knowledge. The learning objectives are all listed at the end of this chapter. There are two types of questions:

- discrete items
- grouped questions

The Free Response sample questions are also linked to learning objectives and can include five types of questions.

- Lab I—includes writing a design for a lab procedure to answer a specific problem
- Lab II—includes analyzing provided laboratory data and drawing conclusions based on the evidence provided by the data
- Representation I—includes explaining how particle behavior at the microscopic or particulate level and then explaining how this observed at the macroscopic level
- Representation II—includes drawing diagrams to explain how particle behavior at the microscopic or particulate level and then explaining how this observed at the macroscopic level
- Quantitative—includes solving mathematical problems with work shown

## Sample AP® Chemistry Style Questions—Section I Multiple-Choice

Question1. The net dipole moment of three compounds with similar molar masses are listed in the table below

| Substance | Net Dipole Moment (D) |
|-----------|----------------------|
| X | 0.1 |
| Y | 2.7 |
| Z | 3.9 |

The three substances are, in no particular order are acetonitrile ($CH_3CN$), acetaldehyde ($CH_3COH$), and propane ($CH_3CH_2CH_3$). If 0.250 mole of each substance is placed in a flask (with a piston at the top) at 228 K ($-45°C$) and the flask is slowly heated under a pressure of 1.00 atm, which substance will exhibit the highest boiling point? What factor is responsible for the high boiling point?

- A. propane, due to having only weak intramolecular forces, London dispersion forces.
- B. acetaldehyde, due to having strong intramolecular forces, hydrogen bonding.
- C. acetonitrile, due to having medium intramolecular forces, dipole-dipole forces.
- D. All three compounds will have about the same boiling point because all three have about the same molar mass and all three have London Dispersion Forces.

This question addresses the following big idea, enduring understanding, essential knowledge, science practice, and learning objectives.

| Big Idea | 6: Any bond or intermolecular attraction that can be formed can be broken. These two processes are in a dynamic competition, sensitive to initial conditions and external perturbations. |
|----------|----------|
| Enduring Understanding | 2.B: Forces of attraction between particles (including the noble gases and also different parts of some large molecules) are important in determining many macroscopic properties of a substance, including how the observable physical state changes with temperature. |
| Essential Knowledge | 2.B.3: Intermolecular forces play a key role in determining the properties of substances, including biological structures and interactions. |
| Science Practices | 6.2: The student can construct explanations of phenomena based on evidence produced through scientific practices.<br>6.4: The student can make claims and predictions about natural phenomena based on scientific theories and models. |

| Learning Objectives | LO 2.16: The student is able to explain the properties (phase, vapor pressure, viscosity, etc.) of small and large molecular compounds in terms of the strengths and types of intermolecular forces. LO 5.9: The student is able to make claims and/or predictions regarding relative magnitudes of the forces acting within collections of interacting molecules based on the distribution of electrons within the molecules and the types of intermolecular forces through which the molecules interact. |
|---|---|

Questions 2–6 refer to the following information

| Half-reaction | E°(V) |
|---|---|
| $Cr^{3+}(aq) + 3e^- \rightarrow Cr(s)$ | −0.74 |
| $Ni^{2+}(aq) + 2e^- \rightarrow Ni(s)$ | −0.23 |
| $Ag^+(aq) + e^- \rightarrow Ag(s)$ | +0.80 |

2. Which reaction will occur spontaneously?

  A. $3Ni(s) + 2Cr^{3+}(aq) \rightarrow 3Ni^{2+}(aq) + 2Cr(s)$

  B. $2Ag(s) + Ni^{2+}(aq) \rightarrow 2Ag^+(aq) + Ni(s)$

  C. $Ni(s) + 2Ag^+(aq) \rightarrow Ni^{2+}(aq) + 2Ag(s)$

  D. $Cr^{3+}(aq) + 3Ag^+(aq) \rightarrow Cr(s) + 3Ag(s)$

Questions 3–5 refer to the above half reactions and the following information and diagram: An electrochemical cell is constructed using two compartments connected by salt bridge. In one compartment silver metal is placed in 1.0 M silver nitrate and in the second compartment nickel metal is placed in 1.0 M nickel(II) nitrate. Wires connect the metal electrodes to a voltmeter.

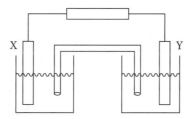

3. If the above electrochemical cell generates a positive emf, the anode is

  A. Ni     B. Ag     C. $Ni^{2+}$     D. $Ag^+$

4. Calculate the cell potential of the above electrochemical cell.

  A. −1.03 V     B. −0.57 V     C. +0.57 V     D. +1.03 V

5. If 0.010 M silver nitrate solution is used instead of 1.0 M for the cell described in question 3, how would this influence the emf of the cell?

  A. the cell voltage would increase

  B. the cell voltage would decrease

  C. the cell voltage would stay the same

  D. there is not sufficient information given to provide an answer

6. Select the statement describing the difference between a Ni-Ag voltaic cell and a Ni-Ag electrolytic cell

  A. In a voltaic cell, oxidation occurs at the anode. In an electrolytic cell, oxidation occurs at the cathode.

  B. An electrolytic cell generates energy without outside help. A voltaic cell needs a continuous input of energy.

C. In a Ni-Ag electrolysis cell, silver cations in the aqueous solution migrate toward the cathode. In a voltaic cell, the cations migrate toward the cathode.

D. In an electrolysis cell, a continuous input of current forces a non-spontaneous reaction to occur, while in a voltaic cell chemical reactions occur to generate energy.

| | |
|---|---|
| **Big Idea** | 3: Changes in matter involve the rearrangement and/or reorganization of atoms and/or the transfer of electrons. |
| **Enduring Understanding** | 3.B: Chemical reactions can be classified by considering what the reactants are, what the products are, or how they change from one into the other. Classes of chemical reactions include synthesis, decomposition, acid–base, and oxidation-reduction reactions. 3.C: Chemical and physical transformations may be observed in several ways and typically involve a change in energy. |
| **Essential Knowledge** | Knowledge 3.C.3: Electrochemistry shows the interconversion between chemical and electrical energy in galvanic and electrolytic cells. <br><br> a. Electrochemistry encompasses the study of redox reactions that occur within electrochemical cells. The reactions either generate electrical current in galvanic cells, or are driven by an externally applied electrical potential in electrolytic cells. Visual representations of galvanic and electrolytic cells are tools of analysis to identify where half-reactions occur and the direction of current flow. <br><br> b. Oxidation occurs at the anode, and reduction occurs at the cathode for all electrochemical cells. <br><br> c. The overall electrical potential of galvanic cells can be calculated by identifying the oxidation half-reaction and reduction half-reaction, and using a table of Standard Reduction Potentials. <br><br> d. Many real systems do not operate at standard conditions; the electrical potential determination must account for the effect of concentrations. LeChâtelier's principle can be used to predict qualitatively the differences in electrical potential and electron flow compared to those at standard conditions. |
| **Science Practices** | 6: The student can work with scientific explanations and theories. |
| **Learning Objectives** | LO 3.8: The student is able to identify redox reactions and justify the identification in terms of electron transfer. <br> LO 3.12: The student can make qualitative or quantitative predictions about galvanic or electrolytic reactions based on half-cell reactions and potentials and/or Faraday's laws. <br> LO 3.13: The student can analyze data regarding galvanic or electrolytic cells to identify properties of the underlying redox reactions. |

## Sample AP® Chemistry Style Free Response or Constructed Response Questions

### Long Question Sample (Lab II)

7. A student runs an experiment measuring the concentration of $N_2O_5$ several times after $N_2O_5$ dissolves in $CCl_4$ at $45\,°C$ and obtains the following data for the decomposition reaction of $N_2O_5$.

$$2N_2O_5 \longrightarrow 4NO_2 + O_2$$

| Time (sec) | $[N_2O_5]$ (M) |
|---|---|
| 0.00 | 1.500 |
| 900.0 | 0.857 |
| 1800.0 | 0.489 |
| 2700.0 | 0.279 |
| 3600.0 | 0.160 |
| 4500.0 | 0.061 |
| 5000.0 | ? |

The student plots a graph of concentration of $N_2O_5$ versus time.

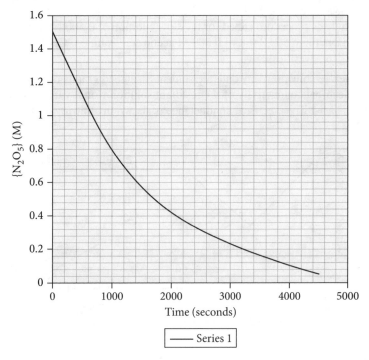

a.  How is the average rate of disappearance of $N_2O_5$ related to the average rate of appearance of $NO_2$? Write a sentence expressing this relationship. Explain how the stoichiometric coefficients are used to relate the rates of $N_2O_5$ and $NO_2$ to each other.

b.  Calculate the average rate of appearance of $NO_2$ between the start of the reaction and 1,800.0 seconds.

c.  Determine the order of this reaction.

d.  Determine the rate constant for this reaction at 45°C.

e.  Determine or estimate the concentration of $N_2O_5$, in units of molarity, at 5,000.0 seconds.

| **Big Idea** | 4: Rates of chemical reactions are determined by details of the molecular collisions. |
|---|---|
| **Enduring Understanding** | Enduring Understanding 4.A: Reaction rates that depend on temperature and other environmental factors are determined by measuring changes in concentrations in reactants or products. |
| **Essential Knowledge** | Essential Knowledge 4.A.2: The rate law shows how the rate depends on reaction concentrations. |

| | Essential Knowledge 4.A.3: The magnitude and temperature dependence of the rate of react ion is contained quantitatively in the rate constant. |
|---|---|
| **Science Practices** | 5.1 The student can analyze data to identify patterns. 7.1 Student can connect phenomena and models across spatial and temporal scales. |
| **Learning Objective** | LO 4.2: The student is able to analyze concentration vs. time data to determine the rate law for a zeroth-, first-, or second-order reaction. |

8.  Several students conduct a series of experiments in which the conductivity of a solution was monitored as a function of how much titrant (or titrator) was added to the analyte (or titrand) during an acid–base titration. One group of students procedure called for the slow addition of 0.500 M KOH($aq$) solution in a buret to 500.0 mL of 0.500 M acetic acid solution, CH$_3$COOH($aq$) in an Erlenmeyer flask.

    Before collecting any data the students sketched graphs of how they thought electrical conductivity of the resultant solution would vary as base is added to the acid. The electrical conductance is shown in arbitrary units.

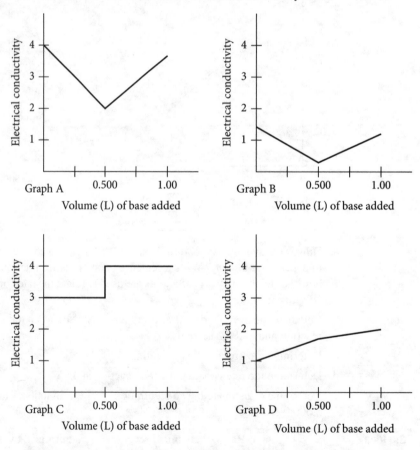

a.  Which graph best matches your expectation for Experiment #1? If none of the graphs match your understanding, sketch your own graph. Explain why the electrical conductivity changed from the point when the titrant was first added to the point at which all of the acid reacted.

b.  Write a balanced chemical equation representing the reaction of an aqueous acetic acid solution with an aqueous potassium hydroxide solution.

c. What volume of base was added to react with all of the acid?

d. Indicate the point on your graph (use the letter "P") just when all of the acid reacted with the base.

e. The diagram below on the left represents a small volume of the acetic acid solution at the particulate nature of matter level before any base is added. Water molecules have been omitted for clarity. The diagram is not to scale. In the circle on the right, make a similar particulate drawing representing the important species present just at the point where enough KOH is added to react with all of the acid in the circle on the left. Be sure to include any newly formed water molecules.

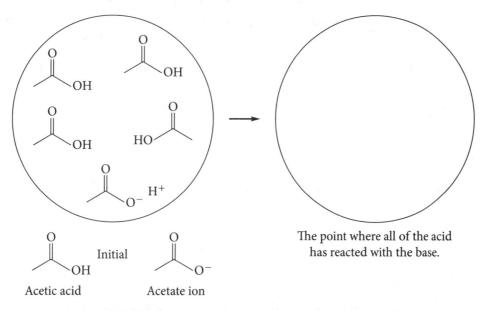

The point where all of the acid has reacted with the base.

f. Is the pH greater than, less than, or equal to 7 at the point in which all of the acid reacts with KOH? Explain. It might be helpful to write a balanced chemical equation representing the interaction of the acetate ion, $CH_3COO^-(aq)$, with water.

| Big Idea | 3: Changes in matter involve the rearrangement and/or reorganization of atoms and/or the transfer of electrons. |
|---|---|
| Enduring Understanding | 3.A: Chemical changes are represented by a balanced chemical equation that identifies the ratios with which reactants and products form.<br>3.B: Chemical reactions can be classified by considering what the reactants are, what the products are, or how they change from one into the other. Classes of chemical reactions include synthesis, decomposition, acid–base, and oxidation-reduction reactions. |
| Essential Knowledge | 3.A.1: A chemical change may be represented by a molecular, ionic, and net ionic equation.<br>a. Chemical equations represent chemical changes, and therefore must contain equal numbers of atoms of every element on each side to be "balanced".<br>3.A.2: Quantitative information can be derived from stoichiometric calculations that utilize the mole ratios from balanced chemical equations.<br>c. Solution chemistry provides additional avenue for laboratory calculations of stoichiometry, including titrations. |
| Science Practices | 6: The student can work with scientific explanations and theories.<br>7.1 The student can connect phenomena and models across spatial and temporal scales. |

| Learning Objectives | LO 1.17: The student is able to express the law of conservation of mass quantitatively and qualitatively using symbolic representations and particulate drawings.<br>LO 3.1: The student can translate among macroscopic observation change, chemical equations, and particulate views.<br>LO 3.3: The student is able to use stoichiometry to predict the results of performing a reaction in the laboratory.<br>LO 3.4: The student is able relate quantities to identify stoichiometric relationships for a reaction. |
|---|---|

9. Students perform an acid–base titration to standardize an HCl solution by placing 20.00 mL of HCl($aq$) in an Erlenmeyer flask, then titrating with a known concentration of NaOH($aq$). Two laboratory technicians have determined the concentration of a sodium hydroxide solution, NaOH($aq$) to be 0.1482 M ± 0.0002 M. and the concentration of the HCl($aq$) solution to be 0.2223 M ± 0.0002 M. The students have the following indicator color chart to consult.

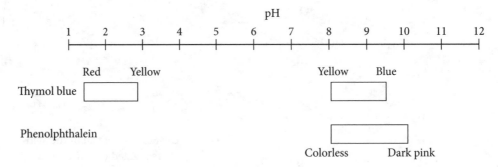

Student X adds a few drops of thymol blue indicator to the acid. Student X rinses a buret with water, then rinses a buret twice with 0.1482 M NaOH($aq$) solution, before filling the buret with fresh 0.1482 M NaOH($aq$). Student X performs a titration of the acid using the 0.1482 M NaOH solution and stops adding NaOH($aq$) when the color of the solution in the Erlenmeyer flask just turns from red to orange. Student X records in his notebook the volume of NaOH($aq$) required to neutralize the HCl($aq$), then calculates the concentration of the HCl($aq$) solution.

Student Y adds a few drops of phenolphthalein indicator to the acid. Student Y rinses a buret twice with water and does not allow most of the water to drain from the buret before filling the buret with 0.1482 M NaOH($aq$). Student Y performs a titration of the acid using the NaOH solution and stops adding NaOH($aq$) when the color of the solution in the Erlenmeyer flask just turns from colorless to faint pink. Student Y records in her notebook the volume of NaOH($aq$) required to neutralize the HCl($aq$), then calculates the concentration of the HCl($aq$) solution.

a. Will the concentration of HCl($aq$) reported by Student X be higher, lower, or about the same as the concentration of HCl($aq$) reported by the technicians? Explain.

b. Will the concentration of HCl($aq$) reported by Student Y be higher, lower, or about the same as the concentration of HCl($aq$) reported by the technicians? Explain.

c. The term *error* indicates the numerical difference between a calculated (or measured) value and the true value. Errors can be classified as determinate (systematic), and indeterminate. Determinate errors can be further classified as *methodic*, *operative*, and *instrumental*. What type of error did Student X make? Explain. What type of error did Student Y make? Explain.

| Big Idea | 3: Changes in matter involve the rearrangement and/or reorganization of atoms and/or the transfer of electrons. |
|---|---|
| Enduring Understanding | 3.A: Chemical changes are represented by a balanced chemical equation that identifies the ratios with which reactants and products form. 3.B: Chemical reactions can be classified by considering what the reactants are, what the products are, or how they change from one into the other. Classes of chemical reactions include synthesis, decomposition, acid–base, and oxidation-reduction reactions. |
| Essential Knowledge | 3.A.1: A chemical change may be represented by a molecular, ionic, and net ionic equation. a. Chemical equations represent chemical changes, and therefore must contain equal numbers of atoms of every element on each side to be "balanced". 3.A.2: Quantitative information can be derived from stoichiometric calculations that utilize the mole ratios from balanced chemical equations. c. Solution chemistry provides additional avenue for laboratory calculations of stoichiometry, including titrations. |
| Science Practices | 2.3: The student can estimate numerically quantities that describe natural phenomena. 4.4: The student can evaluate sources of data to answer a particular scientific question. 6.4: The student can make claims and predictions about natural phenomena based on scientific theories and models. |
| Learning Objectives | LO 2.1: Students can design and or interpret data from an experiment that uses titration to determine the concentration of an analyte in solution. LO 6.13: The student can interpret titration data for monoprotic or polyprotic acids involving titration of a weak or strong acid by a strong base (or a weak or strong base by a strong acid) to determine the concentration of titrant. |

## Answers

### Section I Multiple-Choice

Answers:  *1. C,   2. C;   3. A;   4. D;   5. B;   6. D*

1.  The net dipole moment of three compounds with similar molar mass are listed in the table below

| Substance | Net Dipole Moment (D) |
|---|---|
| X | 0.1 |
| Y | 2.7 |
| Z | 3.9 |

The three substances are, in random listing, acetonitrile ($CH_3CN$), acetaldehyde ($CH_3COH$), and propane ($CH_3CH_2CH_3$). If 0.250 mole of each substance is placed in a flask (with a piston at the top) at $-45°C$ and the flask is slowly heated under a pressure of 1.00 atm, which substance has the highest boiling point. What factor is responsible for the high boiling point.

A.  propane, due to having only weak intermolecular forces, London Dispersion forces.

B.  acetaldehyde, due to having strong intermolecular forces, hydrogen bonding.

C. acetonitrile, due to having medium intermolecular forces, dipole-dipole forces.

D. All three compounds will have about the same boiling point because all three have about the same molar mass and all three have London Dispersion Forces.

Answer: C.

| | |
|---|---|
| **(A)** | This option is incorrect. Propane is a nonpolar compound. Individual London dispersion forces are responsible for keeping propane molecules together as a liquid. London dispersion forces are weak IMFs. Propane has a net dipole moment of 0.1. Propane will have the lowest boiling point of the three compounds. |
| **(B)** | This option is incorrect. Acetaldehyde is a polar compound. Dipole-dipole forces are responsible for keeping acetaldehyde molecules together as a liquid. Dipole-dipole forces are moderate IMFs. Acetaldehyde has a net dipole moment of 2.7. Acetaldehyde does not have an "O—H" group. It does not have hydrogen bonding. Acetaldehyde will have the second highest boiling point of the three compounds. |
| **(C)** | This option is correct. Acetonitrile is a polar compound. Dipole-dipole forces are responsible for keeping acetaldehyde molecules together as a liquid. Dipole-dipole forces are moderate IMFs. Acetaldehyde has a net dipole moment of 3.1. The dipole-dipole IMF in acetonitrile is stronger compare to the dipole-dipole IMF in acetaldehyde. The difference in electronegativity value between the "C" and the "N" is larger compared to the difference in electronegativey between "C" and "O" in Acetaldehyde. Therefore the C—N is more polar compared to the C—O bond. Acetaldehyde will have highest boiling point of the three compounds. |
| **(D)** | This option is incorrect. The compounds do not have similar IMFs and they do not have similar boiling points. |

Questions 2–6 refer to the following information

| Half-reaction | $E°$ (V) |
|---|---|
| $Cr^{3+}(aq) + 3e^- \rightarrow Cr(s)$ | $-0.74$ |
| $Ni^{2+}(aq) + 2e^- \rightarrow Ni(s)$ | $-0.23$ |
| $Ag^+(aq) + e^- \rightarrow Ag(s)$ | $+0.80$ |

2. Which reaction will occur spontaneously?

A. $3Ni(s) + 2Cr^{3+}(aq) \rightarrow 3Ni^{2+}(aq) + 2Cr(s)$

B. $2Ag(s) + Ni^{2+}(aq) \rightarrow 2Ag^+(aq) + Ni(s)$

C. $Ni(s) + 2Ag^+(aq) \rightarrow Ni^{2+}(aq) + 2Ag(s)$

D. $Cr^{3+}(aq) + 3Ag^+(aq) \rightarrow Cr(s) + 3Ag(s)$

| | |
|---|---|
| **(A)** | This option is incorrect. $E° = E°_{cathode} - E°_{anode} = -0.74 \text{ V} - (-0.23 \text{ V}) = -0.51 \text{ V}$ A negative $E°_{reaction}$ values indicates a non-spontaneous reaction. |
| **(B)** | This option is incorrect. $E° = E°_{cathode} - E°_{anode} = -0.23 \text{ V} - (+0.80 \text{ V}) = -1.03 \text{ V}$ A negative $E°_{reaction}$ values indicates a non-spontaneous reaction. |
| **(C)** | This option is correct. $E° = E°_{cathode} - E°_{anode} = +0.80 \text{ V} - (-0.23 \text{ V}) = +1.03 \text{ V}$ A positive $E°_{reaction}$ values indicates a spontaneous reaction. |
| **(D)** | This option is incorrect. The equation is not an oxidation-reduction equation since $Cr^{3+}(aq) + 3e^- \rightarrow Cr(s)$ is a reduction half-reaction and $3Ag^+(aq) + 3e^- \rightarrow 3Ag(s)$ is also a reduction half-reaction. An oxidation half-reaction is missing. |

Questions 3–5 refer to the following information and diagram: An electrochemical cell is constructed using two compartments connected by salt bridge. In one compartment silver metal is placed in 1.0 M silver nitrate and in the second compartment nickel metal is placed in 1.0 M nickel(II) nitrate. Wires connect the metal electrodes to a voltmeter.

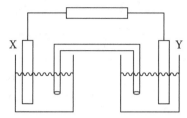

3. If the above electrochemical cell generates a positive emf, _____ is the anode.

   A. Ni        B. Ag        C. $Ni^{2+}$        D. $Ag^+$

| (A) | This option is correct.<br>$Ni^{2+}(aq) + 2e^- \rightarrow Ni(s)$ $E° = -0.23$ V is a reduction half-reaction<br>$Ag^+(aq) + e^- \rightarrow Agi(s)$ $E° = +0.80$ V is a reduction half-reaction<br>Accordingly, Ni is the more active metal compared to Ag. Ni will serve as the anode and Ag will serve as the cathode.<br>$Ni(s) \rightarrow Ni^{2+}(aq) + 2e^-$ oxidation occurs at the anode |
|---|---|
| (B) | This option is incorrect.<br>$Ni^{2+}(aq) + 2e^- \rightarrow Ni(s)$ $E° = -0.23$ V is a reduction half-reaction<br>$Ag^+(aq) + e^- \rightarrow Agi(s)$ $E° = +0.80$ V is a reduction half-reaction<br>Accordingly, Ni is the more active metal compared to Ag. Ni will serve as the anode and Ag will serve as the cathode.<br>$Ag^+(aq) + e^- \rightarrow Agi(s)$ reduction occurs at the cathode |
| (C) | This option is incorrect. The $Ni^{2+}(aq)$ metal cation in aqueous solution can not serve as the anode in part because it can not undergo oxidation (lose electrons). |
| (D) | This option is incorrect. The $Ag^+(aq)$ metal cation in aqueous solution can not serve as the anode in part because it can not undergo oxidation (lose electrons). |

4. Calculate the cell potential of the above electrochemical cell.

   A. $-1.03$ V        B. $-0.57$ V        C. $+0.57$ V        D. $+1.03$ V

| (A) | This option is incorrect.<br>$E° = E°_{cathode} - E°_{anode} = -0.23$ V $- (+0.80$ V$) = -1.03$ V<br>A negative $E°_{reaction}$ values indicates a thermodynamically unfavorable reaction. |
|---|---|
| (B) | This option is incorrect. Students often reverse which $E°$ value represents the cathode and anode.<br>$E° = E°_{cathode} - E°_{anode} = -0.80$ V $- (-0.23$ V$) = -0.57$ V |
| (C) | This option is incorrect. Students often reverse which $E°$ value represents the cathode and anode.<br>$E° = E°_{cathode} - E°_{anode} = 0.80$ V $- (0.23$ V$) = +0.57$ V |
| (D) | This option is correct.<br>$E° = E°_{cathode} - E°_{anode} = +0.80$ V $- (-0.23$ V$) = \pm 1.03$ V |

5. If 0.010 M silver nitrate solution is used instead of 1.0 M for the cell described in question 3, how would this influence the emf of the cell?

   A. the cell voltage would increase        C. the cell voltage would stay the same

   B. the cell voltage would decrease        D. there is not sufficient information given to provide an answer

| (A) | This option is incorrect. For concentration cells,<br>$E° = E°_{cathode} - E°_{anode} = +0.80\text{ V} - (-0.23\text{ V}) = +1.03\text{ V}$<br>Students often incorrectly reverse the values for<br>$Q = [Ag^+]^2/Ni^2 = [0.010\text{ M}]^2/1.0\text{ M} = 0.00010$<br>$E_{cell} = E°_{cell} - (0.0592/n)\log Q = +1.03\text{ V} - (0.0592/2)(-4)$<br>The emf calculates to be greater than $+1.03$ V |
|---|---|
| (B) | This option is correct. $Ni(s) + 2Ag^+(aq) \rightleftharpoons Ni^{2+}(aq) + 2Ag(s)$<br>$E° = E°_{cathode} - E°_{anode} = +0.80\text{ V} - (-0.23\text{ V}) = +1.03\text{ V}$<br>$Q = [Ni^{2+}]/[Ag^+]^2 = 1.0\text{ M}/[0.010\text{ M}]^2 = 10{,}000$<br>$E_{cell} = E°_{cell} - (0.0592/n)\log Q = +1.03\text{ V} - (0.0592/2)(4)$<br>The emf will be less than $+1.03$ V |
| (C) | This option is incorrect. If there is a difference in concentration there will be a different emf, not the same. |
| (D) | This option is incorrect. There is sufficient information given to provide an answer. |

6. Select one statement describing the difference between a Ni-Ag voltaic cell and a Ni-Ag electrolytic cell

   A. In a voltaic cell, oxidation occurs at the anode. In an electrolytic cell, oxidation occurs at the cathode.

   B. An electrolytic cell generates energy without outside help. A voltaic cell needs a continuous input of energy.

   C. In a Ni-Ag electrolysis cell, silver cations in the aqueous solution migrate toward the cathode. In a voltaic cell, the cations migrate toward the cathode.

   D. In an electrolysis cell, a continuous input of current forces a non-spontaneous reaction to occur, while in a voltaic cell chemical reactions occur to generate energy.

| (A) | This option is incorrect. For any electrochemical cell, oxidation occurs at the anode and reduction occurs at the cathode. |
|---|---|
| (B) | This option is incorrect. An electrolytic cell generates energy without outside help. A voltaic cell needs a continuous input of energy. |
| (C) | This option is incorrect. In this voltaic cell, at the cathode cations gain electrons to form atoms. |
| (D) | This option is correct. In an electrolysis cell, a continuous input of current forces a non-spontaneous reaction to occur, while in a voltaic cell chemical reactions occur to generate energy. |

**Section II Free Response**

1. A student runs an experiment measuring the concentration of $N_2O_5$ several times after $N_2O_5$ dissolves in $CCl_4$ at 45 °C and obtains the following data for the decomposition reaction of $N_2O_5$.

   $2N_2O_5 \rightarrow 4NO_2 + O_2(g)$

| Time (sec) | [N₂O₅] (M) | Time (sec) | [N₂O₅] (M) |
|---|---|---|---|
| 0.00 | 1.500 | 3600.0 | 0.160 |
| 900.0 | 0.857 | 4500.0 | 0.0913 |
| 1800.0 | 0.489 | 5000.0 | ? |
| 2700.0 | 0.279 | | |

The student plots a graph of concentration of $N_2O_5$ versus time.

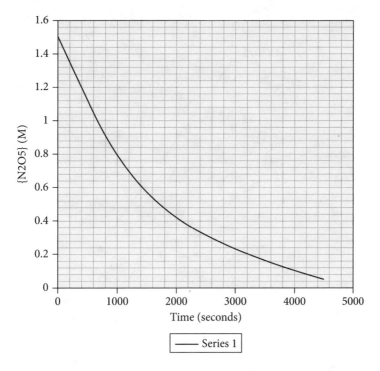

— Series 1

a.  How is the average rate of disappearance of $N_2O_5$ related to the average rate of appearance of $NO_2$? Write a sentence expressing this relationship. Explain how the stoichiometric coefficients are used to relate the relative rates of $N_2O_5$ and $NO_2$ to each other.

The average rate of appearance of $NO_2$ is twice as fast as the rate of disappearance of $N_2O_5$ because 4 moles of $NO_2$ are produced for every 2 moles of $N_2O_5$ that react.

b.  Calculate the average rate of appearance of $NO_2$ between the start of the reaction and 1,800.0 seconds.

Average Rate $= (-1/2)\Delta[N_2O_5]/\Delta t = (1/4)\Delta[NO_2]/\Delta t$

$\Delta[NO_2]/\Delta t = 2(-)\Delta[N_2O_5]/\Delta t = 2(-)$

$\{[0.489\,M - 1.500\,M]/1800.0\,sec - 0.0\,sec\}$

Average rate $= \Delta[N_2O_5]/\Delta t = 2[5.62 \times 10^{-4}\,M/sec]$

$= 1.12 \times 10^{-2}\,M/sec$

c.  Determine the order of this reaction.

Since the plot of $[N_2O_5]$ vs. time is not linear, the reaction is not zero order with respect to $[N_2O_5]$. A plot of $\ln[N_2O_5]$ vs time is linear, therefore the reaction is first-order with respect to $[N_2O_5]$.

| Time (sec) | $[N_2O_5]$ (M) | $\ln[N_2O_5]$ |
|---|---|---|
| 0.00 | 1.500 | 0.405 |
| 900.0 | 0.857 | −0.154 |
| 1800.0 | 0.489 | −0.715 |
| 2700.0 | 0.279 | −1.276 |
| 3600.0 | 0.160 | −1.832 |
| 4500.0 | 0.0913 | −2.797 |
| 5000.0 | ? | |

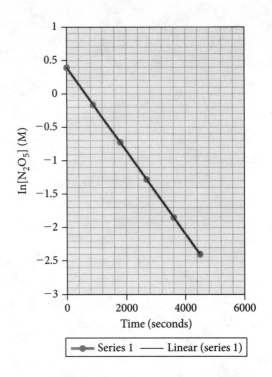

Time (seconds)

Series 1 —— Linear (series 1)

d. Determine the rate constant for this reaction at 45°C.

A first-order reaction with respect to $[N_2O_5]$ follows the equation for a straight line $\ln[N_2O_5]_t = -kt + \ln[N_2O_5]_0$ where t is time and k is the slope of the line. The slope of the line is equal to $-k$. Using the information for 1,800.0 seconds

$$\ln[1.500 \text{ M}] = -k(1,800.0 \text{ sec}) + \ln[0.489 \text{ M}]$$

$$0.405 = -k(1,800.0 \text{ sec}) + (-0.715)$$

$$0.405 + 0.715 = -k(1,800.0 \text{ sec})$$

$$1.120/1,800.0 \text{ sec} = -k$$

$$-6.22 \times 10^{-4} \text{ sec}^{-1} = \text{slope where k, rate constant} = 6.22 \times 10^{-4} \text{ sec}^{-1}$$

e. Determine or estimate the concentration of $N_2O_5$, in units of molarity, at 5,000.0 seconds. If you could not calculate a rate constant use may use $k = 9.00 \times 10^{-4} \text{ sec}^{-1}$.

$$\ln[N_2O_5]_t = -kt + \ln[N_2O_5]_0 \quad \text{For k} = 6.22 \times 10^{-4} \text{ sec}^{-1}$$

$$\ln[x] = -(6.22 \times 10^{-4} \text{ sec}^{-1})(5,000.0 \text{ sec}) + \ln[1.500 \text{ M}]$$

$$\ln[x] = -3.11 + 0.405 = -2.70$$

$$\ln[x] = -2.70 \quad \text{note: } e^{\ln x} = x$$

$$x = e^{(-2.70)} = x = 0.0669 \text{ M}$$

Alternatively, since the average rate of disappearance of $[N_2O_5]$ between 4,500 sec and 3,600 sec is $-7.60 \times 10^{-5}$ M/sec, assume the average rate between 5,000 sec and 4,500 sec is $-7.00 \times 10^{-5}$ M/sec

$$\text{Average rate} = -\Delta[N_2O_5]/\Delta t = -7.00 \times 10^{-5} \text{ M/sec}$$

$$\text{rate} = -\Delta[N_2O_5]/\Delta t = \{[N_2O_5]_2 - [N_2O_5]_1/(t_2 - t_1)\}$$

$$-7.00 \times 10^{-5} \, \text{M/sec} = \{ [N_2O_5]_2 - 0.0913 \, \text{M/}$$
$$(5,000.0 \, \text{sec} - 4,500.0 \, \text{sec}) \}$$

$$-7.00 \times 10^{-5} \, \text{M/sec} = (x - 0.0913 \, \text{M})/500.0 \, \text{sec}$$

$$(-7.00 \times 10^{-5} \, \text{M/sec})(500.0 \, \text{sec}) = (x - 0.0913 \, \text{M})$$

$$-0.035 \, \text{M} = x - 0.0913 \, \text{M}$$

$$x = 0.056 \, \text{M}$$

Exercising the option of using $k = 9.00 \times 10^{-4} \, \text{sec}^{-1}$

$$\ln[N_2O_5]_t = -kt + \ln[N_2O_5]_0$$

$$\ln[x] = -(9.00 \times 10^{-4} \, \text{sec}^{-1})(5,000.0 \, \text{sec}) + \ln[1.500 \, \text{M}]$$

$$\ln[x] = -4.50 + 0.405$$

$$-4.09 = \ln[x]$$

$$e^{(.155)} = x = 0.0166 \, \text{M}$$

2. Several students conduct a series of experiments in which the conductivity of a solution was monitored as a function of how much titrant (or titrator) was added to the analyte (or titrand) during an acid–base titration. One group of students procedure called for the slow addition of 0.500 M KOH($aq$) solution in a buret to 500.0 mL of 0.500 M acetic acid solution, $CH_3COOH(aq)$ in an Erlenmeyer flask.

   Before collecting any data the students sketched graphs of how they thought electrical conductivity of the resultant solution would vary as base is added to the acid. The electrical conductance is shown in arbitrary units.

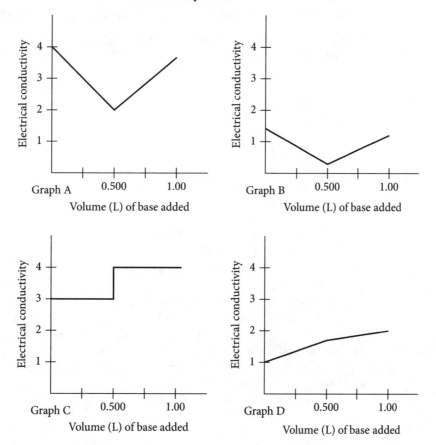

a.  Which graph best matches your expectation for Experiment #1? If none of the graphs match your understanding, sketch your own graph. Explain why the electrical conductivity changed from the point when the titrant was first added to the point at which all of the acid reacted.

Graph D. A weak acid has low conductivity because most of the acid is in the form of molecules which do not conduct, approximately 8% of the weak acid is ionized. KOH is a strong base. As KOH is added, some of the acetic acid molecules react and form acetate ions. For each acetate ion formed a $K^+$ ion is associated with it. This means for every one acetic acid molecule that reacts two ions form. Even though the solution becomes more dilute, there are more ions present in the solution. Electrical conductivity in a solution is a measure of the number of ions present. The more ions present, the greater the conductivity. Positive and negative ions migrating in solution constitutes a current. The relative electrical conductivity of the solution will increase steadily as KOH is added.

b.  Write a balanced chemical equation representing the reaction of an aqueous acetic acid solution with an aqueous potassium hydroxide solution.

$$CH_3COOH(aq) + KOH(aq) \rightarrow K^+(aq), CH_3COO^-(aq) + H_2O(l)$$

c.  What volume of base was added to react with all of the acid?

Moles of $CH_3COOH(aq)$ initially present

$0.500\,L \times 0.500\,mol/L = 0.250\,mol\,CH_3COOH(aq)$

Moles of KOH needed to react with all of the acid

$0.250\,mol\,CH_3COOH(aq) \times 1\,mole\,KOH/1\,mole\,CH_3COOH$

$$= 0.250\,mol\,KOH$$

$M$ = moles solute/L solution

L KOH solution = moles solute/$M$ = $0.250\,mol/0.500\,mol/L = 0.500\,L$

d.  Indicate the point on your graph (use the letter "P") just when all of the acid reacted with the base.

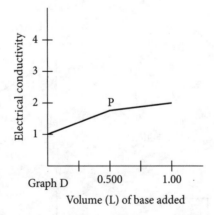

Graph D

e.  The diagram on the next page, on the left represents a small volume of the acetic acid solution at the particulate nature of matter level before any base is added. Water molecules have been omitted for clarity. The diagram is not to scale. In the circle on the right, make a similar particulate drawing representing the important species present just at the point where enough KOH is added to react with all of the acid in the circle on the left. Be sure to include any newly formed water molecules.

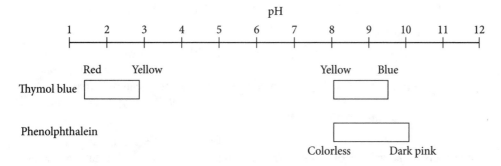

The point where all of the acid
has reacted with the base.

Initial

Acetate ion

f.  Is the pH greater than, less than, or equal to 7 at the point in which all
of the acid reacts with KOH? Explain. It might be helpful to write a balanced chemical equation representing the interaction of the acetate ion,
$CH_3COO^-(aq)$, with water.

The pH will be slightly greater than 7. At the equivalence point, all of the initial
acid reacts with the added KOH, creating acetate ions, $CH_3COO^-(aq)$ and $K^+(aq)$ ions. Some
of the acetate ions react with water to form new hydroxide ions (not from the KOH) and new
acetic acid molecules. The reverse reaction also occurs. An equilibrium system is established.

$$CH_3COO^-(aq) + H_2O(l) \rightleftharpoons CH_3COOH(aq) + OH^-(aq)$$

The acetic acid molecules stay intact as molecules and do not release $H^+$ ions.
The presence of hydroxide ions in solution, in addition to the hydroxide ions from the autoionization of water, creates a slightly basic solution.

3.  Students perform an acid–base titration to standardize an HCl solution by placing 20.00 mL of HCl(aq) in an Erlenmeyer flask, then titrating with a known
concentration of NaOH(aq). Two laboratory technicians have determined the
concentration of a sodium hydroxide solution, NaOH(aq) to be 0.1482 M
$\pm$ 0.0002 M. and the concentration of the HCl(aq) solution to be 0.2223 M
$\pm$ 0.0002 M. The students have the following indicator color chart to consult.

pH

| 1 | 2 | 3 | 4 | 5 | 6 | 7 | 8 | 9 | 10 | 11 | 12 |

Thymol blue: Red — Yellow / Yellow — Blue

Phenolphthalein: Colorless — Dark pink

Student X adds a few drops of thymol blue indicator to the acid. Student X rinses a buret with water, then rinses a buret twice with 0.1482 M NaOH(aq) solution, before filling the buret
with fresh 0.1482 M NaOH(aq). Student X performs a titration of the acid using the 0.1482 M
NaOH solution and stops adding NaOH(aq) when the color of the solution in the Erlenmeyer flask
just turns from red to orange. Student X records in his notebook the volume of NaOH(aq) required
to neutralize the HCl(aq), then calculates the concentration of the HCl(aq) solution.

Student Y adds a few drops of phenolphthalein indicator to the acid. Student Y rinses a buret twice with water and does not allow most of the water to drain from the buret before filling the buret with 0.1482 M NaOH($aq$). Student Y performs a titration of the acid using the NaOH solution and stops adding NaOH($aq$) when the color of the solution in the Erlenmeyer flask just turns from colorless to faint pink. Student Y records in her notebook the volume of NaOH($aq$) required to neutralize the HCl($aq$), then calculates the concentration of the HCl($aq$) solution.

    a. Will the concentration of HCl($aq$) reported by Student X be higher, lower, or about the same as the concentration of HCl($aq$) reported by the technicians? Explain.

The concentration of the HCl($aq$) solution as reported by Student X will be lower compared to the 0.2223 M value reported by the lab technicians. 20.00 mL of 0,2223 M HCl contains 0.00446 mole of HCl. The technicians used about 30.00 mL of 0.1482 M NaOH to neutralize the HCl. Student X stops the titration well before all of the acid is completely neutralized. Since thymol blue turns a solution orange around pH = 2, we can estimate Student X added about 15 mL of NaOH($aq$). The student would show the following calculations

$$0.01500\,\text{L NaOH} \times 0.1482\,\text{mol/L NaOH} = 0.002223\,\text{mol NaOH}$$

$$\text{HCl}(aq) + \text{NaOH}(aq) \rightarrow \text{NaCl}(aq) + \text{H}_2\text{O}(l)$$

$$0.002223\,\text{mol NaOH} \times 1\,\text{mole HCl}/1\,\text{mole NaOH} = 0.002223\,\text{mol HCl}$$

$$M_{\text{HCl}} = 0.002223\,\text{mol HCl}/0.02000\,\text{L} = 0.1112\,\text{M}$$

    b. Will the concentration of HCl($aq$) reported by Student Y be higher, lower, or about the same as the concentration of HCl($aq$) reported by the technicians? Explain.

The concentration of the HCl($aq$) solution as reported by Student X will be higher compared to the 0.2223 M value reported by the lab technicians. As stated aboe, 20.00 mL of 0,2223 M HCl contains 0.00446 mole of HCl. The technicians used about 30.00 mL of 0.1482 M NaOH to neutralize the HCl. Student Y did not rinse her buret with the sodium hydroxide solution, therefore when the sodium hydroxide solution was added to the buret some of the water in the buret mixed with the NaOH and made the solution dilute. We can estimate the concentration of the NaOH($aq$) in the buret as 0.120 M. Student Y stops the titration when all of the acid is completely neutralized. We can estimate about 35 mL of base was used to neutralize the acid because the NaOH solution in the buret was a bit more dilute compared to what the technicians used. The student would show the following calculations using a higher value for the concentration of NaOH compared to the true value.

$$0.03500\,\text{L NaOH} \times 0.1482\,\text{mol/L NaOH} = 0.005187\,\text{mol NaOH}$$

$$\text{HCl}(aq) + \text{NaOH}(aq) \rightarrow \text{NaCl}(aq) + \text{H}_2\text{O}(l)$$

$$0.005187\,\text{mol NaOH} \times 1\,\text{mole HCl}/1\,\text{mole NaOH} = 0.005187\,\text{mol HCl}$$

$$M_{\text{HCl}} = 0.005187\,\text{mol HCl}/0.02000\,\text{L} = 0.2593\,\text{M}$$

    c. The term *error* indicates the numerical difference between a calculated (or measured) value and the true value. Errors can be classified as determinate (systematic), and indeterminate. Determinate errors can be further classified as *methodic*, *operative*, and *instrumental*. What type of error did Students X and Y make? Explain.

Although the measured values of volume do have some error, in this experiment, measurements of the volume of solutions are not the prime source of error. Students X and Y each made a different type of operative error. This type of error can be corrected in a subsequent trial of the experiment. Operative errors are a type of determinate error. Determinate errors are unidirectional with respect to the true value and can be reproduced by a scientist who understands the procedures, calculations and the theory of the experiment.

# Correlation Guide for AP® Chemistry

## Big Idea 1 Learning Objectives

The chemical elements are fundamental building materials of matter, and all matter can be understood in terms of arrangements of atoms. These atoms retain their identity in chemical reactions.

| | Learning Objective | Science Practice | Chapter and Section |
|---|---|---|---|
| 1.1 | The student can justify the observation that the ratio of the masses of the constituent elements in any pure sample of that compound is always identical on the basis of the atomic molecular theory. | 6.1 | 2.5-2.8, 3.9-3.10 |
| 1.2 | The student is able to select and apply mathematical routines to mass data to identify or infer the composition of pure substances and/or mixtures. | 2.2 | 3.9-3.10 |
| 1.3 | The student is able to select and apply mathematical relationships to mass data in order to justify a claim regarding the identity and/or estimated purity of a substance. | 2.2 | Labs in Mastering: Experiment 2, 4 |
| 1.4 | The student is able to connect the number of particles, moles, mass, and volume of substances to one another, both qualitatively and quantitatively. | 7.1 | 2.8-2.9, 3.8-3.11 |
| 1.5 | The student is able to explain the distribution of electrons in an atom or ion based upon data. | 1.5, 6.2 | You can access coverage of this learning objective at www.PearsonSchool.com/Advanced |
| 1.6 | The student is able to analyze data relating to electron energies for patterns and relationships. | 5.1 | 7.1-7.6, 8.1-8.8 |
| 1.7 | The student is able to describe the electronic structure of the atom, using PES data, ionization energy data, and/or Coulomb's Law to construct explanations of how the energies of electrons within shells in atoms vary. | 5.1, 6.2 | 8.2-8.9 |
| 1.8 | The student is able to explain the distribution of electrons using Coulomb's Law to analyze measured energies. | 6.2 | 8.3 |
| 1.9 | The student is able to predict and/or justify trends in atomic properties based on location on the periodic table and/or the shell model. | 6.4 | 7.3-7.6, 8.2-8.9 |
| 1.10 | Students can justify with evidence the arrangement of the periodic table and can apply periodic properties to chemical reactivity. | 6.1 | 7.3-7.6, 8.2-8.9 |
| 1.11 | The student can analyze data, based on periodicity and the properties of binary compounds, to identify patterns and generate hypotheses related to the molecular design of compounds for which data are not supplied. | 3.1, 5.1 | 8.9 |
| 1.12 | The student is able to explain why a given set of data suggests, or does not suggest, the need to refine the atomic model from a classical shell model with the quantum mechanical model. | 6.3 | 2.3-2.4, 7.3-7.6, 8.3-8.4 |
| 1.13 | Given information about a particular model of the atom, the student is able to determine if the model is consistent with specified evidence. | 5.3 | 1.2, 2.3-2.5, 7.3-7.6, 8.1-8.8 |

| | Learning Objective | Science Practice | Chapter and Section |
|---|---|---|---|
| 1.14 | The student is able to use data from mass spectrometry to identify the elements and the masses of individual atoms of a specific element. | 1.4, 1.5 | 2.8 |
| 1.15 | The student can justify the selection of a particular type of spectroscopy to measure properties associated with vibrational or electronic motions of molecules. | 4.1 | 7.2-7.6 |
| 1.16 | The student can design and/or interpret the results of an experiment regarding the absorption of light to determine the concentration of an absorbing species in a solution. | 4.2, 5.1 | Labs in Mastering: Experiment 9, 18B |
| 1.17 | The student is able to express the law of conservation of mass quantitatively and qualitatively using symbolic representations and particulate drawings. | 1.5 | 1.2-1.4, 3.11, 4.2 |
| 1.18 | The student is able to apply conservation of atoms to the rearrangement of atoms in various processes. | 1.4 | 2.8-2.9, 3.3-3.11 |
| 1.19 | The student can design, and/or interpret data from, an experiment that uses gravimetric analysis to determine the concentration of an analyte in a solution. | 4.2, 5.1 | Labs in Mastering: Experiment 4 |
| 1.20 | The student can design, and/or interpret data from, an experiment that uses titration to determine the concentration of an analyte in a solution. | 4.2, 5.1 | 4.8, 16.4 |

## Big Idea 2 Learning Objectives

Chemical and physical properties of materials can be explained by the structure and rearrangement of atoms, ions, molecules and the forces between them.

| | Learning Objective | Science Practice | Chapter and Section |
|---|---|---|---|
| 2.1 | Students can predict properties of substances based on their chemical formulas, and provide explanations of their properties based on particle views. | 6.4, 7.1 | 3.2-3.6, 3.12, 4.5, 4.8, 11.2, 11.3, 11.11 |
| 2.2 | The student is able to explain the relative strengths of acids and bases based on molecular structure, interparticle forces, and solution equilibrium. | 7.2 | 4.4-4.8, 15.2, 15.4 |
| 2.3 | The student is able to use aspects of particulate models (i.e., particle spacing, motion, and forces of attraction) to reason about observed differences between solid and liquid phases and among solid and liquid materials. | 6.4, 7.1 | 11.2-11.4, 11.7-11.12 |
| 2.4 | The student is able to use KMT and concepts of intermolecular forces to make predictions about the macroscopic properties of gases, including both ideal and nonideal behaviors. | 1.4, 6.4 | 5.4-5.10 |
| 2.5 | The student is able to refine multiple representations of a sample of matter in the gas phase to accurately represent the effect of changes in macroscopic properties on the sample. | 1.3, 6.4, 7.2 | 5.3-5.10 |
| 2.6 | The student can apply mathematical relationships or estimation to determine macroscopic variables for ideal gases. | 2.2, 2.3 | 5.3-5.4 |

| | Learning Objective | Science Practice | Chapter and Section |
|---|---|---|---|
| 2.7 | The student is able to explain how solutes can be separated by chromatography based on intermolecular interactions. | 6.2 | Labs in Mastering: Experiment 15A |
| 2.8 | The student can draw and/or interpret representations of solutions that show the interactions between the solute and solvent. | 1.1, 1.2, 6.4 | 12.2, 12.3 |
| 2.9 | The student is able to create or interpret representations that link the concept of molarity with particle views of solutions. | 1.1, 1.4 | 4.4-4.5, 12.5 |
| 2.10 | The student can design and/or interpret the results of a separation experiment (filtration, paper chromatography, column chromatography, or distillation) in terms of the relative strength of interactions among and between the components. | 4.2, 5.1 | Labs in Mastering: Experiment 2, 15A |
| 2.11 | The student is able to explain the trends in properties and/or predict properties of samples consisting of particles with no permanent dipole on the basis of London dispersion forces. | 6.2, 6.4 | 11.3 |
| 2.12 | The student can qualitatively analyze data regarding real gases to identify deviations from ideal behavior and relate these to molecular interactions. | 5.1, 6.5 | 11.2-11.3, 12.12 |
| 2.13 | The student is able to describe the relationships between the structural features of polar molecules and the forces of attraction between the particles. | 1.4 | 11.2-11.3 |
| 2.14 | The student is able to apply Coulomb's Law qualitatively (including using representations) to describe the interactions of ions, and the attractions between ions and solvents to explain the factors that contribute to the solubility of ionic compounds. | 1.4, 6.4 | 8.3, 11.3 |
| 2.15 | The student is able to explain observations regarding the solubility of ionic solids and molecules in water and other solvents on the basis of particle views that include intermolecular interactions and entropic effects. | 1.4, 6.2 | 11.3-11.5, 5.4, 5.10 |
| 2.16 | The student is able to explain the properties (phase, vapor pressure, viscosity, etc.) of small and large molecular compounds in terms of the strengths and types of intermolecular forces. | 6.2 | 11.3-11.5 |
| 2.17 | The student can predict the type of bonding present between two atoms in a binary compound based on position in the periodic table and the electronegativity of the elements. | 6.4 | 9.2-9.6 |
| 2.18 | The student is able to rank and justify the ranking of bond polarity on the basis of the locations of the bonded atoms in the periodic table. | 6.1 | 9.2-9.6, 9.8, 11.3, |
| 2.19 | The student can create visual representations of ionic substances that connect the microscopic structure to macroscopic properties, and/or use representations to connect the microscopic structure to macroscopic properties (e.g., boiling point, solubility hardness, brittleness, low volatility, lack of malleability, ductility, or conductivity). | 1.1, 1.4, 7.1 | 9.4, 11.1-11.3, 1.3-1.4 |
| 2.20 | The student is able to explain how a bonding model involving delocalized electrons is consistent with macroscopic properties of metals (e.g., conductivity, malleability, ductility and low volatility) and the shell model of the atom. | 6.2, 7.1 | 9.11, 1.3-1.4, 20.7 |
| 2.21 | The student is able to use Lewis diagrams and VSEPR to predict the geometry of molecules, identify hybridization, and make predictions about polarity. | 1.4 | 9.6-9.10, 10.2-10.8 |

| | Learning Objective | Science Practice | Chapter and Section |
|---|---|---|---|
| 2.22 | The student is able to design or evaluate a plan to collect and/or interpret data needed to deduce the type of bonding in a sample of a solid. | 4.2 | You can access coverage of this learning objective at www.PearsonSchool.com/Advanced |
| 2.23 | The student can create a representation of an ionic solid that shows essential characteristics of the structure and interactions present in the substance. | 1.1 | 9.2, 11.1-11.3, 8.3, |
| 2.24 | The student is able to explain a representation that connects properties of an ionic solid to its structural attributes and to the interactions present at the atomic level. | 1.1, 6.2, 7.1 | 9.2, 11.1-11.3, 8.3, |
| 2.25 | The student is able to compare the properties of metal alloys with their constituent elements to determine if an alloy has formed, identify the type of alloy formed, and explain the differences in properties using particulate level reasoning. | 1.4, 7.2 | 9.2, 11.2, 23.2-23.4 |
| 2.26 | Students can use the electron sea model of metallic bonding to predict or make claims about the macroscopic properties of metals or alloys. | 6.4, 7.1 | 9.2, 11.2, 23.2-23.4 |
| 2.27 | The student can create a representation of a metallic solid that shows essential characteristics of the structure and interactions present in the substance. | 1.1 | 9.2, 11.2, 23.2-23.4 |
| 2.28 | The student is able to explain a representation that connects properties of a metallic solid to its structural attributes and to the interactions present at the atomic level. | 1.1, 6.2, 7.1 | 9.2, 11.2, 23.2-23.4 |
| 2.29 | The student can create a representation of a covalent solid that shows essential characteristics of the structure and interactions present in the substance. | 1.1 | 11.2-11.3, 22.3-22.5 |
| 2.30 | The student is able to explain a representation that connects properties of a covalent solid to its structural attributes and to the interactions present at the atomic level. | 1.1, 6.2, 7.1 | 11.2-11.3, 22.3-22.5 |
| 2.31 | The student can create a representation of a molecular solid that shows essential characteristics of the structure and interactions present in the substance. | 1.1 | 9.2-9.3, 11.2 |
| 2.32 | The student is able to explain a representation that connects properties of a molecular solid to its structural attributes and to the interactions present at the atomic level. | 1.1, 6.2, 7.1 | 9.2-9.3, 11.2 |

## Big Idea 3 Learning Objectives

Changes in matter involve the rearrangement and/or reorganization of atoms and/or the transfer of electrons.

| | Learning Objective | Science Practice | Chapter and Section |
|---|---|---|---|
| 3.1 | Students can translate among macroscopic observations of change, chemical equations, and particle views. | 1.5, 7.1 | 1.3, 1.4, 3.11, 4.6-4.8, 5.3, 13.5-13.7, 15.3, 18.3 |
| 3.2 | The student can translate an observed chemical change into a balanced chemical equation and justify the choice of equation type (molecular, ionic, or net ionic) in terms of utility for the given circumstances. | 1.5, 7.1 | 1.4, 3.11, 4.6-4.9 |

| | | Learning Objective | Science Practice | Chapter and Section |
|---|---|---|---|---|
| 3.3 | | The student is able to use stoichiometric calculations to predict the results of performing a reaction in the laboratory and/or to analyze deviations from the expected results. | 2.2, 5.1 | 3.11, 4.2-4.3, 4.8-4.9, 5.7 |
| 3.4 | | The student is able to relate quantities (measured mass of substances, volumes of solutions, or volumes and pressures of gases) to identify stoichiometric relationships for a reaction, including situations involving limiting reactants and situations in which the reaction has not gone to completion. | 2.2, 5.1, 6.4 | 3.11, 4.2-4.3, 4.8-4.9, 5.7 |
| 3.5 | | The student is able to design a plan in order to collect data on the synthesis or decomposition of a compound to confirm the conservation of matter and the law of definite proportions. | 2.1, 4.2 | 2.3 |
| 3.6 | | The student is able to use data from synthesis or decomposition of a compound to confirm the conservation of matter and the law of definite proportions. | 2.2, 6.1 | 2.3, 3.10 |
| 3.7 | | The student is able to identify compounds as Brensted-Lowry acids, bases, and/or conjugate acid–base pairs, using proton-transfer reactions to justify the identification. | 6.1 | 4.8, 15.3 |
| 3.8 | | The student is able to identify redox reactions and justify the identification in terms of electron transfer. | 6.1 | 4.9, 18.1-18.3, 21 |
| 3.9 | | The student is able to design and/or interpret the results of an experiment involving a redox titration. | 4.2, 5.1 | |
| 3.10 | | The student is able to evaluate the classification of a process as a physical change, chemical change, or ambiguous change based on both macroscopic observations and the distinction between rearrangement of covalent interactions and noncovalent interactions. | 1.4, 6.1 | 1.4-1.5, 4.2-4.9, |
| 3.11 | | The student is able to interpret observations regarding macroscopic energy changes associated with a reaction or process to generate a relevant symbolic and/or graphical representation of the energy changes. | 1.5, 4.4 | 6.1-6.6 |
| 3.12 | | The student can make qualitative or quantitative predictions about galvanic or electrolytic reactions based on half-cell reactions and potentials and/or Faraday's laws. | 2.2, 2.3, 6.4 | 18.3-18.8 |
| 3.13 | | The student can analyze data regarding galvanic or electrolytic cells to identify properties of the underlying redox reactions. | 5.1 | 18.4 |

## Big Idea 4 Learning Objectives

Rates of chemical reactions are determined by details of the molecular collisions.

| | | Learning Objective | Science Practice | Chapter and Section |
|---|---|---|---|---|
| 4.1 | | The student is able to design and/or interpret the results of an experiment regarding the factors (i.e., temperature, concentration, surface area) that may influence the rate of a reaction. | 4.2, 5.1 | 13.1-13.5 |
| 4.2 | | The student is able to analyze concentration vs. time data to determine the rate law for a zeroth-, first-, or second-order reaction. | 5.1 | 13.1-13.5 |
| 4.3 | | The student is able to connect the half-life of a reaction to the rate constant of a first-order reaction and justify the use of this relation in terms of the reaction being a first-order reaction. | 2.1, 2.2 | 13.1-13.5 |

| | Learning Objective | Science Practice | Chapter and Section |
|---|---|---|---|
| 4.4 | The student is able to connect the rate law for an elementary reaction to the frequency and success of molecular collisions, including connecting the frequency and success to the order and rate constant, respectively. | 7.1 | 13.2-13.5 |
| 4.5 | The student is able to explain the difference between collisions that convert reactants to products and those that do not in terms of energy distributions and molecular orientation. | 6.2 | 13.5 |
| 4.6 | The student is able to use representations of the energy profile for an elementary reaction (from the reactants, through the transition state, to the products) to make qualitative predictions regarding the relative temperature dependence of the reaction rate. | 1.4, 6.4 | 13.5 |
| 4.7 | The student is able to evaluate alternative explanations, as expressed by reaction mechanisms, to determine which are consistent with data regarding the overall rate of a reaction, and data that can be used to infer the presence of a reaction intermediate. | 6.5 | 13.6 |
| 4.8 | The student can translate among reaction energy profile representations, particulate representations, and symbolic representations (chemical equations) of a chemical reaction occurring in the presence and absence of a catalyst. | 1.5 | 13.7 |
| 4.9 | The student is able to explain changes in reaction rates arising from the use of acid–base catalysts, surface catalysts, or enzyme catalysts, including selecting appropriate mechanisms with or without the catalyst present. | 6.2, 7.2 | 13.7 |

## Big Idea 5 Thermochemistry

The laws of thermodynamics describe the essential role of energy and explain and predict the direction of changes in matter.

| | Learning Objective | Science Practice | Chapter and Section |
|---|---|---|---|
| 5.1 | The student is able to create or use graphical representations in order to connect the dependence of potential energy to the distance between atoms and factors, such as bond order (for covalent interactions) and polarity (for intermolecular interactions), which influence the interaction strength. | 1.1, 1.4, 7.2 | 9.5, 9.6, 9.10, 8.3 |
| 5.2 | The student is able to relate temperature to the motions of particles, either via particulate representations, such as drawings of particles with arrows indicating velocities, and/or via representations of average kinetic energy and distribution of kinetic energies of the particles, such as plots of the Maxwell-Boltzmann distribution. | 1.1, 1.4, 7.1 | 6.1-6.4, 17.3 |
| 5.3 | The student can generate explanations or make predictions about the transfer of thermal energy between systems based on this transfer being due to a kinetic energy transfer between systems arising from molecular collisions. | 7.1 | 6.1-6.4 |
| 5.4 | The student is able to use conservation of energy to relate the magnitudes of the energy changes occurring in two or more interacting systems, including identification of the systems, the type (heat versus work), or the direction of energy flow. | 1.4, 2.2 | 6.1-6.8 |

| | Learning Objective | Science Practice | Chapter and Section |
|---|---|---|---|
| 5.5 | The student is able to use conservation of energy to relate the magnitudes of the energy changes when two nonreacting substances are mixed or brought into contact with one another. | 2.2 | 6.3-6.4 |
| 5.6 | The student is able to use calculations or estimations to relate energy changes associated with heating/cooling a substance to the heat capacity, relate energy changes associated with a phase transition to the enthalpy of fusion/vaporization, relate energy changes associated with a chemical reaction to the enthalpy of the reaction, and relate energy changes to P$\Delta$V work. | 2.2, 2.3 | 6.1-6.9 |
| 5.7 | The student is able to design and/or interpret the results of an experiment in which calorimetry is used to determine the change in enthalpy of a chemical process (heating/ cooling, phase transition, or chemical reaction) at constant pressure. | 4.2, 5.1 | 6.5-6.7 |
| 5.8 | The student is able to draw qualitative and quantitative connections between the reaction enthalpy and the energies involved in the breaking and formation of chemical bonds. | 2.3, 7.1, 7.2 | 6.6-6.9, 9.10, 8.3 |
| 5.9 | The student is able to make claims and/or predictions regarding relative magnitudes of the forces acting within collections of interacting molecules based on the distribution of electrons within the molecules and the types of intermolecular forces through which the molecules interact. | 6.4 | 11.1-11.9 |
| 5.10 | The student can support the claim about whether a process is a chemical or physical change (or may be classified as both) based on whether the process involves changes in intramolecular versus intermolecular interactions. | 5.1 | 11.1-11.9 |
| 5.11 | The student is able to identify the noncovalent interactions within and between large molecules, and/or connect the shape and function of the large molecule to the presence and magnitude of these interactions. | 7.2 | 11.3, 20.14, 21.1-21.7 |
| 5.12 | The student is able to use representations and models to predict the sign and relative magnitude of the entropy change associated with chemical or physical processes. | 1.4 | 17.4-17.9 |
| 5.13 | The student is able to predict whether or not a physical or chemical process is thermodynamically favored by determination of (either quantitatively or qualitatively) the signs of both $\Delta H°$ and $\Delta S°$, and calculation or estimation of $\Delta G°$ when needed. | 2.2, 2.3, 6.4 | 17.1-17.9 |
| 5.14 | The student is able to determine whether a chemical or physical process is thermodynamically favorable by calculating the change in standard Gibbs free energy. | 2.2 | 17.5-17.7 |
| 5.15 | The student is able to explain how the application of external energy sources or the coupling of favorable with unfavorable reactions can be used to cause processes that are not thermodynamically favorable to become favorable. | 6.2 | 18.8, 17.7 |
| 5.16 | The student can use LeChâtelier's principle to make qualitative predictions for systems in which coupled reactions that share a common intermediate drive formation of a product. | 6.4 | 17.7 |
| 5.17 | The student can make quantitative predictions for systems involving coupled reactions that share a common intermediate, based on the equilibrium constant for the combined reaction. | 6.4 | 14.3 |

| | Learning Objective | Science Practice | Chapter and Section |
|---|---|---|---|
| 5.18 | The student can explain why a thermodynamically favored chemical reaction may not produce large amounts of product (based on consideration of both initial conditions and kinetic effects), or why a thermodynamically unfavored chemical reaction can produce large amounts of product for certain sets of initial conditions. | 1.3, 7.2 | 17.1-17.9 |

## Big Idea 6 Equilibrium

Any bond or intermolecular attraction that can be formed can be broken. These two processes are in a dynamic competition, sensitive to initial conditions and external perturbations.

| | Learning Objective | Science Practice | Chapter and Section |
|---|---|---|---|
| 6.1 | The student is able to, given a set of experimental observations regarding physical, chemical, biological, or environmental processes that are reversible, construct an explanation that connects the observations to the reversibility of the underlying chemical reactions or processes. | 6.2 | 14.1-14.2, 15.6, 16.2 |
| 6.2 | The student can, given a manipulation of a chemical reaction or set of reactions (e.g., reversal of reaction or addition of two reactions), determine the effects of that manipulation on $Q$ or $K$. | 2.2 | 14.3-14.5, 16.6 |
| 6.3 | The student can connect kinetics to equilibrium by using reasoning about equilibrium, such as LeChâtelier's principle, to infer the relative rates of the forward and reverse reactions. | 7.2 | You can access coverage of this learning objective at www.PearsonSchool.com/Advanced |
| 6.4 | The student can, given a set of initial conditions (concentrations or partial pressures) and the equilibrium constant, $K$, use the tendency of $Q$ to approach $K$ to predict and justify the prediction as to whether the reaction will proceed toward products or reactants as equilibrium is approached. | 2.2, 6.4 | 14.3-14.7 |
| 6.5 | The student can, given data (tabular, graphical, etc.) from which the state of a system at equilibrium can be obtained, calculate the equilibrium constant, $K$. | 2.2 | 14.6 |
| 6.6 | The student can, given a set of initial conditions (concentrations or partial pressures) and the equilibrium constant, $K$, use stoichiometric relationships and the law of mass action ($Q$ equals $K$ at equilibrium) to determine qualitatively and/or quantitatively the conditions at equilibrium for a system involving a single reversible reaction. | 2.2, 6.4 | 14.2-14.6 |
| 6.7 | The student is able, for a reversible reaction that has a large or small $K$, to determine which chemical species will have very large versus very small concentrations at equilibrium. | 2.2, 2.3 | 14.2-14.7, 15.4 |
| 6.8 | The student is able to use LeChâtelier's principle to predict the direction of the shift resulting from various possible stresses on a system at chemical equilibrium. | 1.4, 6.4 | 14.9 |
| 6.9 | The student is able to use LeChâtelier's principle to design a set of conditions that will optimize a desired outcome, such as product yield. | 4.2 | 14.9 |

| | Learning Objective | Science Practice | Chapter and Section |
|---|---|---|---|
| 6.10 | The student is able to connect LeChâtelier's principle to the comparison of $Q$ to $K$ by explaining the effects of the stress on $Q$ and $K$. | 1.4, 7.2 | 14.9 |
| 6.11 | The student can generate or use a particulate representation of an acid (strong or weak or polyprotic) and a strong base to explain the species that will have large versus small concentrations at equilibrium. | 1.1, 1.4, 2.3 | 15.1-15.4, 15.7, 16.2, 16.4 |
| 6.12 | The student can reason about the distinction between strong and weak acid solutions with similar values of pH, including the percent ionization of the acids, the concentrations needed to achieve the same pH, and the amount of base needed to reach the equivalence point in a titration. | 1.4 | 15.1-15.4, 15.7, 16.2, 16.4 |
| 6.13 | The student can interpret titration data for monoprotic or polyprotic acids involving titration of a weak or strong acid by a strong base (or a weak or strong base by a strong acid) to determine the concentration of the titrant and the $pK_a$ for a weak acid, or the $pK_b$ for a weak base. | 5.1 | 16.1-16.4 |
| 6.14 | The student can, based on the dependence of $K_w$ on temperature, reason that neutrality requires $[H^+] = [OH^-]$ as opposed to requiring pH = 7, including especially the applications to biological systems. | 2.2, 6.2 | 15.5 |
| 6.15 | The student can identify a given solution as containing a mixture of strong acids and/or bases and calculate or estimate the pH (and concentrations of all chemical species) in the resulting solution. | 2.2, 2.3, 6.4 | 15.1-16.4 |
| 6.16 | The student can identify a given solution as being the solution of a monoprotic weak acid or base (including salts in which one ion is a weak acid or base), calculate the pH and concentration of all species in the solution, and/or infer the relative strengths of the weak acids or bases from given equilibrium concentrations. | 2.2, 6.4 | 15.1-16.4 |
| 6.17 | The student can, given an arbitrary mixture of weak and strong acids and bases (including polyprotic systems), determine which species will react strongly with one another (i.e., with $K > 1$) and what species will be present in large concentrations at equilibrium. | 6.4 | 15.9, 15.10 |
| 6.18 | The student can design a buffer solution with a target pH and buffer capacity by selecting an appropriate conjugate acid–base pair and estimating the concentrations needed to achieve the desired capacity. | 2.3, 4.2, 6.4 | 16.1 |
| 6.19 | The student can relate the predominant form of a chemical species involving a labile proton (i.e., protonated/deprotonated form of a weak acid) to the pH of a solution and the $pK_a$ associated with the labile proton | 2.3, 5.1, 6.4 | 15.1-15.4 |
| 6.20 | The student can identify a solution as being a buffer solution and explain the buffer mechanism in terms of the reactions that would occur on addition of acid or base. | 6.4 | 16.1-16.4 |
| 6.21 | The student can predict the solubility of a salt, or rank the solubility of salts, given the relevant $K_{sp}$ values. | 2.2, 2.3, 6.4 | 16.5-16.7 |
| 6.22 | The student can interpret data regarding solubility of salts to determine, or rank, the relevant $K_{sp}$ values. | 2.2, 2.3, 6.4 | 16.5-16.7 |
| 6.23 | The student can interpret data regarding the relative solubility of salts in terms of factors (common ions, pH) that influence the solubility. | 5.1 | 16.5-16.7 |

| | Learning Objective | Science Practice | Chapter and Section |
|---|---|---|---|
| 6.24 | The student can analyze the enthalpic and entropic changes associated with the dissolution of a salt, using particulate level interactions and representations. | 1.4, 7.1 | 12.3 |
| 6.25 | The student is able to express the equilibrium constant in terms of $\Delta G°$ and $RT$ and use this relationship to estimate the magnitude of $K$ and, consequently, the thermodynamic favorability of the process. | 2.3 | 17.9 |

Upon publication, this text was correlated to the College Board's AP® Chemistry Curriculum Framework for the 2013–2014 school year. We continually monitor the College Board's AP® Course Description for updates to exam topics. For the most current AP® correlation for this textbook, visit PearsonSchool.com/Advanced.

AP® Chemistry is broken down into six big ideas. These big ideas all have enduring understandings, science practices, and learning objectives which accompany them. Each chapter will identify the learning objectives and science practices within the chapter to be mastered. Some of the objectives may be listed for several chapters where different parts of an objective may be addressed.

Five questions similar to the AP® style questions accompany each chapter. Some of these questions are foundational in nature and will not be on an actual AP® Chemistry Exam but will be expected as part of the steps to solve actual AP® problems. For instance the AP® Exam will not ask you to change measurements from grams to moles and milliliters to liters but both of these will need to be done as a part of solving a problem to determine a molarity when the mass of the solute is given in grams and the volume of solution is given in milliliters.

This manual is a quick review of vocabulary and concepts needed to be successful in AP® Chemistry. Refer to Chemistry: A Molecular Approach, 3rd Edition, by Nivaldo Tro for additional examples and problems on each concept.

# MATTER, MEASUREMENT, AND PROBLEM SOLVING

This is a foundational chapter and many of the concepts and skills discussed here will be review from your first-year chemistry course or other science classes. Every chapter has vocabulary you must recognize and understand to determine what a given problem on the AP Exam is asking you to address. It is important you recognize some vocabulary words have very specific definitions in chemistry, which may be different from how they are used in general language. Be sure to review Section 1.8 "Solving Chemical Problems" and the definitions in Section 1.5 "Energy: A Fundamental Part of Physical and Chemical Change" in the text. In addition, pay close attention to the following sections to review concepts:

1.3 **Classification of Matter: Solid, Liquid, and Gas**

1.4 **Physical and Chemical Changes and Physical and Chemical Properties**

1.6 **The Units of Measurement**

1.7 **The Reliability of a Measurement**

## Specific Learning Objectives Addressed in This Chapter:

**Learning objective 1.3** The student is able to select and apply mathematical relationships to mass data in order to justify a claim regarding the identity and/or estimated purity of a substance. [*See* **SP 2.2, 6.1**]

**Learning Objective 1.13** Given information about a particular model of the atom, the student is able to determine if the model is consistent with specified evidence. [*See* **SP 5.3**]

**Learning Objective 1.17** The student is able to express the law of conservation of mass quantitatively and qualitatively using symbolic representations and particulate drawings. [*See* **SP 1.5**]

**Learning Objective 2.19** The student can create visual representations of ionic substances that connect the microscopic structure to macroscopic properties, and/or use representations to connect the microscopic structure to macroscopic properties (e.g., boiling point, solubility, hardness, brittleness, low volatility, lack of malleability, ductility, or conductivity). [*See* **SP 1.1, 1.4, 7.1**]

**Learning Objective 2.20** The student is able to explain how a bonding model involving delocalized electrons is consistent with macroscopic properties of metals (e.g., conductivity, malleability, ductility, and low volatility) and the shell model of the atom. [*See* **SP 6.2, 7.1**]

**Learning Objective 3.1** Students can translate among macroscopic observations of change, chemical equations, and particle views. [*See* **SP 1.5, 7.1**]

**Learning Objective 3.2** The student can translate an observed chemical change into a balanced chemical equation and justify the choice of equation type (molecular, ionic, or net ionic) in terms of utility for the given circumstances. [*See* **SP 1.5, 7.1**]

**Learning Objective 3.10** The student is able to evaluate the classification of a process as a physical change, chemical change, or ambiguous change based on both macroscopic observations and the distinction between rearrangement of covalent interactions and noncovalent interactions. [*See* **SP 1.4, 6.1**]

## Specific Science Practices Addressed in This Chapter:

**Science Practice 1:** The student can use representations and models to communicate scientific phenomena and solve scientific problems.

> 1.1 The student can *create representations and models* of natural or man-made phenomena and systems in the domain.
>
> 1.4 The student can *use representations and models* to analyze situations or solve problems qualitatively and quantitatively.
>
> 1.5 The student can *re-express key elements* of natural phenomena across multiple representations in the domain.

**Science Practice 2:** The student can use mathematics appropriately.

> 2.2 The student can *apply mathematical routines to quantities* that describe natural phenomena.
>
> 2.3 The student can *estimate numerically quantities* that describe natural phenomena.

**Science Practice 5:** The student can perform data analysis and evaluation of evidence.

> 5.1 The student can *analyze data to identify patterns and relationships*.
>
> 5.3 The student can *evaluate the evidence provided by data sets* in relation to a particular scientific question.

**Science Practice 6:** The student can work with scientific explanations and theories.

  6.1  The student can *justify claims with evidence.*

  6.2  The student can *construct explanations of phenomena based on evidence* produced through scientific practices.

**Science Practice 7:** The student is able to connect and relate knowledge across various scales, concepts, and representations in and across domains.

  7.1  The student can *connect phenomena and models* across spatial and temporal scales.


## Concepts and Vocabulary to Review:

## Atoms and Molecules                    Section 1.1

**Atoms** are the building blocks of matter. Atoms can combine to form molecules and compounds. Atoms are "conserved"—they are never created or destroyed (except through nuclear processes). Molecules, on the other hand, can be restructured in chemical reactions.


## The Scientific Approach to Knowledge          Section 1.2

The **Law of Conservation of Mass** states "In a chemical reaction, matter is neither created nor destroyed." Antoine Lavoisier and others demonstrated this law through very careful measurements. The Law of Conservation of Mass forms the basis of chemistry predictions for the amounts of products produced in chemical reactions, given the starting amounts. (This law remains true for chemical reactions in this course. For nuclear equations, Albert Einstein explained the equation $E = mc^2$, which indicates matter and energy can be interchanged. The conservation of mass–energy as a combined property is now a fundamental principle in physics.)


## Classification of Matter: Solid, Liquid, and Gas          Section 1.3

**Matter** has mass and takes up space, although the space may be very small. Atoms are the fundamental chemical components of matter and are not visible to the naked eye. They can now be visualized using recently developed equipment called *atomic force microscopes*. Atoms in matter may be made up of molecules—atoms closely organized in small groups. In the following descriptions, the term *species* applies to atoms, ions, or molecules, or in some cases, mixtures of these.

**Solid** matter is closely packed together and the species composing the solid are in relatively fixed positions. A solid has a fixed volume and shape.

**Crystalline** solids have an ordered pattern in their shape. A few examples are salt (sodium chloride) and ice (solid water). Crystals generally have well-defined internal and external shapes, and can only be compressed under extremely high pressures.

In **amorphous** solids, there is a lack of an ordered arrangement although the species composing the solid may be arranged in long chains or rings. An example of an amorphous solid is glass.

**Liquid** matter, like solid matter, is closely packed together. However, liquid matter can move independent to each other. Water molecules in liquid water move over, under, and around other water molecules. Liquids take the shape of the container they occupy and can only be compressed under high pressure.

**Gases** are a type of matter not closely packed together, which results in their ability to be easily compressed. If a substance is not a gas under standard conditions of 1 atmosphere and 25°C, when it changes to a gas it is called a *vapor*. Liquid water when heated changes to gaseous water vapor.

**Elements** are composed of one or more atoms, each having the same number of protons. Elements cannot be chemically broken down into smaller substances.

**Compounds** are substances with two or more elements bonded together in fixed proportions, such as water with two hydrogen atoms and one oxygen atom.

**Pure substances** are composed of a single type of component (either an element or a compound) and the composition of the substance does not vary.

**Mixtures** are composed of more than one component and the composition can vary.

**Heterogeneous mixtures** are mixtures with a varied composition. An example is hot cocoa with marshmallows on top.

**Homogeneous mixtures** are mixtures with a uniform composition as a result of uniform mixing. An example is lemonade (without pulp). The sugar, water, and lemon juice are uniformly mixed. Poorly stirred lemonade may well be heterogeneous! To be homogeneous it must be well mixed. Mixtures can also be gases. Air is such an example. While air seems truly homogenous, its composition varies from place to place and day to day, so it is classified as heterogeneous.

Classifying Matter can be quickly reviewed by using the chart on page 5. You will be expected to know how to physically or chemically test to see what type of matter is present. Figure 1.1 represents an illustration of how one might classify matter.

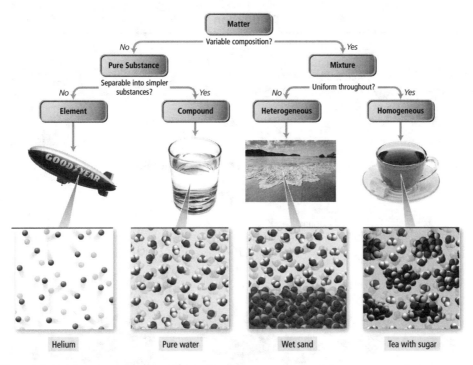

**Figure 1.1** Chart to determine if a substance is an element, compound, homogeneous mixture or heterogeneous mixture.

Some procedures or techniques used to determine the classification of matter include decanting, filtering, and distilling. Refer to Figure 1.2 for how to set up distillation and filtration.

**Volatile** is a term used for a liquid easily changed to its vapor state. Ammonia, a volatile liquid, easily changes to vapor as evidenced by the way the odor moves through a room when a bottle is opened. However, the ammonia you see in the lab is not pure ammonia, but a solution of ammonia in water. The pure vapor is easily released from the solution.

**Decanting** is a technique during which a heterogeneous mixture can be separated carefully by pouring one substance from the other. A mixture such as sand and water can be decanted by pouring off the layer of water.

**Distillation** is a technique used to separate liquid substances, often in a homogeneous mixture, with different boiling points. The lower boiling point substance will boil off first and can be collected in a different flask, thereby separating two liquid substances. When a water and ethanol mixture is distilled, the ethanol will evaporate first.

**Filtration** is a technique used to separate solids from liquids in a heterogeneous mixture. Filtration takes place by pouring a heterogeneous mixture through a funnel fitted with a piece of filter paper. Only liquids will move through the paper, separating solids such as precipitates from the liquid.

**Distillation**

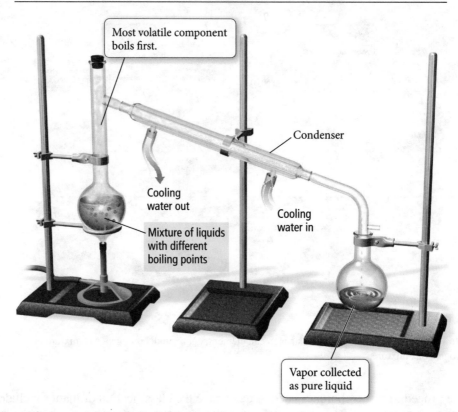

**Figure 1.2  Separating Substances by Distillation**   When a liquid mixture is heated, the component with the lowest boiling point vaporizes first, leaving behind less volatile liquids or dissolved solids. The vapor is then cooled, condensing it back to a liquid, and collected.

## Section 1.4   Physical and Chemical Changes and Physical and Chemical Properties

The properties of matter are either physical or chemical properties. Physical properties are observed without the substance undergoing a chemical reaction. Identifying a sample as a white solid or blue solution are physical properties. Some other physical properties are the temperatures at which a substance undergoes boiling, freezing, condensation, evaporation, sublimation, and deposition. Other examples can be observing whether a substance has an odor, has a certain color, has a certain appearance, and from calculations based on measurements has a certain density. Physical changes occur when a substance changes state but it remains the same substance. Boiling, freezing, subliming are some examples of conditions where a change of state occurs. Another example of a physical change is when one substance dissolves in another substance. Chemical properties are observed when a substance undergoes a chemical reaction. The flammability of a gas (ease of burning in air), corrosiveness, rusting, and toxicity are some examples. Chemical changes occur when the substance reacts and changes into a new substance.

**Physical properties** are observed without the substance undergoing change in identity. For example, the color and state of matter of a substance can be observed. However, some physical properties can only be observed by adding or removing energy, such as boiling or freezing, so the substance undergoes a change of state.

**Chemical properties** are only observed when the substance changes its composition in a chemical reaction. Gasoline is a flammable gas. Its chemical property of flammability is observed as gasoline undergoes a combustion reaction with oxygen to form the new substances of carbon dioxide and water.

**Physical changes** involve changes to the physical state or form of the substance without changing its identity. The changes in states from liquid water to water vapor by boiling or from liquid water to ice by freezing are examples of physical changes. The composition is still two hydrogen atoms to one oxygen atom within the molecule. For example, cutting a sample of a solid substance in half will result in two pieces, both with the same original chemical identity despite their difference in physical appearance (shape).

**Chemical changes** involve chemical reactions where the substances change into other substances. Gasoline combusting into carbon dioxide and water is an example. The original material is no longer present and new chemical substances can be identified as having been produced.

## Energy: A Fundamental Part of Physical and Chemical Change

Section 1.5

**Kinetic energy** is the energy of motion. Atoms and/or molecules are constantly in motion as in the vibration motion within a solid or the translational motion in a gas.

**Potential energy** is the energy of position or composition. Compounds have potential energy in bonds. Substances have potential energy by virtue of their relative positions.

The **Law of Conservation of Energy** states that energy is neither created nor destroyed, although the energy may change into different types. (Refer to the law of conservation of mass *about* matter and energy being interchangeable.)

**Thermal energy** is the kinetic energy associated with the temperature of an object.

**Temperature** is a measure of molecular motion. Molecules moving quickly will have a higher temperature than those moving slowly.

**Heat** is thermal energy transferred when two objects are in the process of exchanging energy with each other. Thermal energy is thought to move from the hot object to the cooler object. If the two objects are at the same temperature, heat dynamically exchanges, but there is no net heat change.

## Section 1.6    The Units of Measurement

In the United States, both metric and nonmetric units are common. Conversions between metric and nonmetric units are not expected in the AP curriculum. Although chemistry only uses metric units, not all those units used are expressed in the standard basic SI unit. For instance, the basic SI unit of mass is the kilogram, but, in chemistry lab, the masses are usually measured in grams or smaller fractions of grams (such as milligrams) (a sub-unit in SI). Review the symbols and the units in Table 1.1.

**Mass** is a measure of the quantity of matter. Mass is different from weight. Weight is affected by gravitational force. An object on the moon has the same mass on Earth but has a different weight since the gravitational force (gravity) is different in both locations.

Knowledge of conversions between some units is necessary, such as converting between the temperature scales of Celsius and Kelvin. In this instance, the conversion is °C + 273.15 is the temperature in Kelvin since the degree itself is the same size in both scales, only the starting points of the scales differ.

Prefixes and how to use them to perform conversions between units are reviewed in Table 1.2, which shows the SI prefix multipliers.

**Volume** is a measure of the space matter occupies. Two volume units and their equivalents important to be familiar with in AP chemistry are: 1 mL, which is equal in volume to 1 $cm^3$, and 1 L, which is equal to 1,000 mL or 1 $dm^3$ at standard conditions.

**Derived units** are units that are not directly observed because they are combinations of units. Examples include units for density and speed. Measurements of volume and mass can be observed and then used to determine the density of an object. Distance traveled and the time it took can be measured and then used to calculate speed. Derived units are usually ratios such as km/hr. It is important to be familiar with how to use them as conversion factors in problems.

**Table 1.1**    SI base units.

| Quantity | Unit | Symbol |
|---|---|---|
| Length | Meter | m |
| Mass | Kilogram | kg |
| Time | Second | s |
| Temperature | Kelvin | K |
| Amount of substance | Mole | mol |
| Electric current | Ampere | A |
| Luminous intensity | Candela | cd |

**Table 1.2**  SI prefix multipliers.

| Prefix | Symbol | Multiplier | |
|--------|--------|------------|---|
| exa | E | 1,000,000,000,000,000,000 | $(10^{18})$ |
| peta | P | 1,000,000,000,000,000 | $(10^{15})$ |
| tera | T | 1,000,000,000,000 | $(10^{12})$ |
| giga | G | 1,000,000,000 | $(10^{9})$ |
| mega | M | 1,000,000 | $(10^{6})$ |
| kilo | k | 1000 | $(10^{3})$ |
| deci | d | 0.1 | $(10^{-1})$ |
| centi | c | 0.01 | $(10^{-2})$ |
| milli | m | 0.001 | $(10^{-3})$ |
| micro | μ | 0.000001 | $(10^{-6})$ |
| nano | n | 0.000000001 | $(10^{-9})$ |
| pico | p | 0.000000000001 | $(10^{-12})$ |
| femto | f | 0.000000000000001 | $(10^{-15})$ |
| atto | a | 0.000000000000000001 | $(10^{-18})$ |

**Density** is a physical property which is calculated from measurements of the mass and volume of an object. The density ratio is the mass divided by the volume of the object. No matter how the mass or volume of the substance changes, the ratio between them for a given substance remains the same. Whether 175 g of water or 25 mL of water are present in a beaker, the ratio of mass to volume for water under standard conditions is 1.0 g/mL. When identifying an unknown in a laboratory setting, the density of an object can be used as evidence for substance identification.

## The Reliability of a Measurement    Section 1.7

How to make or read measurements is an important skill. Every scientific measurement is reported, so every digit in the measurement is certain except for the last digit, which is approximate. A measurement reported as 22.46 g indicates for certain 22.4 grams are present but the last digit in the hundredths position indicates the 6 was close but not certain. The approximate digit is part of the significant figures in a measurement. This means the actual value was between 22.45 g and 22.47 g. In other words, there is a chance the last digit could be different by $\pm 0.01$.

**Significant figures** are the measured digits in a reported measurement and they do not include placeholders. The zero in 0.1 g is a placeholder and not significant while the one was measured and is significant. The measurement 0.1 g has one significant figure.

Review how to determine the number of significant figures in a measurement with the following rules:

**Nonzero digits** are ALL significant.

### Zeros in a measurement

- Zeros between two nonzero digits were measured and are significant. The measurement 204 g has three significant figures.

- Zeros at the beginning of a number are placeholders and are not significant. The measurement 0.0021 cm has only two significant figures (the 2 and the 1).

- Zeros which are at the end of a number when a decimal is present were measured and are significant. 21.00 g has four significant figures. 20. g has two significant figures.

  - Zeros at the end of a number without a decimal are placeholders and are not significant figures. The measurement 210 g has two significant figures (the 2 and the 1). If all three digits were measured and the 210 g is exact, AP uses a decimal point after the zero to make the zero "significant," 210. g. It can also be written in scientific notation as $2.10 \times 10^2$ g. All digits in scientific notation are significant.

Exact numbers and whole numbers in conversion factors have unlimited significant figures. These include defined equivalency numbers used in conversion factor ratios, such as 1000 mL = 1 L.

### Significant Figures in Calculations

The proper use of significant figures is expected in all calculations. "Rounding" is the process used for reporting results of complex calculations correctly. Remember to only round once in a problem—at the end. Keeping track of the number of significant figures to record when there are multiple operations is important. Why only round once? Rounding each time there is a calculation compounds the error in the answer.

The following rules are used in calculations with significant figures:

- Multiplication and division both round to the least number of digits found in the measurements being used in the calculation. To find the density of a compound the mass is divided by the volume. If the mass is 10.0 g, a three digit number, and the volume is 5.0 mL, a two digit number, then the density is 10.0 g ÷ 5.0 mL = 2.0 g/mL. The two digits in the volume indicate the final answer will have two digits.

- Addition and subtraction round to the least precise of the starting measurements. For instance in the example 120.0 g − 58 g, 120.0 g is measured to the tenth and 58 g is measured to the whole number. 58 g is the least precise indicating the final answer would be rounded to the whole number or 62 g.

- Only look at the next digit to determine how to round to the correct number of significant figures. A 5 or higher in the next digit rounds up and a 4 or lower rounds down. 22.47 g rounded to the tenth is 22.5 g, whereas 22.445 g rounded to the tenth is 22.4 g.

**Accuracy** is how close a measurement is to its true value (when this is known).

**Precision** has two definitions. Depending on the context, one definition may work better than the other. It may mean how close a series of measurements are to each other (what you actually measure). Often precision is expressed relative to the mean (average) value of a series of measurements of the same parameter. How close repeated measurements are to each other is an example of precision. For example if one measures the mass of a bar of copper on the same balance three times: 5.258 g, 5.257 g, 5.257 g, the measurements are considered precise. Precision may also refer to the exactness of a single measurement. A measurement having a large number of decimal places and consequently a small uncertainty is considered very precise. For example, if a balance measures the mass of a bar of copper as 5.2583 g, it is more precise compared to a balance providing a measurement of 5.28 g.

Measurements can be precise and accurate (a measurement close to the true value multiple times), precise and inaccurate (the same wrong measurement several times), and accurate and imprecise (averaging close to the true value, but the measurements are not close to each other).

## Solving Chemical Problems    Section 1.8

**Conversion factors** are ratios using the relationship between the two units to convert from one unit to the other. The ratio is written so the units cancel to result in the new desired unit. For example, if you are converting from liters to milliliters, $\dfrac{1000 \text{ mL}}{1 \text{ L}}$ is the conversion factor to cancel the L, but if the conversion is from milliliters to liters it would be written as $\dfrac{1 \text{ L}}{1000 \text{ mL}}$ to cancel the mL.

**Dimensional analysis** uses relationships among units as a way to solve problems. For instance, if converting the speed 21.4 km per hour ($km \cdot hr^{-1}$ or km/hr) to meters per second ($m \cdot s^{-1}$ or m/s), there will be two conversions steps. One step converts kilometers to meters and the other step converts hours to seconds. Using the conversion factors $\dfrac{1000 \text{ m}}{1 \text{ km}}$ and $\dfrac{1 \text{ hr}}{3600 \text{ s}}$, the problem would be written as $\dfrac{21.4 \text{ km}}{1 \text{ hr}} \times \dfrac{1000 \text{ m}}{1 \text{ km}} \times \dfrac{1 \text{ hr}}{3600 \text{ s}}$. The first step converted the km units and the second step converted the hr units. This process is used throughout the chemistry curriculum in numerical problems.

**Additional Practice**

*Self-Assessment Quiz Questions Q2, Q7, Q8, Q9, and Q11*
*Problems 35, 41, 42, 43, 45, 47, 49, 59, 60, 68, 73, 74, 77, 79, 81, 83, and 87*

**Practice AP® Test Questions**

1. This thermometer is measuring the temperature of a liquid in units of Celsius. What is the correct temperature using the proper number of significant figures?

   A) 19.7

   B) 19.68

   C) 19.70

   D) 19.59

2. Which of the following is not a physical property of chlorine gas?

   A) Chlorine gas has a pale green color.

   B) The normal boiling point of chlorine gas is 239 K.

   C) Chlorine gas irritates the mucus membranes.

   D) The density of chlorine gas at STP is 3.2 g/L.

3. Which of the following can be separated using filtration?

   A) A solution of sodium chloride

   B) Copper turnings in water

   C) Oxygen and helium gas in a gas cylinder

   D) 5% skim milk

4. Provide the reason for selection of your answer to the previous problem.

   A) All mixtures can be easily separated using physical techniques such as filtration, decanting, and evaporation.

   B) The solvent in a solution can be separated from the solute by filtration since the solute and solvent do not react.

   C) Any component of a homogeneous mixture that is visible can be separated by filtration because the particles are too large to pass through the small holes in the filter paper.

   D) If a substance is not soluble in a solvent, filtration can be used to separate the two components because the insoluble substance is too large to pass through the holes in the filter paper.

5. Which drawing at the particulate level of matter best represents a small sample of Helium gas?

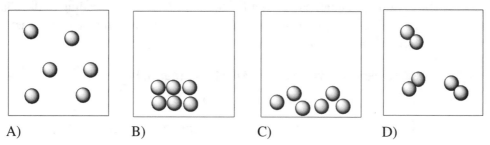

A)          B)          C)          D)

# ATOMS AND ELEMENTS

To understand the development of our current knowledge of atoms and their structure, there are several points in this chapter that require your attention. In the past, some concepts that we now accept regarding the atom were met with skepticism and were not readily accepted. Other ideas have been discarded in light of more recent evidence. In this chapter, pay particular attention to the **DATA** leading to the change or new concept being introduced and the new MODEL created by this evidence. The most important sections to review are as follows:

2.3  **Modern Atomic Theory and the Laws That Led to It**

2.5  **Structure of the Atom**

2.6  **Subatomic Particles: Protons, Neutrons, and Electrons in Atoms**

2.8  **Atomic Mass: The Average Mass of an Element's Atoms**

2.9  **Molar Mass: Counting Atoms by Weighing Them**

## Specific Learning Objectives Addressed in This Chapter:

**Learning objective 1.1** The student can justify the observation that the ratio of the masses of the constituent elements in any pure sample of that compound is always identical on the basis of the atomic molecular theory. [*See* **SP 6.1**]

**Learning objective 1.4** The student is able to connect the number of particles, moles, mass, and volume of substances to one another, both qualitatively and quantitatively. [*See* **SP 7.1**]

**Learning objective 1.12** The student is able to explain why a given set of data suggests, or does not suggest, the need to refine the atomic model from a classical shell model with the quantum mechanical model. [*See* **SP 6.3**]

**Learning objective 1.13** Given information about a particular model of the atom, the student is able to determine if the model is consistent with specified evidence. [*See* **SP 5.3**]

**Learning objective 1.14** The student is able to use data from mass spectrometry to identify the elements and the masses of individual atoms of a specific element. [*See* **SP 1.4, 1.5**]

**Learning objective 1.17** The student is able to express the law of conservation of mass quantitatively and qualitatively using symbolic representations and particulate drawings. [*See* **SP 1.5**]

**Learning objective 1.18** The student is able to apply conservation of atoms to the re-arrangement of atoms in various processes. [*See* **SP 1.4**]

**Learning objective 3.5** The student is able to design a plan in order to collect data on the synthesis or decomposition of a compound to confirm the conservation of matter and the law of definite proportions. [*See* **SP 2.1, 4.2**]

**Learning objective 3.6** The student is able to use data from synthesis or decomposition of a compound to confirm the conservation of matter and the law of definite proportions. [*See* **SP 2.2, 6.1**]

## Specific Science Practices Addressed in This Chapter:

**Science Practice 1:** The student can use representations and models to communicate scientific phenomena and solve scientific problems.

   1.1   The student can *create representations and models* of natural or man-made phenomena and systems in the domain.

   1.4   The student can *use representations and models* to analyze situations or solve problems qualitatively and quantitatively.

   1.5   The student can *re-express key elements* of natural phenomena across multiple representations in the domain.

**Science Practice 2:** The student can use mathematics appropriately.

   2.2   The student can *apply mathematical routines* to quantities that describe natural phenomena.

   2.3   The student can *estimate numerically quantities* that describe natural phenomena.

**Science Practice 4:** The student can plan and implement data collection strategies in relation to a particular scientific question.

   4.2   The student can *design a plan* for collecting data to answer a particular scientific question.

**Science Practice 5:** The student can perform data analysis and evaluation of evidence.

   5.1   The student can analyze data to identify patterns and relationships.

   5.3   The student can *evaluate the evidence provided by data sets* in relation to a particular scientific question.

**Science Practice 6:** The student can work with scientific explanations and theories.

6.1   The student can *justify claims with evidence*.

6.3   The student can *articulate the reasons that scientific explanations and theories are refined or replaced*.

**Science Practice 7:** The student is able to connect and relate knowledge across various scales, concepts, and representations in and across domains.

7.1   The student can *connect phenomena and models* across spatial and temporal scales.

### Concepts and Vocabulary to Review:

Section 2.3

## Modern Atomic Theory and the Laws That Led to It

With the **Law of Definite Proportions**, Joseph Proust stated that all the elements composing a specific compound are always found in exact or fixed ratios of weight (mass) in the compound. In contrast, mixtures can have a variety of ratios. The compound water ($H_2O$) is always 16.0 g of oxygen atoms to 2.0 g of hydrogen atoms, which is a ratio of 8:1.

With the **Law of Multiple Proportions**, John Dalton stated that when two elements combine to form different compounds, the atoms in each of the compounds formed have a different fixed ratio. For instance, both water and hydrogen peroxide are both made of only hydrogen and oxygen atoms. Water as noted above has a ratio of 8:1 by mass, but hydrogen peroxide ($H_2O_2$) has 32.0 g of oxygen atoms to 2.0 g of hydrogen atoms, which is a ratio of 16:1 by mass. The ratio of mass of oxygen in water (8:1) to mass of oxygen in hydrogen peroxide (16:1) is 1:2. Using Dalton's theory, there must be twice as many oxygen atoms in hydrogen peroxide compared to the number of oxygen atoms in water.

In a series of experiments, a chemist analyzed two different compounds containing only titanium and bromine and determined the mass of each element in each compound.

| Compound | Mass of Bromine (g) | Mass of Titanium (g) |
|---|---|---|
| 1 | 17.394 | 2.605 |
| 2 | 15.390 | 4.610 |

Calculate the mass of bromine per gram of titanium in each compound. How do the numbers support the atomic theory?

$$Compound\ 1 \quad \frac{17.394\ \text{g Br}}{2.605\ \text{g Ti}} = \frac{6.69\ \text{g Br}}{1\ \text{g Ti}}$$

$$Compound\ 2 \quad \frac{15.390\ \text{g Br}}{4.610\ \text{g Ti}} = \frac{3.34\ \text{g Br}}{1\ \text{g Ti}}$$

$$\frac{Compound\ 1}{Compound\ 2} = \frac{6.69\ \text{g Br}}{3.34\ \text{g Br}} = \frac{2}{1}$$

The ratio of mass in units of grams of bromine in compound 1 to mass of bromine in compound 2 is 2:1. This ratio uses small whole numbers. The two compounds obey the law of multiple proportions. The only way for this to occur is for the bromine and titanium to combine using atoms. For every one bromine atom in compound 2 there are two bromine atoms in compound 1. Possible compounds include $TiBr$, $TiBr_2$ and $TiBr_4$ or $TiBr_3$ and $TiBr_6$. Additional calculations can be done using the above data to determine which formulas fit the data.

Dalton reintroduced the idea of the existence atoms, saying that all matter is composed of atoms; the atoms combine in whole number ratios; and in chemical reactions, atoms cannot change into other types of atoms. A hydrogen atom is always a hydrogen atom. (Only nuclear reactions can change the type.) He also stated ALL atoms of the same element have the same mass, which was later disproved. There is no single mass for a given element due to the existence of isotopes, which creates a range of masses for each element. A periodic table of the elements will list the weighted average mass of all of the naturally occurring isotopes of the element.

## The Discovery of the Electron    Section 2.4

J.J. Thompson using cathode ray tubes discovered the electron, a negatively charged subatomic particle with very little mass.

Robert Millikan followed this up with his oil drop experiment indicating the charge of a single electron was $-1.60 \times 10^{-19}$ C (coulombs). Using this data, the mass of the electron was then calculated to be $9.10 \times 10^{-28}$ g

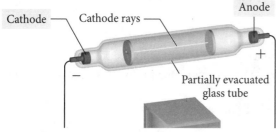

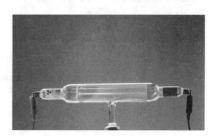

**Figure 2.1  Cathode Ray Tube**

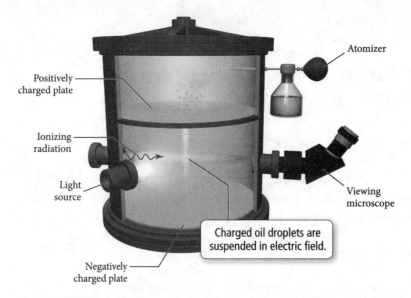

**Figure 2.2  Millikan's Measurement of the Electron's Charge**   Millikan calculated the charge on oil droplets falling in an electric field. He found that it was always a whole-number multiple of $-1.60 \times 10^{-19}$ C, the charge of a single electron.

## Section 2.5    Structure of the Atom

From the discovery of the electron, **J.J. Thompson** suggested the atom was like a positive pudding with electrons spread through it—this is known as the **plum pudding model**.

**Ernest Rutherford** changed the concept of the plum pudding model to a **nuclear model** after doing the gold foil experiment. Rutherford found there had to be a dense, positively charged area in the atom to repel alpha particles ($He^{2+}$) being shot through the atom. The core of the atom, where the dense positive charge was located, was called the nucleus of the atom. The positive particles were called protons. In contrast to the dense, closely packed nucleus, the rest of the atom where the electrons were found was mostly empty space.

The last particle was hard to observe since it was neutral in charge. This was the neutron and was identified by James Chadwick although it had been observed earlier.

## Section 2.6    Subatomic Particles: Protons, Neutrons, and Electrons in Atoms

**Atomic mass unit** is $1/12$ th the mass of a carbon-12 atom with six protons and six neutrons (carbon can have different numbers of neutrons). One proton has a mass of 1 amu.

**Atomic number** is the number of protons in the atom.

**Mass number** is the sum of the protons and neutrons present in the atom.

**Isotopes** are atoms of the same element with different masses. They have the same number of protons and electrons, but greater or lesser numbers of neutrons.

**Ions** are a charged species due to atoms or groups of atoms losing or gaining electrons.

**Cations** are positively charged ions due to the loss of electrons.

**Anions** are negatively charged ions due to the gain of electrons.

### Calculating numbers of protons, neutrons, and electrons:

✓ The proton number is the atomic number of the atom.

✓ The mass number is the sum of the number of protons and neutrons.

✓ The neutron number is the mass number minus the number of protons.

✓ The electron number equals the proton number in an atom but for an ion, the sum of the proton charge and electron charge equals the charge of the ion. So positive ions have more protons than electrons whereas anions have more electrons than protons.

Note that it is easier to use mass values in amu or Daltons (symbol Da) than grams because the mass is so small. A carbon-12 atom is defined to have a mass of 12.0000 Da or 12.0000 amu.

Summary table of subatomic particles:

| Particle | Charge (Relative) | Mass (g) | Mass (amu or Da) |
|----------|-------------------|----------|------------------|
| Proton   | +1                | $1.672 \times 10^{-24}$ | 1.00727 |
| Neutron  | 0                 | $1.674 \times 10^{-24}$ | 1.00866 |
| Electron | −1                | $9.10 \times 10^{-20}$  | 0.00055 |

## Atomic Mass: The Average Mass of an Element's Atoms    Section 2.8

**Atomic mass** is the average mass of an atom of an element. Because elements can have isotopes, the mass on the periodic table is a weighted average of the isotopic masses. If you know the main isotopes of carbon have masses of 12, 13, and 14, and the mass on the table is 12.01 amu, we know there must be a much higher percentage of carbon with a mass of 12 than carbon with a mass of 13 or 14.

$$\text{Atomic mass} = \sum (\text{fraction of isotope } z \times \text{mass of isotope } z)$$
$$+ (\text{fraction of isotope } y \times \text{mass of isotope } y).$$

Copper has two isotopes: copper 63(62.94) with an abundance of 69.17% and copper 65(64.93) with an abundance of 62.94%. The weighted average atomic mass of copper can be calculated as follows:

$$\text{Atomic mass Cu} = (0.6917 \times 62.94 \text{ amu})$$
$$+ (0.3083 \times 64.93 \text{ amu}) = 63.55 \text{ amu}$$

Be sure you do not confuse atomic mass and mass number. The mass number is an integer sum of the numbers of neutrons and protons; the atomic mass is the actual mass (in appropriate relative units) of the atoms and so does not come to an exact whole number (integer).

**Mass spectrometry** is a technique or method used to separate particles by mass. It separates isotopes of atoms by mass so the relative abundance of an isotope can be determined. From this, the average mass can be determined. It can be used to identify what is in a sample.

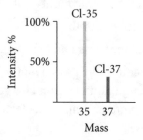

**Figure 2.3  The Mass Spectrum of Chlorine**    The position of each peak on the *x*-axis indicates the mass of the isotope. The intensity (or height) of the peak indicates the relative abundance of the isotope. The intensity of the highest peak is usually set to 100% and the intensity of all other peaks is reported relative to the most intense one.

## Section 2.9    Molar Mass: Counting Atoms by Weighing Them

**1 Mole** represents $6.022 \times 10^{23}$ items. It is similar to using the word dozen. When we hear one dozen, we think of the number 12. It could be oranges, apples, anything. Two dozen is 24, half a dozen is 6 and so on. When you hear mole, think of $6.022 \times 10^{23}$. You can also have multiples or fractions of a mole.

**Avogadro's number** (he did not find the number, but it is named after him) is the number of things (usually atoms or molecules) in a mole, so $6.022 \times 10^{23}$.

**Molar mass** is the mass of one mole of the same thing; this could be atoms, molecules, formula units, etc.

Calculating grams, moles, and number of particles in a species and converting between them requires using a periodic table to find the mass of a mole of each type of atom in the species.

**Additional Practice**

*Self-Assessment Questions Q1, Q5, Q6, Q7, Q11, and Q15*
*Problems 41, 42, 47, 48, 51, 53, 57, 58, 72, 76, 79, 81, 82, 83, 85, and 86*

**Practice AP® Test Questions**

1. Iodine–131 is radioactive and is used to treat thyroid cancer. In $^{131}I^{1-}$, there are
   ____ protons, ____neutrons, and ____ electrons.

   A) 131, 53, 54

   B) 131, 53, 52

   C) 53, 78, 54

   D) 53, 131, 53

2. The elements in Groups 1, 16, and 17 are called ____, ____, and ____,
   respectively.

   A) alkaline earth metals, halogens, chalcogens

   B) alkali metals, chalcogens, halogens

   C) alkali metals, halogens, noble gases

   D) alkaline earth metals, transition metals, halogens

3. If different circles represent different atoms, which "particulate diagram" best
   shows a mixture of two compounds?

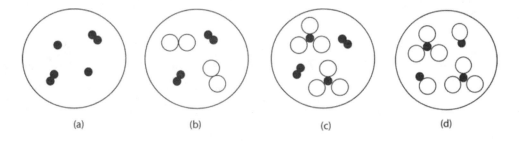

4. Use the following block diagram of the Periodic Table. Which group of elements is most likely to react with calcium to form an ionic compound with the formula $Ca_3X_2$?

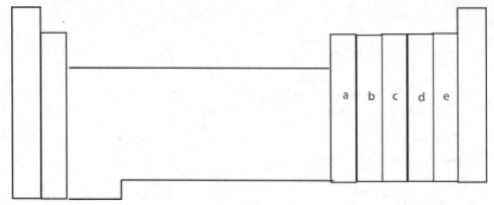

5. Chlorine has two naturally occurring isotopes chlorine-35 and chlorine-37 with masses and natural abundances 34.97 amu (75.77%) and 36.97 amu (24.23%) respectively. Which mass spectrum most likely will look like the mass spectrum of the charged molecular ions of chlorine gas, $Cl_2$?

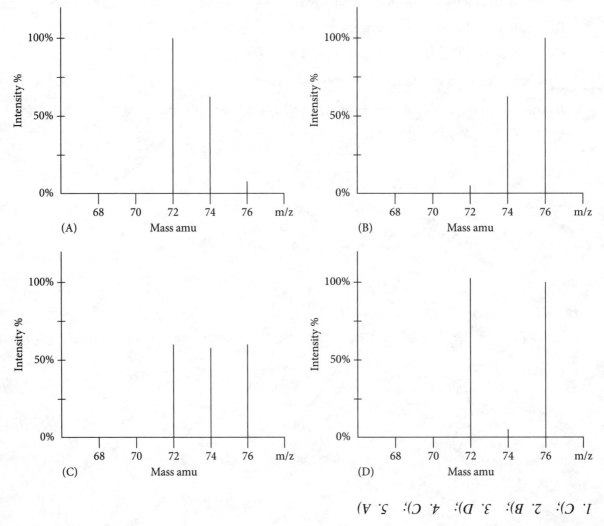

# MOLECULES, COMPOUNDS, AND CHEMICAL EQUATIONS

To understand chemistry, you must first learn the language of chemistry, including all the naming systems of different types of compounds. The majority of this chapter is reviewing the basics of naming ionic- and covalent-bonded compounds. You need to know the molecular and atomic elements in Section 3.4. There is also a short introduction to naming organic compounds, but this will be covered more thoroughly in a later chapter. All of this is foundational knowledge that must be mastered in order to complete any of the problems on the AP exam.

Calculation of molar mass, percent composition, empirical formulas, and molecular formulas are calculations in this chapter that must be mastered. The most important sections to review are as follows:

3.2 **Chemical Bonds**

3.3 **Representing Compounds: Chemical Formulas and Molecular Models**

3.5 **Ionic Compounds: Formulas and Names**

3.6 **Molecular Compounds: Formulas and Names**

3.8 **Formula Mass and the Mole Concept for Compounds**

3.9 **Composition of Compounds**

3.10 **Determining a Chemical Formula from Experimental Data**

3.11 **Writing and Balancing Chemical Equations**

## Specific Learning Objectives Addressed in This Chapter:

**Learning objective 1.1** The student can justify the observation that the ratio of the masses of the constituent elements in any pure sample of that compound is always identical on the basis of the atomic molecular theory. [*See* **SP 6.1**]

**Learning objective 1.2** The student is able to select and apply mathematical routines to mass data to identify or infer the composition of pure substances and/or mixtures. [*See* **SP 2.2**]

**Learning objective 1.4** The student is able to connect the number of particles, moles, mass, and volume of substances to one another, both qualitatively and quantitatively. [*See* **SP 7.1**]

**Learning objective 1.17** The student is able to express the law of conservation of mass quantitatively and qualitatively using symbolic representations and particulate drawings. [*See* **SP 1.5**]

**Learning objective 1.18** The student is able to apply conservation of atoms to the rearrangement of atoms in various processes. [*See* **SP 1.4**]

**Learning objective 2.1** Students can predict properties of substances based on their chemical formulas, and provide explanations of their properties based on particle views. [*See* **SP 6.4, 7.1**]

**Learning objective 3.1** Students can translate among macroscopic observations of change, chemical equations, and particle views. [*See* **SP 1.5, 7.1**]

**Learning objective 3.2** The student can translate an observed chemical change into a balanced chemical equation and justify the choice of equation type (molecular, ionic, or net ionic) in terms of utility for the given circumstances. [*See* **SP 1.5, 7.1**]

**Learning objective 3.3** The student is able to use stoichiometric calculations to predict the results of performing a reaction in the laboratory and/or to analyze deviations from the expected results. [*See* **SP 2.2, 5.1**]

**Learning objective 3.4** The student is able to relate quantities (measured mass of substances, volumes of solutions, or volumes and pressures of gases) to identify stoichiometric relationships for a reaction, including situations involving limiting reactants and situations in which the reaction has not gone to completion. [*See* **SP 2.2, 5.1, 6.4**]

**Learning objective 3.6** The student is able to use data from synthesis or decomposition of a compound to confirm the conservation of matter and the law of definite proportions. [*See* **SP 2.2, 6.1**]

## Specific Science Practices Addressed in This Chapter:

**Science Practice 1:** The student can use representations and models to communicate scientific phenomena and solve scientific problems.

  1.4  The student can *use representations and models* to analyze situations or solve problems qualitatively and quantitatively.

  1.5  The student can *re-express key elements* of natural phenomena across multiple representations in the domain.

**Science Practice 2:** The student can use mathematics appropriately.

2.2 The student can apply mathematical routines to quantities that describe natural phenomena.

2.3 The student can estimate numerically quantities that describe natural phenomena.

**Science Practice 5:** The student can perform data analysis and evaluation of evidence.

5.1 The student can analyze data to identify patterns and relationships.

**Science Practice 6:** The student can work with scientific explanations and theories.

6.1 The student can *justify claims with evidence*.

6.4 The student can *make claims and predictions about natural phenomena* based on scientific theories and models.

**Science Practice 7:** The student is able to connect and relate knowledge across various scales, concepts, and representations in and across domains.

7.1 The student can *connect phenomena and models* across spatial and temporal scales.

## Concepts and Vocabulary to Review:

## Chemical Bonds      Section 3.2

What holds the atoms in compounds together? This is called *chemical bonding*. Two basic bonding concepts exist—ionic and covalent. Some chemical atoms more readily bond by one form than the other.

Ionic bonds result from the formation of ions. Ions are formed when one or more electrons are removed from atoms of one element and transferred to atoms of a second element. This results in an actual charge on those atoms. The electrostatic attractions between the positively and negatively charged ions hold the solid compound together in a three-dimensional lattice. The positively charged ions (cations) and negatively charged ions (anions) alternate. The ionic compound is NOT a discrete molecule. When sodium atoms and chlorine atoms combine to form sodium chloride, NaCl, a sodium atom transfers one electron to a chlorine atom. The sodium atom becomes a sodium cation and the chlorine atoms becomes chloride anion. The $Na^+-Cl^-$ bond is an ionic bond. However, since a group of cations and anions pack close together they form a lattice. The basic unit (the smallest number ratio of each ion in the solid) of the lattice is called a *formula unit* (Section 3.4).

## The Formation of an Ionic Compound

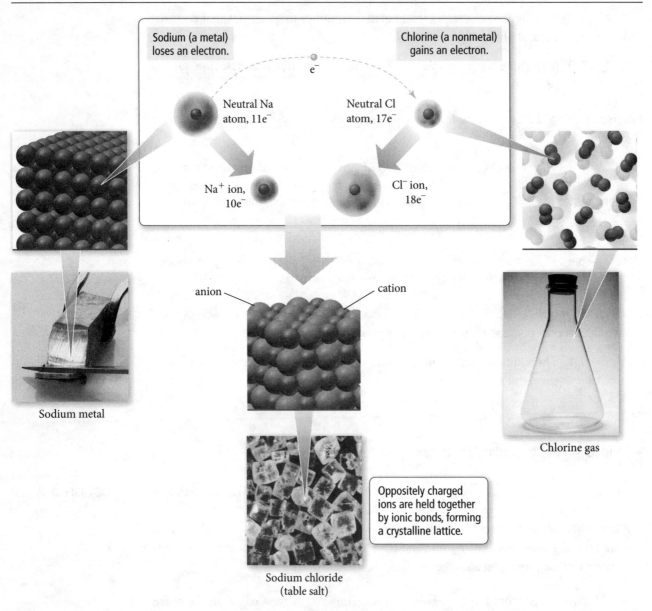

Sodium (a metal) loses an electron.

Chlorine (a nonmetal) gains an electron.

$e^-$

Neutral Na atom, $11e^-$

Neutral Cl atom, $17e^-$

$Na^+$ ion, $10e^-$

$Cl^-$ ion, $18e^-$

Sodium metal

Chlorine gas

anion

cation

Oppositely charged ions are held together by ionic bonds, forming a crystalline lattice.

Sodium chloride (table salt)

**Figure 3.1** The Formation of an Ionic Compound. An atom of sodium (a metal) transfers an electron to a chlorine atom. The sodium atom becomes a $Na^+$ cation and the chlorine atom becomes a $Cl^-$ anion, creating a pair of oppositely charged ions. The sodium cation is attracted to the chloride anion and the two are held together as part of a crystalline lattice.

Covalent bonds, by contrast, are formed by the sharing of electrons between two or more atoms. The atoms may be of the same element (as in hydrogen, $H_2$, or oxygen, $O_2$), or they may be between atoms of differing elements (as in carbon monoxide, CO, or nitrogen dioxide, $NO_2$). The sharing of electrons takes place because the resulting compound is more stable than the individual atoms, meaning that it has a lower potential energy compared to the atoms. When two chlorine atoms combine to share electron density equally, as in $Cl_2$, the Cl–Cl bond is called a covalent bond. $Cl_2$ is a *molecule*.

# Representing Compounds: Chemical Formulas and Molecular Models

Section 3.3

There are many ways to represent a chemical substance on paper and it is important to understand what each type of representation indicates and does not indicate.

The **empirical formula** is the reduced, whole-number formula giving the smallest whole-number ratio of each atom to each of the others. $H_2O_2$ can be reduced to HO; a ratio of one atom of oxygen to every atom of hydrogen. $H_2O$ cannot be reduced and has a ratio of two hydrogen atoms to every oxygen atom. Only integers are used in empirical formulas so $HO_{0.5}$ would not be correct.

A **molecular formula** is the unreduced, full formula of the compound representing the actual composition found by an experiment. In an experiment, data would indicate the ratio of hydrogen atoms to oxygen atoms in hydrogen peroxide is one to one or HO. The molecular formula is always a whole-number multiple of the empirical formula. In the case of hydrogen peroxide, the empirical formula HO is multiplied by 2 to give the molecular formula of $H_2O_2$. While this type of formula fully describes the constituent parts and is used in many calculations, it does not give any idea of the actual geometry or of the arrangement of the atoms in the compound.

A **structural formula** shows how atoms are arranged in the molecule and how they are connected with bonds (represented by lines), providing the position of covalent bonds. If two lines are between two atoms sharing four electrons, the connecting bond is a double bond; if there are three lines, the bond is a triple bond sharing six electrons. A triple bond is the highest order bond between two atoms. There are no quadruple bonds, and so on. While the structural formula tells us more about the connectivity and orders of bonding within the molecule, it still does not tell us anything about the geometry of the molecule.

The **ball-and-stick molecular model** represents atoms as balls and bonds as sticks. This model is a good representation of the connectivity of the atoms in a molecule, and of the three dimensional structure and bond angles. At the same time, however, it is much less convenient in many cases, particularly where calculations are being performed.

The **space-filling molecular model** represents how the model would look scaled to size, with the electron orbitals included from the outside of the molecule. It is a fair approximation to how the molecule would look, should we be able to see something that small.

The following table shows a comparison of several molecules between the different representations.

$CH_4$

Molecular formula

H
|
H—C—H
|
H

Structural formula

Ball-and-stick model

Space-filling model

**TABLE 3.1**   Benzene, Acetylene, Glucose, and Ammonia

| Name of Compound | Empirical Formula | Molecular Formula | Structural Formula | Ball-and-Stick Model | Space-Filling Model |
|---|---|---|---|---|---|
| Benzene | CH | $C_6H_6$ | | | |
| Acetylene | CH | $C_2H_2$ | H—C≡C—H | | |
| Glucose | $CH_2O$ | $C_6H_{12}O_6$ | | | |
| Ammonia | $NH_3$ | $NH_3$ | | | |

## Section 3.5   Ionic Compounds: Formulas and Names

Ionic compounds are usually stable because the attraction between the cations and anions are strong, especially when the ions are packed tightly in a solid lattice. The most familiar is common salt, NaCl, which consists of $Na^+$ and $Cl^-$ ions in a closely packed lattice. To determine the formula of ionic compounds, write the cation symbol first and the anion symbol second; determine what ratio of cations and anions results in the charges adding up to zero; and then write the smallest whole-number ratio in the formula. For NaCl, the $Na^+$ is the cation, the $Cl^-$ the anion, and the ratio is 1:1. In calcium fluoride, there are two fluorine ions for each calcium ion, resulting in a ratio of 1:2. The resulting formula is, then, $CaF_2$.

Naming ionic compounds requires knowledge of the different cation and anion names. In AP, you need to know the systematic naming of ionic compounds. The general format is metal name (Roman numeral if needed) and then the anion name. Roman numerals are needed if a metal can show more than one possible valence state (or oxidation number) leading to alternative compound formulas. Be sure to be able to name the ions and compounds from all the different types of examples given in the text. Following are lists of some cations and anions to know.

**Table 3.2**    Metals Whose Charge Is Invariant from One Compound to Another

| Metal | Ion | Name | Group Number |
|---|---|---|---|
| Li | $Li^+$ | Lithium | 1A |
| Na | $Na^+$ | Sodium | 1A |
| K | $K^+$ | Potassium | 1A |
| Rb | $Rb^+$ | Rubidium | 1A |
| Cs | $Cs^+$ | Cesium | 1A |
| Be | $Be^{2+}$ | Beryllium | 2A |
| Mg | $Mg^{2+}$ | Magnesium | 2A |
| Ca | $Ca^{2+}$ | Calcium | 2A |
| Sr | $Sr^{2+}$ | Strontium | 2A |
| Ba | $Ba^{2+}$ | Barium | 2A |
| Al | $Al^{3+}$ | Aluminum | 3A |
| Zn | $Zn^{2+}$ | Zinc | * |
| Sc | $Sc^{3+}$ | Scandium | * |
| Ag** | $Ag^+$ | Silver | * |

*The charge of these metals cannot be inferred from their group number.
**Silver sometimes forms compounds with other charges, but these are rare.

**Table 3.3**    Some Common Monoatomic Anions

| Nonmetal | Symbol for Ion | Base Name | Anion Name |
|---|---|---|---|
| Fluorine | $F^-$ | fluor | Fluoride |
| Chlorine | $Cl^-$ | chlor | Chloride |
| Bromine | $Br^-$ | brom | Bromide |
| Iodine | $I^-$ | iod | Iodide |
| Oxygen | $O^{2-}$ | ox | Oxide |
| Sulfur | $S^{2-}$ | sulf | Sulfide |
| Nitrogen | $N^{3-}$ | nitr | Nitride |
| Phosphorus | $P^{3-}$ | phosph | Phosphide |

**Table 3.4**    Some Metals That Form Cations with Different Charges

| Metal | Ion | Name | Older Name* |
|-------|-----|------|-------------|
| Chromium | $Cr^{2+}$ | Chromium(II) | Chromous |
|  | $Cr^{3+}$ | Chromium(III) | Chromic |
| Iron | $Fe^{2+}$ | Iron(II) | Ferrous |
|  | $Fe^{3+}$ | Iron(III) | Ferric |
| Cobalt | $Co^{2+}$ | Cobalt(II) | Cobaltous |
|  | $Co^{3+}$ | Cobalt(III) | Cobaltic |
| Copper | $Cu^{+}$ | Copper(I) | Cuprous |
|  | $Cu^{2+}$ | Copper(II) | Cupric |
| Tin | $Sn^{2+}$ | Tin(II) | Stannous |
|  | $Sn^{4+}$ | Tin(IV) | Stannic |
| Mercury | $Hg_2^{2+}$ | Mercury(I) | Mercurous |
|  | $Hg^{2+}$ | Mercury(II) | Mercuric |
| Lead | $Pb^{2+}$ | Lead(II) | Plumbous |
|  | $Pb^{4+}$ | Lead(IV) | Plumbic |

*An older naming system substitutes the names found in this column for the name of the metal and its charge. Under this system, chromium(II) oxide is named chromous oxide. Additionally, the suffix *-ous* indicates the ion with the lesser charge and *-ic* indicates the ion with the greater charge. We will *not* use the older system in this text.

**Table 3.5**    Some Common Polyatomic Ions

| Name | Formula | Name | Formula |
|------|---------|------|---------|
| Acetate | $C_2H_3O_2^-$ | Hypochlorite | $ClO^-$ |
| Carbonate | $CO_3^{2-}$ | Chlorite | $ClO_2^-$ |
| Hydrogen carbonate (or bicarbonate) | $HCO_3^-$ | Chlorate | $ClO_3^-$ |
| Hydroxide | $OH^-$ | Perchlorate | $ClO_4^-$ |
| Nitrite | $NO_2^-$ | Permanganate | $MnO_4^-$ |
| Nitrate | $NO_3^-$ | Sulfite | $SO_3^{2-}$ |
| Chromate | $CrO_4^{2-}$ | Hydrogen sulfite (or bisulfite) | $HSO_3^-$ |
| Dichromate | $Cr_2O_7^{2-}$ | Sulfate | $SO_4^{2-}$ |
| Phosphate | $PO_4^{3-}$ | Hydrogen sulfate (or bisulfate) | $HSO_4^-$ |
| Hydrogen phosphate | $HPO_4^{2-}$ | Cyanide | $CN^-$ |
| Dihydrogen phosphate | $H_2PO_4^-$ | Peroxide | $O_2^{2-}$ |
| Ammonium | $NH_4^+$ | Carbonate | $CO_3^{2-}$ |

Some ionic compounds have enough space between the ions and have enough attraction for water molecules that they actually incorporate the water into the lattice. This makes the lattice even more stable. These types of compounds are called **hydrates**. *Hydrates* are indicated by a molecular formula followed by a dot and a number of water molecules such as in copper (II) sulfate pentahydrate: $CuSO_4 \cdot 5H_2O$. The number of water molecules incorporated into the hydrate is called the water of hydration. You will need to know how to name and write the formula of hydrated ionic compounds.

The water of hydration contained in hydrates can be removed by heating. After waters of hydration are removed from the compounds the remaining **anhydrous** (literally "without water" in Latin) forms have different properties. An example is copper(II) sulfate pentahydrate, whose formula is given above, which is blue, whereas anhydrous copper(II) sulfate $(CuSO_4)$ appears white.

## Molecular Compounds: Formulas and Names      Section 3.6

Molecular (covalently bonded) compounds have a different naming system. These compounds are made of two nonmetals. The format for naming is prefix (except *mon-*) name of first element, prefix base name of second element, then *–ide*. $N_2O_5$ is dinitrogen pentoxide, CO is carbon monoxide (NOT monocarbon monoxide), and $CO_2$ is carbon dioxide (NOT monocarbon dioxide). You should know the first ten prefixes.

A few compounds go by common names, such as water (which would be dihydrogen monoxide). Another common name to know is ammonia, which has the formula $NH_3$.

Another group of compounds frequently encountered are acids. *Acids* are molecular compounds that release hydrogen ions $(H^+)$ when dissolved in water. Naming acids depends on which anion is present in the acid. Generally, compounds are only named as acids when dissolved in water or when water is present.

- If the anion ends in *–ide*, the acid follows the pattern *hydro* (base name of the nonmetal)*ic acid*. In HCl, the anion is chloride so it is named is hydrochloric acid. In the complete absence of water, it is a gas at room temperature and its name is simply hydrogen chloride.

- If the anion ends in *–ate*, the acid follows the pattern (base name of the nonmetal)*ic acid*. In $HNO_3$, the anion is nitrate, so the acid name is nitric acid, NOT hydronitric acid.

- If the anion ends in *–ite*, the acid follows the pattern (base name of the nonmetal)*ous acid*. In $HNO_2$, the anion is nitrite, so the acid name is nitrous acid.

All the naming rules are summarized in the following table:

**Inorganic Nomenclature Flow Chart**

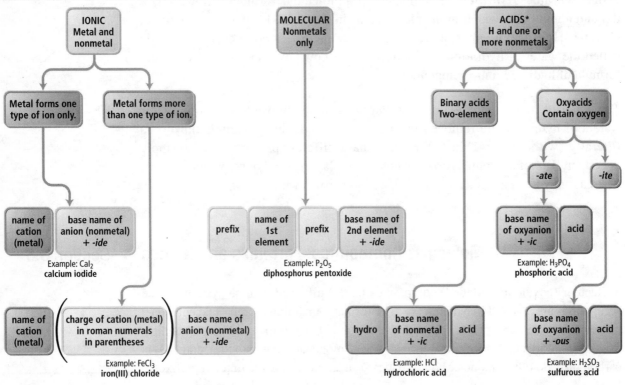

**Figure 3.2** Inorganic Nomenclature Flow Chart. The chart summarizes how to name inorganic compounds. Begin by determining if the compound to be named is ionic, molecular, or an acid. Then follow the flow chart for that category from top to bottom until you arrive at a name for the compound.

You should practice both approaches—writing formulas from names and writing names from formulas.

## Section 3.8    Formula Mass and the Mole Concept for Compounds

**Molar Mass** is the mass of 1 mole of a substance. The mole represents $6.022 \times 10^{23}$ atoms or molecules and is the number necessary to make the number of atomic mass units on the periodic table equal to the mass in grams. Therefore, the mass an atom of an element in amu and of a mole of those same atoms in grams per mole are the same. A carbon atom has a mass of 12.01 amu and a mole of carbon atoms ($6.022 \times 10^{23}$ atoms C) has a mass of 12.01 g. To calculate the molar mass of a compound, add the molar masses of all the atoms making up the compound from the atomic masses on the periodic table. The units of molar mass are g/mol. Determination of the correct molar mass is a calculation that must be mastered at the AP level. Be sure to use all given digits on the periodic table and to use correct significant figures for the result. For example, the mass of carbon on the periodic table is 12.01 g/mol and the mass of oxygen is 16.00 g/mol. Thus, the molar mass of $CO_2$ is 12.01 g/mol + 2(16.00 g/mol) = 44.01 g/mol. Remember, this works because the data given on the periodic table can be interpreted two ways: (1) as the relative mass of the atoms in atomic mass units OR (2) the molar mass in grams/mol of the atoms.

## Composition of Compounds    Section 3.9

Mass percent or mass percent composition can be determined from the molar mass and the atomic masses. After adding the molar mass, use the mass each element contributed to the total molar mass and put it over the total molar mass to form a ratio. This ratio is multiplied by 100 to indicate the mass percent. For $CO_2$, the C is 12.0 g/mol of the total 44.01 g/mol, which would be 27.29%. The same ratio of masses in grams without the multiplier of 100 can be used as a conversion factor, such as

$$\frac{12.01\frac{g}{mol} \text{ of C}}{44.01\frac{g}{mol} \text{ of } CO_2}.$$

There are a variety of problems in which this can be used, such as calculating the number of grams used to form a certain amount of compound.

It is important to recognize percent literally means "out of 100." In some cases, it is convenient to assume the sample size is 100 grams of the compound. What is the mass of C in 50.0 g $CO_2$? If we assume we have 100 grams of $CO_2$, then we can ask what is the mass of C in 100.00 grams of $CO_2$? Since the percentage of C in $CO_2$ is 27.29%, the mass of carbon in 100.0 g of $CO_2$ is 27.29 grams. The number of grams of C in 50.0 grams would be half this amount or 13.6 grams. This also means that oxygen is 100.00 g − 27.29 g = 72.71 grams, so the mass percent of oxygen in $CO_2$ is 72.71%

### Example:

How many grams of iron are in 40.00 g of iron (III) sulfate?

The formula mass or molar mass of $Fe_2(SO_4)_3$ is 400.0 g/mol.

$$\frac{111.7 \text{ g Fe}}{400.0 \text{ } Fe_2(SO_4)_3} \times 100\% = 27.92\% \text{ Fe}$$

$$40.00 \text{ g } Fe_2(SO_4)_3 \times 0.2792 = 11.17 \text{ g Fe}$$

Chemical formulas can also provide ratios to help solve problems. For instance, in $C_6H_{12}O_6$, the ratio of moles of carbon atoms per mole of compound is 6:1 or 6 mol of C per 1 mol of $C_6H_{12}O_6$. Mastery of conversions between grams of one species to grams of another species using mass and molar conversion factors is a necessity.

**Example:**

How many grams of sulfur are in 40.0 g of $Fe_2(SO_4)_3$?

$$40.00 \text{ g} \times \frac{1 \text{ mol Fe}_2(SO_4)_3}{400.0 \text{ g Fe}_2(SO_4)_3} \times \frac{3 \text{ mol S}}{1 \text{ mol Fe}_2(SO_4)_3} \times \frac{32.06 \text{ g S}}{1 \text{ mol S}} = 9.619 \text{ g S}$$

Another source of a ratio sometimes needed in solving problems is the density of the substance. For example, the density of water is 1.00 g/mL. In this case, the ratio of mass to volume can be used to determine the total mass or total volume present.

**Example:**

How many molecules of methanol $(CH_3OH)$ are in 14.8 mL of methanol? The density of methanol is 0.7918 g/mL.

$$14.8 \text{ mL CH}_3OH \times \frac{0.7918 \text{ g}}{1 \text{ mL}} \times \frac{1 \text{ mol CH}_3OH}{32.01 \text{ g CH}_3OH} \times \frac{6.02 \times 10^{23} \text{ molecules CH}_3OH}{1 \text{ mol CH}_3OH}$$

$$= 2.20 \times 10^{23} \text{ molecules CH}_3OH$$

It is always required to show work and use units on the AP Test. If properly set up, the units will cancel so the desired final units are left. Well-practiced, problem-solving skills for problems of varying types and approaches are needed to be a successful student in AP chemistry.

## Section 3.10    Determining a Chemical Formula from Experimental Data

The AP course is data driven, so understanding how to determine a formula from data is an important skill. This also works with chemical equations.

**Example:**

Assuming a 100.0 gram sample, 69.94 g is iron and 30.06 g is oxygen. Convert the mass of each element to moles. Calculate a mole O to mole Fe ratio.

$$69.94 \text{ g Fe} \times \frac{1 \text{ mol Fe}}{55.85 \text{ g Fe}} = 1.252 \text{ mol Fe}$$

$$30.06 \text{ g O} \times \frac{1 \text{ mol O}}{16.00 \text{ g O}} = 1.879 \text{ mol O}$$

$$\frac{1.879 \text{ mol O}}{1.252 \text{ mol Fe}} = \frac{1.50 \text{ mol O}}{1 \text{ mol Fe}} \times \frac{2}{2} = \frac{3 \text{ mol O}}{2 \text{ mol Fe}}$$

The empirical formula is $Fe_2O_3$.

This experimental data only leads to the determination of the empirical formula, not the molecular formula. When working on these problems, remember the ratios of atom to atom must be whole numbers, so you must recognize what certain decimals need to have as a multiplier to get the nearest whole number. For instance, 0.50 needs to be multiplied by 2 to get the whole number 1, 0.3 would most likely be multiplied by 3. Additionally, experiments rarely give perfect data as all experiments have some measureable error. Sometimes the data will not result in a perfect whole number answer. For instance if the data results in the calculations yielding a ratio of 1.9:1, it is much more likely to really be a 2:1 ratio.

To determine the molecular formula from your calculated empirical formula and empirical mass, the molar mass must be known. The ratio of the molar mass to the empirical mass will yield the multiplier needed to transform the empirical formula into the molecular formula.

### Example:

Caffeine contains 49.50% C, 5.15% H, 28.90% N, and 16.50% O by mass. Determine the empirical formula and the molecular formula of caffeine. The formula mass or molar mass of caffeine is 195 g/mol.

From the percent by mass data the empirical formula is $C_4H_5N_2O$. The empirical mass is 97.5 g/mol.

$$\frac{\text{Molar Mass}}{\text{Empirical Mass}} = \frac{195\frac{g}{mol}}{97.5\frac{g}{mol}} = \frac{2}{1}$$

Molecular formula $= C_4H_5N_2O \times 2 = C_8H_{10}N_4O_2$

One way to get the data to calculate the percent composition is to burn the material. In **combustion analysis**, organic compounds are burned in oxygen or air completely to produce $CO_2$ and $H_2O$. The amounts of these products can be used to determine the amount of starting reactants. In complete combustion of a hydrocarbon, all the carbon in the hydrocarbon is combined with oxygen to make carbon dioxide. All the hydrogen combines with oxygen to make water. From the amount of carbon dioxide, the amount of the original carbon can be determined and from the amount of water formed, the amount of the original hydrogen in the hydrocarbon can be determined. With this data, the formula of the compound can be determined. In these types of experiments, it is safe to assume that no other products have been formed.

### Example:

A 0.1507 g sample of menthol, a substance used in mentholated cough drops and composed of C, H, and O was combusted and produced 0.4243 g of carbon dioxide and 0.1738 g of water. Determine the empirical formula of menthol.

All of the carbon in the carbon dioxide must be from the carbon in the sample of menthol. Calculate the number of moles and grams of carbon present in the carbon dioxide.

$$0.4243 \text{ g CO}_2 \times \frac{1 \text{ mol CO}_2}{44.0 \text{ g CO}_2} \times \frac{1 \text{ mol C}}{1 \text{ mol CO}_2} = 0.00964 \text{ mol C}$$

All of the hydrogen in the water must be from the hydrogen in the sample of menthol. Calculate the number of moles and grams of hydrogen present in the water.

$$0.1738 \text{ g H}_2\text{O} \times \frac{1 \text{ mol H}_2\text{O}}{18.01 \text{ g H}_2\text{O}} = 0.01930 \text{ mol H}$$

In order to determine the moles of oxygen in the sample, the mass of oxygen in the sample should be calculated. First, determine the mass of carbon and hydrogen present in the sample of menthol.

$$0.00964 \text{ mol C} \times \frac{12.01 \text{ g C}}{1 \text{ mol C}} = 0.1158 \text{ g C}$$

$$0.01930 \text{ mol H} \times \frac{1.007 \text{ g H}}{1 \text{ mol H}} = 0.0195 \text{ g H}$$

$$\text{mass of oxygen} = \text{total mass sample} - \text{mass C} - \text{mass H}$$

$$\text{mass of oxygen} = 0.1507 \text{ g} - 0.1158 \text{ g C} - 0.0195 \text{ g H} = 0.0156 \text{ g O}$$

$$\text{moles of O} = 0.0156 \text{ g O} \times \frac{1 \text{ mol of O}}{16.00 \text{ g O}} = 0.000964 \text{ mol O}$$

Determine the mole to mole ratio of the elements.

$$\frac{0.01930 \text{ mol H}}{0.00964 \text{ mol C}} = \frac{2 \text{ mol H}}{1 \text{ mol C}}$$

$$\frac{0.00964 \text{ mol C}}{0.000975 \text{ mol O}} = \frac{10 \text{ mol C}}{1 \text{ mol O}}$$

The empirical formula of menthol is $C_{10}H_{20}O$.

## Section 3.11    Writing and Balancing Chemical Equations

A **chemical reaction** can be represented by symbols, using the molecular formulas that you have learned to write. The **reactants** are the starting materials and are found on the left-hand side of the equation; the **products** that are formed are found on the right-hand side. An arrow which means "to form," is placed between the reactants and the products. Sometimes an equals sign is used instead of an arrow, hence the words *chemical equation*. Once the skeleton equation with the chemical species is present, **coefficients** are put in front of each chemical species to balance the equation to get the same number of each type of atom on each side of the equation. This is what an equals sign would indicate. If it is unbalanced then it really isn't an equation. This is called *conservation of atoms* and it is the foundation of writing and balancing equations. Atoms cannot be changed into other types of atoms nor can they be lost in the reaction (unless it is a nuclear reaction which is not covered here). The coefficients are applied to every element in the chemical species they are placed in front of; $2CO_2$ indicates 2C atoms and 4O atoms. Using proper math notations, this would be written $2(CO_2)$, but chemists leave out the parentheses.

**Example:**

Balance the following equation and write a sentence describing what occurs at the atom level and at the mole level.

$$\_\_Fe(s) + \_\_ O_2(g) \rightarrow \_\_ Fe_2O_3(s)$$
$$4\,Fe(s) + 3\,O_2(g) \rightarrow 2\,Fe_2O_3(s)$$

Four atoms of iron react with 3 molecules of oxygen gas to form two units of iron(III) oxide.

Four moles of iron react with three moles of oxygen gas to form two moles of iron(III) oxide.

This chapter contains a variety of fundamental skills you must master to be successful in AP chemistry. Practice and continue to practice these foundations throughout the year.

## Additional Practice

*Self-Assessment Quiz Questions Q1, Q2, Q3, Q4, Q5, Q6, Q7, Q8, Q9, Q10, Q11, Q12, Q13, Q14, and Q15*

*Problems 23, 25, 29, 31, 32, 37, 41, 43, 45, 47, 49, 51, 53, 59, 61, 66, 72, 79, 83, 87, 99, 100, 102, 105, 106, 109, 126, 131, and 132*

## Practice AP® Test Questions

1. Which one of the following is the formula of hypochlorous acid?

   A) $HClO_3$

   B) $HClO_2$

   C) $HClO$

   D) $H_2ClO_2$

2. The correct name for $Fe(NO_2)_2$ is _____.

   A) Iron(II) nitrite

   B) Iron(II) nitrate

   C) Ferric nitrite

   D) Iron dinitrite

3. The correct name for $K_2O_2$ is _____.

   A) Potassium oxide

   B) Potassium dioxide

   C) Dipotassium oxide

   D) Potassium peroxide

4. The formula for the compound formed between aluminum ions and carbonate ions is _____.

   A) $Al_3(CO_3)_3$

   B) $Al_2(CO_3)_3$

   C) $AlCO_3$

   D) $Al(CO_3)_3$

5. The name of the compound $N_2O_4$ is ___.

   A) Dinitrogen tetroxide

   B) Dinitrogen quatroxide

   C) Nitrogen(IV) oxide

   D) Nitric oxide

6. Which series of compounds have a common empirical formula?

   A) $C_2H_6$    $C_3H_8$    $C_4H_{10}$

   B) $HClO$, $HClO_2$ $HClO_3$

   C) $Al_2(CO_3)_3$    $Al_2S_3$    $Al_2O_3$

   D) $C_2H_4$    $C_3H_6$    $C_4H_8$

# CHEMICAL QUANTITIES AND AQUEOUS REACTIONS

This chapter has two parts: mathematical calculations and types of chemical reactions. Mathematical calculations are important to master because they are the basis of many other types of problems in later chapters and all are tested on the AP exam. The math here should be review. The types of reactions are useful ways to classify many chemical reactions we see everyday. Understanding how to decide on a specific type of reaction is important. There is a lot packed into this chapter, but the most important sections for quantitative calculations are as follows:

The most important sections for reaction classification types are as follows:

## Specific Learning Objectives Addressed in this Chapter:

**Learning objective 1.17** The student is able to express the law of conservation of mass quantitatively and qualitatively using symbolic representations and particulate drawings. [*See* **SP 1.5**]

**Learning objective 1.20** The student can design, and/or interpret data from, an experiment that uses titration to determine the concentration of an analyte in a solution. [*See* **SP 4.2, 5.1**]

**Learning objective 2.1** Students can predict properties of substances based on their chemical formulas, and provide explanations of their properties based on particle views. [*See* **SP 6.4, 7.1**]

**Learning objective 2.2** The student is able to explain the relative strengths of acids and bases based on molecular structure, interparticle forces, and solution equilibrium. [*See* **SP 7.2**]

**Learning objective 2.9** The student is able to create or interpret representations that link the concept of molarity with particle views of solutions. [*See* **SP 1.1**, **1.4**]

**Learning objective 3.1** Students can translate among macroscopic observations of change, chemical equations, and particle views. [*See* **SP 1.5**, **7.1**]

**Learning objective 3.2** The student can translate an observed chemical change into a balanced chemical equation and justify the choice of equation type (molecular, ionic, or net ionic) in terms of utility for the given circumstances. [*See* **SP 1.5**, **7.1**]

**Learning objective 3.3** The student is able to use stoichiometric calculations to predict the results of performing a reaction in the laboratory and/or to analyze deviations from the expected results. [*See* **SP 2.2**, **5.1**]

**Learning objective 3.4** The student is able to relate quantities (measured mass of substances, volumes of solutions, or volumes and pressures of gases) to identify stoichiometric relationships for a reaction, including situations involving limiting reactants and situations in which the reaction has not gone to completion. [*See* **SP 2.2**, **5.1**, **6.4**]

**Learning objective 3.7** The student is able to identify compounds as Brønsted-Lowry acids, bases, and/or conjugate acid–base pairs, using proton-transfer reactions to justify the identification. [*See* **SP 6.1**]

**Learning objective 3.8** The student is able to identify redox reactions and justify the identification in terms of electron transfer. [*See* **SP 6.1**]

**Learning objective 3.10** The student is able to evaluate the classification of a process as a physical change, chemical change, or ambiguous change based on both macroscopic observations and the distinction between rearrangement of covalent interactions and noncovalent interactions. [*See* **SP 1.4**, **6.1**]

## Specific Science Practices Addressed in This Chapter:

**Science Practice 1:** The student can use representations and models to communicate scientific phenomena and solve scientific problems.

> 1.1 The student can *create representations and models* of natural or man-made phenomena and systems in the domain.

> 1.2 The student can *describe representations and models* of natural or man-made phenomena and systems in the domain.

> 1.4 The student can *use representations and models* to analyze situations or solve problems qualitatively and quantitatively.

> 1.5 The student can *re-express key elements* of natural phenomena across multiple representations in the domain.

**Science Practice 2:** The student can use mathematics appropriately.

> 2.2 The student can *apply mathematical routines* to quantities that describe natural phenomena.

**Science Practice 4:** The student can plan and implement data collection strategies in relation to a particular scientific question.

> 4.2   The student can *design a plan* for collecting data to answer a particular scientific question.

**Science Practice 5:** The student can perform data analysis and evaluation of evidence.

> 5.1   The student can *analyze data* to identify patterns or relationships.

**Science Practice 6:** The student can work with scientific explanations and theories.

> 6.1   The student can *justify claims with evidence*.

> 6.2   The student can *construct explanations of phenomena based on evidence* produced through scientific practices.

> 6.4   The student can *make claims and predictions about natural phenomena* based on scientific theories and models.

**Science Practice 7:** The student is able to connect and relate knowledge across various scales, concepts, and representations in and across domains.

> 7.1   The student can *connect phenomena and models* across spatial and temporal scales.

> 7.2   The student can *connect concepts* in and across domain(s) to generalize or extrapolate in and/or across enduring understandings and/or big ideas.

### Concepts and Vocabulary to Review:

Section 4.2

## Reaction Stoichiometry: How Much Carbon Dioxide?

The foundation of most chemistry problems is stoichiometry. When reactions occur, how can we predict how much product can be made? We use stoichiometry: using the coefficients from a balanced equation to provide the mole ratios of one chemical to another. Often, we refer to the mathematical calculation of changing from one type of chemical substance to another as a conversion.

In the equation $2H_2(g) + O_2(g) \rightarrow 2H_2O(g)$ there are several ratios of moles to moles: $\dfrac{2 \text{ mol } H_2}{1 \text{ mol } O_2}, \dfrac{2 \text{ mol } H_2O}{1 \text{ mol } O_2}, \dfrac{1 \text{ mol } O_2}{2 \text{ mol } H_2}, \dfrac{1 \text{ mol } O_2}{2 \text{ mol } H_2O}, \dfrac{2 \text{ mol } H_2}{2 \text{ mol } H_2O},$ and $\dfrac{2 \text{ mol } H_2O}{2 \text{ mol } H_2}$. The ratio you would choose to use depends on what substance you are starting with and to which one you want to convert. If you have 3 moles of oxygen and you want to convert to moles of water, you would use $\dfrac{2 \text{ mol } H_2O}{1 \text{ mol } O_2}$. This ratio will cancel the unit of moles of oxygen and convert to the unit moles of water.

$$3 \text{ mol O}_2 \times \frac{2 \text{ mol H}_2\text{O}}{1 \text{ mol O}_2} = 6 \text{ mol H}_2\text{O}$$

There are two types of conversions to review: mole–mole conversions as shown above and mass–mass conversions. Unfortunately, there is no way to directly go from mass of one species to moles or mass of another species in the reaction. The chemical equation used indicates the relationships between all the species but only in molecules, or, more conveniently, moles. Mass-mass conversions must include mole-to-mole conversions as a step as well as adding a step before and after the mole–mole step. Converting the starting substance from grams to moles occurs first, then the moles to mole stoichiometry step is done, and the final step is converting the formed substance from moles to grams. Of course, there are different types of combinations in which you can start in grams but end in moles. Throughout all conversions, it is important to recognize that atoms are being conserved. They MUST add up!

If you start with 18.0 grams of hydrogen, how many grams of oxygen will be required to react completely to form water? The first step is to identify the chemical equation to know the moles ratios needed.

$$2\text{H}_2 + \text{O}_2 \rightarrow 2\text{H}_2\text{O}$$

The equation indicates the ratio of two moles of hydrogen gas is needed to completely react with one mole of oxygen gas. In the calculation grams of hydrogen are converted to moles of hydrogen followed by the stoichiometry step of multiplying by the ratio 1 mole of oxygen to two moles of hydrogen and finally converting the moles of oxygen to grams:

$$180 \text{ g H}_2 \times \frac{1 \text{ mol H}_2}{2.016 \text{ g H}_2} \times \frac{1 \text{ mol O}_2}{2 \text{ mol H}_2} \times \frac{32.00 \text{ g O}_2}{1 \text{ mol O}_2} = 143 \text{ g O}_2$$

You need to be able to read a problem and determine where you need to start—moles or grams—and where you need to stop. Practice this skill and performing the necessary set up. On the AP exam, you are required to show work in all your calculations in the free response section, so always write everything out with units and labels even during practice sessions. There are also calculations in the multiple-choice section of the exam; if you do the set up, often numbers will cancel and will be easy to solve.

## Limiting Reactant, Theoretical Yield, and Percent Yield     Section 4.3

Using the skills in the above section, we can also calculate to further analyze chemical reaction yields. There are several types of calculations you need to be able to do.

A *limiting reactant* is the reactant you do not have enough of to fully react the other reactant(s). In other words, it is the ingredient that runs out first. This is also calculated through stoichiometry. If you were making cookies and the recipe called for 1 cup of sugar and 1 cup of flour to make 6 cookies, and you had 12 cups of sugar, but only 2 cups of flour, the flour is the limiting reactant. You could not make 72 cookies, but only 12 cookies, at the most. At this point, you have run out of flour, and can make no more cookies. In chemistry, the recipe, in the analogy above, is the chemical reaction. The coefficients are the guide to how much of each reactant are needed to make the products, and those coefficients count atoms and molecules. This means the number of grams of each reactant does not indicate which reactant is the limiting reactant because it is NOT a direct count of atoms; you must do the math to determine the numbers by converting to moles. The reactant you have a surplus of is called the *excess reactant*. For the cookies, the excess reactant was the sugar. You will be expected to be able to determine how much excess reactant is present after the reaction occurs as well. For the cookies, it would be 12 – 2 cups of sugar, or 10 cups of sugar.

The amount of product indicated by stoichiometry is the *maximum yield*; this predicted amount is called the *theoretical yield*. In reality, things external to the reaction can affect the amount that actually gets made—and the amount is always less than or equal to the amount predicted should be made. When the reaction is actually completed, the amount really made is called the *actual yield*. If stoichiometry predicted 50.0 grams of water to be made, this is the theoretical yield. If the reaction only made 40.0 grams, this is the actual yield. These two numbers are used to calculate percent yield, which is calculated by taking the actual yield and dividing it by the theoretical yield, then multiplying by 100 to make it a percent.

$$\frac{\text{actual yield}}{\text{theoretical yield}} \times 100 = \% \text{ yield.}$$

In the cookies example, the theoretical yield was 12 cookies, but suppose you left some batter on the sides of the mixing bowl, so only 10 cookies were made. This is the actual yield. The percent yield is 10 cookies/12 cookies $\times$ 100 = 83%. Note percent yield has no units.

It is vital in all chemistry calculations to associate every quantity with a unit. Rarely will a quantity be unitless. Even *grams* have an associated label, e.g., grams of hydrogen, and so does *moles*. This is important as grams/grams may appear to cancel, but grams hydrogen/grams water does NOT cancel.

## Section 4.4    Solution Concentration and Solution Stoichiometry

To discuss solutions, you must remember the following vocabulary words.

**Solute** is the substance being dissolved.

**Solvent** is the substance doing the dissolving, and in water solutions, the solvent is the water.

A **dilute solution** is one containing only a few solute particles in a large amount of solvent. A **concentrated solution** has much more solute than a dilute solution. In a **saturated solution**, the solution contains the maximum amount of solute that the solvent can dissolve. This **solubility limit** depends on several factors and is different for different substances; there is no standard rule.

**Molarity (M)** is used to indicate the concentration of a solution in moles solute per liter of solution. The definition of molarity is the ratio of $\dfrac{\text{mol solute}}{\text{liters of solution}}$. In many problems, you will need to change grams of solute to moles of solute in order to calculate molarity.

**How to make a solution is an important LAB SKILL.** Make sure you know the steps. You may be asked to make a whole liter of solution, but more often than not, you will be asked to make another amount on the AP test, such as 250 mL. You need to be able to calculate the number of grams needed to make any amount of solution. To solve this, you can set up a proportion:

$$\frac{\text{mol solute}}{\text{liters solution}} = \frac{x \text{ mol solute}}{\text{desired liters of solution}}$$

In this proportion, the given molarity is on one side and the desired volume in liters is on the other to determine how many moles of solute is needed. This can then be

**Preparing a Solution of Specified Concentration**

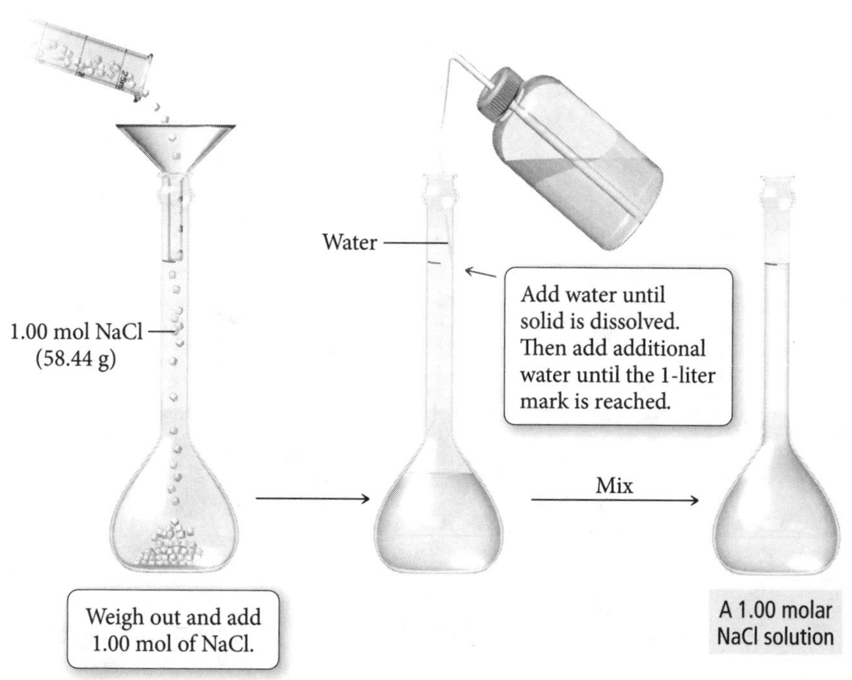

1.00 mol NaCl (58.44 g)

Water

Add water until solid is dissolved. Then add additional water until the 1-liter mark is reached.

Weigh out and add 1.00 mol of NaCl.

Mix

A 1.00 molar NaCl solution

**Figure 4.1  Preparing a 1-Molar NaCl Solution.**

converted into grams of solute. Once this number is known, there are three basic steps to follow after putting on proper personal protection equipment (PPE) such as goggles: (Note these steps may vary at your institution.)

1. Measure the solute in grams. Dissolve the solute in a small amount of water (solvent) in a beaker.** see note below if using acids.

2. Pour the solute in the appropriate volume volumetric flask.

3. Add water (solvent) to the mark in the flask.

Since molarity is a ratio, it can be used in stoichiometry calculations too because molarity times volume in liters equals moles; $\dfrac{\text{Mol solute}}{\text{L solution}} \times \text{L} = \text{mol.}$

Another lab-related skill is to make a more dilute solution from a concentrated solution. The concentrated solution is called a *stock solution*. The equation for solution

### Diluting a Solution

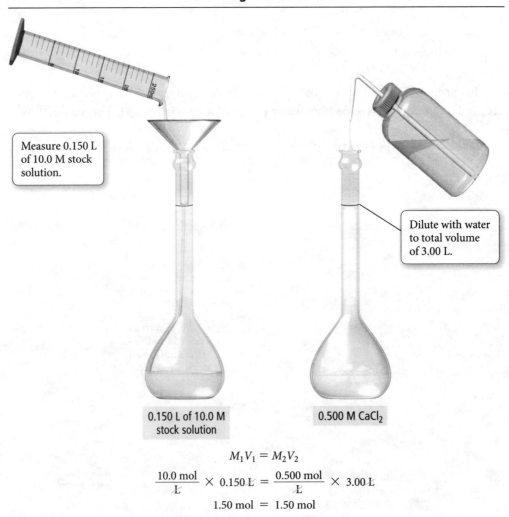

Measure 0.150 L of 10.0 M stock solution.

Dilute with water to total volume of 3.00 L.

0.150 L of 10.0 M stock solution

0.500 M CaCl$_2$

$$M_1 V_1 = M_2 V_2$$

$$\frac{10.0\ \text{mol}}{\text{L}} \times 0.150\ \text{L} = \frac{0.500\ \text{mol}}{\text{L}} \times 3.00\ \text{L}$$

$$1.50\ \text{mol} = 1.50\ \text{mol}$$

**Figure 4.2  Preparing 3.00 L of 5.00 M CaCl$_2$ from a 10.0 M Stock Solution.**

dilution is $M_1V_1 = M_2V_2$, where the subscript 1 refers to the stock solution and the subscript 2 refers to the new diluted solution.

**Solution dilution steps, after putting on PPE, are as follows:**

1. Measure out the specific volume of stock solution.

2. Pour into the appropriate volumetric flask,** which already contains 1/2 to 2/3 of the needed solvent to be added.

3. Add water to the mark.

**Regardless of which steps your institution follows,** if you are diluting an acid solution on the AP test, pour 1/2 to 2/3 of the water needed in the appropriate flask. Then SLOWLY add the acid while swirling it. Finish by adding the last amount of water to the mark. This is considered a safety issue.

# Types of Aqueous Solutions and Solubility    Section 4.5

This section builds the foundation for other sections by introducing vocabulary.

**Strong electrolytes** are differentiated from nonelectrolytes and weak electrolytes. The strong electrolytes, which include the strong acids, disassociate (break apart into ions) completely in water. The individual ions of the strong electrolytes are more attracted to the water molecules than they are to themselves. Sodium chloride or table salt is an example of a strong electrolyte.

**Weak electrolytes**, which include weak acids and bases, do not disassociate completely in solution and will actually have only some degree of ionization (dissociation). Acetic acid is an example of a weak electrolyte.

**Nonelectrolytes** also dissolve in water because they are more attracted to the water molecules than they are to themselves, BUT when they dissolve they stay intact as molecules. Typically, non-electrolytes are made up of covalently bonded molecules. Sugar is an example of a nonelectrolyte.

It is important to be able to draw and explain the solute–solvent interactions seen below. These are often asked on the AP exam and indicate an understanding of how different species dissolve.

Those compounds that dissolve in a solute are called *soluble* and those that do not are *insoluble*. There are rules to predict if a compound will be soluble in water. These are used to see if newly formed products will be soluble as well. Alkali metal ions, nitrate, and ammonium ions are always soluble are the only rules you are expected to know. You do not need to memorize Table 4.1, but you should be familiar with its data. It is the forces within and between the solute and solvent molecules determining the type of solution that will form.

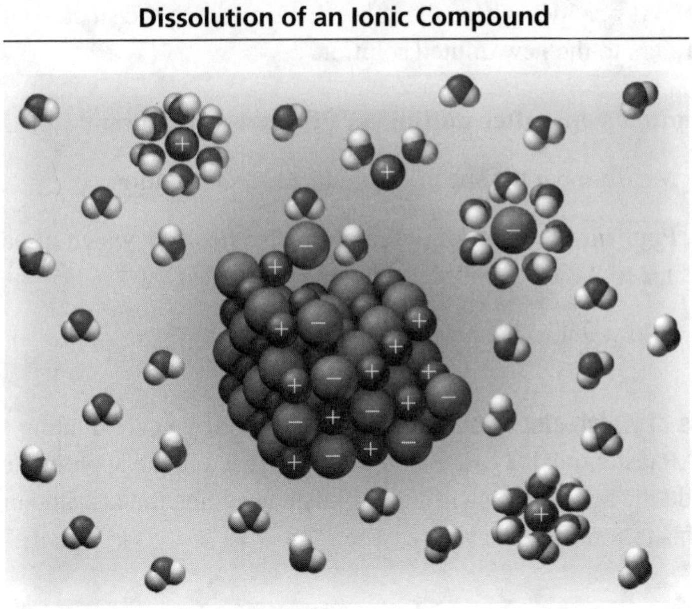

**Dissolution of an Ionic Compound**

**Figure 4.3  Sodium Chloride Dissolving in Water**   The attraction between water molecules and the ions of sodium chloride causes NaCl to dissolve in the water.

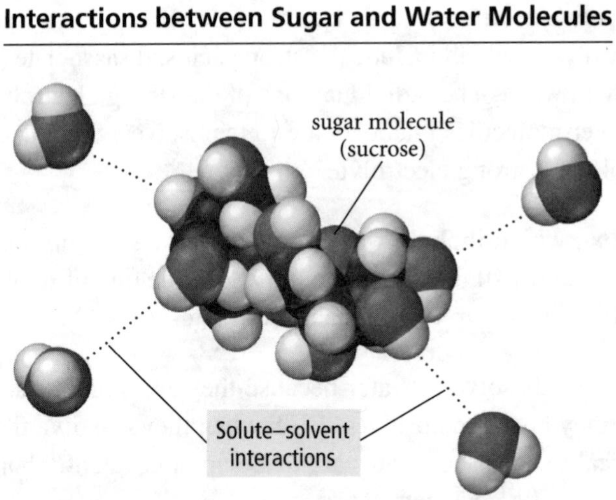

**Interactions between Sugar and Water Molecules**

sugar molecule
(sucrose)

Solute–solvent
interactions

**Figure 4.4  Sugar and Water Interactions**   Partial charges on sugar molecules and water molecules (discussed more fully in Chapter 11) result in attractions between the sugar molecules and water molecules.

## Section 4.6    Precipitation Reactions

During a reaction in solution (usually in water) in which insoluble compounds form, the insoluble compound is called a *precipitate*. You should be able to describe what is occurring in a precipitation reaction. Usually these reactions start by combining two aqueous solutions. By trading the cations in the two solutions, you can predict what possible products could form.

**Table 4.1** Solubility Rules for Ionic Compounds in Water

| Compounds Containing the Following Ions Are Generally Soluble | Exceptions |
|---|---|
| $Li^+$, $Na^+$, $K^+$, and $NH_4^+$ | None |
| $NO_3^-$ and $C_2H_3O_2^-$ | None |
| $Cl^-$, $Br^-$, and $I^-$ | When these ions pair with $Ag^+$, $Hg_2^{2+}$, or $Pb^{2+}$, the resulting compounds are insoluble. |
| $SO_4^{2-}$ | When $SO_4^{2-}$ pairs with $Sr^{2+}$, $Ba^{2+}$, $Pb^{2+}$, $Ag^+$, or $Ca^{2+}$, the resulting compound is insoluble. |
| **Compounds Containing the Following Ions Are Generally Insoluble** | **Exceptions** |
| $OH^-$ and $S^{2-}$ | When these ions pair with $Li^+$, $Na^+$, $K^+$, or $NH_4^+$, the resulting compounds are soluble. |
| | When $S^{2-}$ pairs with $Ca^{2+}$, $Sr^{2+}$, or $Ba^{2+}$, the resulting compound is soluble. |
| | When $OH^-$ pairs with $Ca^{2+}$, $Sr^{2+}$, or $Ba^{2+}$, the resulting compound is slightly soluble. |
| $CO_3^{2-}$ and $PO_4^{3-}$ | When these ions pair with $Li^+$, $Na^+$, $K^+$, or $NH_4^+$, the resulting compounds are soluble. |

## Representing Aqueous Reactions: Molecular, Ionic, and Complete Ionic Equations

Section 4.7

Molecular equations, balanced net ionic equations, and complete ionic equations have different uses. Molecular equations keep all the reactants and products as whole species with their coefficients. These equations are used to indicate all the reactants and products, atom conservation, and the mole-to-mole ratios between them. Sometimes, however, it is more convenient to only look at the species as they exist in solution, rather than as complete molecules. For this, we use **ionic equations**. In balanced complete ionic equations, strong electrolytes are written as disassociated ions, so all reactants and products are written showing how they exist in the solution before and after the reaction also with coefficients to balance the equation. In other cases, we are only concerned with the ions that are actually reacting in the experiment. So, in balanced **net ionic equations**, species not participating in the reaction are crossed out and only the species undergoing a change are left. It is important to understand what each type of equation indicates. The following is a common example.

## Precipitation Reaction

$$2\ KI(aq)\ +\ Pb(NO_3)_2(aq)\ \longrightarrow\ 2\ KNO_3(aq)\ +\ PbI_2(s)$$
(soluble)        (soluble)                          (soluble)      (insoluble)

When a potassium iodide solution is mixed with a lead(II) nitrate solution, a yellow lead(II) iodide precipitate forms.

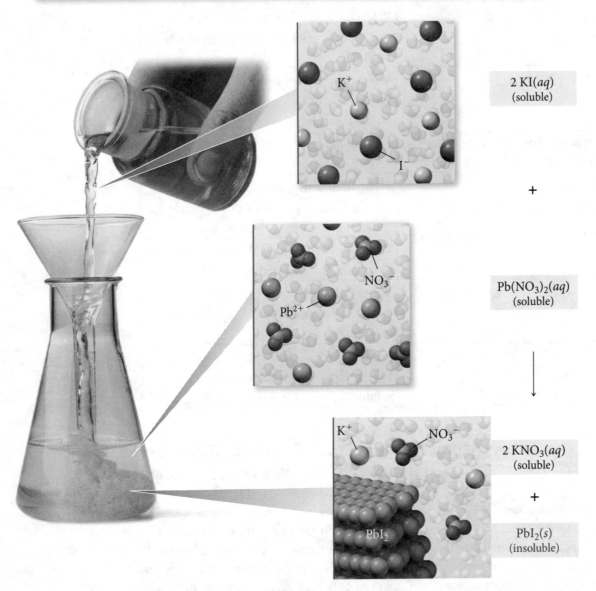

$2\ KI(aq)$
(soluble)

+

$Pb(NO_3)_2(aq)$
(soluble)

$2\ KNO_3(aq)$
(soluble)

+

$PbI_2(s)$
(insoluble)

**Figure 4.5  Precipitation of Lead(II) Iodide**   When a potassium iodide solution is mixed with a lead(II) itrate solution, a yellow lead(II) iodide precipitate forms.

Molecular equation: $AgNO_3(aq) + NaCl(aq) \rightarrow NaNO_3(aq) + AgCl(s)$

Changed to ionic equation: $Ag^+(aq) + NO_3^-(aq) + Na^+(aq) + Cl^-(aq) \rightarrow Na^+(aq) + NO_3^-(aq) + AgCl(s)$

Changed to net Ionic equation: $Ag^+(aq) + Cl^-(aq) \rightarrow AgCl(s)$

The unchanged ions in the complete ionic equation ($NO_3^-$ and $Na^+$) were removed as spectator ions to create the net ionic equation.

## Acid–Base and Gas Evolution Reactions    Section 4.8

This section includes vocabulary and background about acid and base concepts. An acid–base reaction is also called a **neutralization** reaction because the acid neutralizes the base. When the acid and base react, they form a salt and water. The salt contains the cation of the base and the anion of the acid. For example, in the reaction, $KOH + HCl \rightarrow KCl + H_2O$, the cation $K^+$ and the anion $Cl^-$ produce the salt KCl. The net ionic representation of the whole reaction is $OH^- + H^+ H_2O$ because the salt ions are water soluble and the $K^+$ and $Cl^-$ are spectator ions.

**Arrhenius** developed a theory of acids and bases. His theory states acids produce $H^+$ in solution and bases produce $OH^-$ in solution. When an acid disassociates into an

### Acid–Base Titration

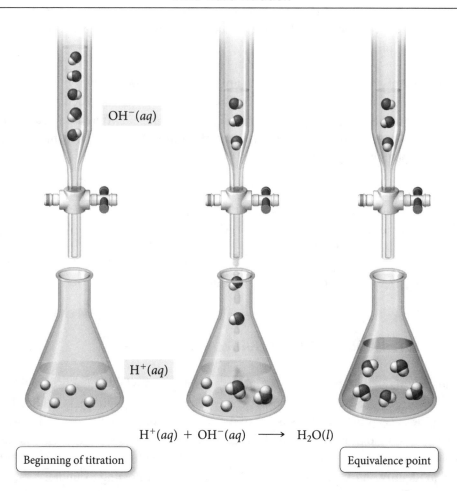

$$H^+(aq) + OH^-(aq) \longrightarrow H_2O(l)$$

Beginning of titration                    Equivalence point

**Figure 4.6  Titration**    In this Indicator in Titration titration, NaOH is added to a dilute HCl solution. When the NaOH and HCl reach stoichiometric proportions (the equivalence point), the phenolphthalein indicator changes color to pink.

**Table 4.2** Types of Compounds That Undergo Gas-Evolution Reactions

| Reactant Type | Intermediate Product | Gas Evolved | Example |
|---|---|---|---|
| Sulfides | None | $H_2S$ | $2\,HCl(aq) + K_2S(aq) \rightarrow H_2S(g) + 2\,KCl(aq)$ |
| Carbonates and bicarbonates | $H_2CO_3$ | $CO_2$ | $2\,HCl(aq) + K_2CO_3(aq) \rightarrow H_2O(l) + CO_2(g)$ $+ 2\,KCl(aq)$ |
| Sulfites and bisulfites | $H_2SO_3$ | $SO_2$ | $2\,HCl(aq) + K_2SO_3(aq) \rightarrow H_2O(l) + SO_2(g)$ $+ 2\,KCl(aq)$ |
| Ammonium | $NH_4OH$ | $NH_3$ | $NH_4Cl(aq) + KOH(aq) \rightarrow H_2O(l) + NH_3(g)$ $+ KCl(aq)$ |

$H^+$ and an anion, the $H^+$ combines with a water molecule to form a hydronium ion, $H_3O^+$.

Polyprotic acids have more than one hydrogen ion that can disassociate into solution. If there are two hydrogen ions going into solution, it is called a *diprotic acid*. $H_2SO_4$ is an example of a diprotic acid. Triprotic acids, such as $H_3PO_4$, phosphoric acid, can release three protons into solution.

In the laboratory, acid–base reactions are done quantitatively in a process called *titration*. Often, an indicator is added to show progress. When the reaction reaches its endpoint or equivalence point, there will be a color change. Different indicators turn different colors and are sensitive to different pH points. At equivalence, the moles of acid will equal the moles of base.

A very important LAB SKILL is to be able to do a titration as shown in the following figure. You may be asked to describe such an experiment, and perform calculations with the data from the experiment on the AP exam.

Gas-evolution reactions in aqueous solutions produce observable bubbling. Predicting which reactions will produce gas is outlined in Table 4.2.

## Section 4.9    Oxidation–Reduction Reactions

Oxidation–reduction, or *redox*, reactions are reactions in which there is a transfer of electrons from one species to another. The species losing electrons is **oxidized** and the species accepting electrons is being **reduced**. It is important to recognize which species is being oxidized and which is reduced in an equation. To do this, you must identify an oxidation state or oxidation number for each atom in a species. Rules used to identify an oxidation state are illustrated in the following example:

For example, to find the oxidation number of the Mn in $KMnO_4$, you write an equation assigning Mn oxidation state as $x$, assign the known oxidation states, in this case

K is always $+1$ and each O is almost always $-2$ (except in peroxides), and then set the equation equal to zero since it is a neutral compound; $+1 + x + -8 = 0$. Thus, Mn is in the $+7$ oxidation state. This section must be mastered before the electrochemistry chapter.

In a reaction such as $Cu(s) + 2\,AgNO_3(aq) \rightarrow Cu(NO_3)_2(aq) + 2Ag(s)$, writing the net ionic equation.

$Cu + Ag^+(aq) \rightarrow Cu^{2+}(aq) + Ag(s)$ emphasizes the electron transfer occcuring. Cu loses two electrons and changes to $Cu^{2+}$ (oxidation), whereas each $Ag^+$ gains an electron to form Ag (reduction). Once the net ionic equation is written, it is easier to see that this is an oxidation–reduction reaction.

Oxidizing agents and reducing agents are not part of the AP curriculum.

In combustion reactions, a compound reacts with oxygen. These are always redox reactions because elemental oxygen has an oxidation state of zero, changes in the reaction to $-2$, and is therefore reduced. If an organic hydrocarbons or substance containing only C, H, and O atoms is completely combusted, the products will be water and carbon dioxide. An example reaction is methane reacting with oxygen:

$$CH_4(g) + 2\,O_2(g) \rightarrow CO_2(g) + 2\,H_2O(l).$$

Note the C atom is unchanged at $+4$ and each of the 4H atoms are oxidized from $-1$ to $+1$.

## Additional Practice

*Self-Assessment Quiz Questions Q1, Q2, Q3, Q4, Q5, Q6, Q7, Q8, Q9, Q10, Q11, Q12, Q13, and Q15*
*Problems 25, 29, 35, 37, 39, 40, 41, 43, 49, 50, 53, 55, 57, 59, 60, 62, 63, 65, 67, 70, 72, 73, 75, 77, 79, 82, 85, 88, 90, 91, 93, 97, 101, 102, 108, 116, 119, 120, 136, 137, and 138*

## Practice AP® Test Questions

1. The following diagram represents the reaction of $A_2$ (two joined triangles) with $X_2$ (two joined shaded spheres) at the particulate nature of matter level representation.

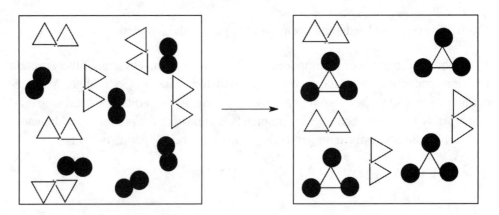

   Write a balanced chemical equation for the process and identify the limiting reagent.

   A) $A + X_2 \rightarrow AX_3$

      $A_2$ is the limiting reagent

   B) $2A + 6X \rightarrow 2\,AX_3$

      $X_2$ is the limiting reagent

   C) $A_2 + 3X_2 \rightarrow 2\,AX_3$

      $A_2$ is the limiting reagent

   D) $A_2 + 3X_2 \rightarrow 2\,AX_3$

      $X_2$ is the limiting reagent

2. Based on the picture diagram in the previous problem, how many moles of product, $AX_3$, can be made if 2.0 moles of $A_2$ are allowed to react with 2.0 moles of $X_2$?

   A) 1.33 mol $AX_3$

   B) 2.0 mol $AX_3$

   C) 4.0 mol $AX_3$

   D) 6.0 mol $AX_3$

3. Iron reacts with oxygen gas in the presence of some water to form iron (III) oxide.

$$4\ Fe(s)\ +\ 3\ O_2(g) \rightarrow 2\ Fe_2O_3(s)$$

When 16 g of oxygen gas are allowed to react with 28 g of iron, allowing for rounding, what is the maximum amount of iron (III) oxide that can form?

A)  20. g

B)  40. g

C)  80. g

D)  160 g

4. When aluminum reacts with chlorine gas, aluminum chloride, $AlCl_3$ can form.

$$2Al(s)\ +\ 3Cl_2(g) \rightarrow 2\ AlCl_3(s)$$

If the percentage yield for the above reaction is 50.0%, how many grams of chlorine gas must react to produce 27 g of $AlCl_3$?

A)  11 g

B)  19 g

C)  22 g

D)  43 g

5. The following diagram represents the reaction of a strong acid HX (a square joined to an X) with strong base, NaOH (the $Na^+$ ion, and a circle joined to a square) at the particulate nature of matter level representation.

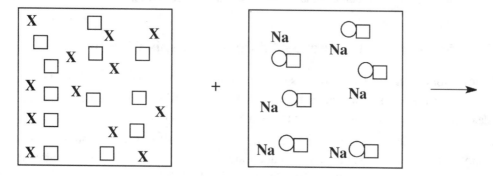

The volume represented by the interior of the square A is the same as Square B. If the concentration of the acid is 0.50 M and the volume of the acid solution is 20. mL, what volume of the base is required to neutralize the acid?

A)  10. mL

B)  20. mL

C)  30. mL

D)  40. mL

# GASES

Gases were the first state of matter to be effectively explained. Since gases automatically fill the container they are in, their volume can be externally controlled. This behavior introduces many unique concepts the AP student must know and are the easiest to model both qualitatively and quantitatively. These ideas are addressed in Learning Objectives 2.4, 2.5, and 2.6 of Big Idea 2. The most important sections to know are:

5.3   **The Simple Gas Laws: Boyle's Law, Charles's Law, and Avogadro's Law**

5.4   **The Ideal Gas Law**

5.5   **Applications of the Ideal Gas Law: Molar Volume, Density, and Molar Mass of a Gas**

5.6   **Mixtures of Gases and Partial Pressures**

5.8   **Kinetic Molecular Theory (KMT): A Model for Gases**

5.10   **Real Gases: The Effects of Size and Intermolecular Forces**

## Specific Learning Objectives Addressed in This Chapter:

**Learning objective 2.4** The student is able to use KMT and concepts of intermolecular forces to make predictions about the macroscopic properties of gases, including both ideal and nonideal behaviors. [*See* **SP 1.4, 6.4**]

**Learning objective 2.5** The student is able to refine multiple representations of a sample of matter in the gas phase to accurately represent the effect of changes in macroscopic properties on the sample. [*See* **SP 1.3, 6.4**]

**Learning objective 2.6** The student can apply mathematical relationships or estimation to determine macroscopic variables for ideal gases. [*See* **SP 2.2, 2.3**]

**Learning objective 2.15** The student is able to explain observations regarding the solubility of ionic solids and molecules in water and other solvents on the basis of particle views that include intermolecular interactions and entropic effects. [*See* **SP 1.4, 6.2**]

**Learning objective 3.1** Students can translate among macroscopic observations of change, chemical equations, and particle views. [*See* **SP 1.5, 7.1**]

**Learning objective 3.3** The student is able to use stoichiometric calculations to predict the results of performing a reaction in the laboratory and/or to analyze deviations from the expected results. [*See* **SP 2.2, 5.1**]

**Learning objective 3.4** The student is able to relate quantities (measured mass of substances, volumes of solutions, or volumes and pressures of gases) to identify stoichiometric relationships for a reaction, including situations involving limiting reactants and situations in which the reaction has not gone to completion. [*See* **SP 2.2**, **5.1**, **6.4**]

## Specific Science Practices Addressed in This Chapter:

**Science Practice 1:** The student can use representations and models to communicate scientific phenomena and solve scientific problems.

1.3  The student can *refine representations and models* of natural or man-made phenomena and systems in the domain.

1.4  The student can *use representations and models* to analyze situations or solve problems qualitatively and quantitatively.

1.5  The student can *re-express key elements* of natural phenomena across multiple representations in the domain.

**Science Practice 2:** The student can use mathematics appropriately.

2.2  The student can *apply mathematical routines* to quantities that describe natural phenomena.

2.3  The student can *estimate numerically* quantities that describe natural phenomena.

**Science Practice 5:** The student can perform data analysis and evaluation of evidence.

5.1  The student can *analyze data* to identify patterns or relationships.

**Science Practice 6:** The student can work with scientific explanations and theories.

6.1  The student can *justify claims with evidence.*

6.2  The student can *construct explanations of phenomena based on evidence* produced through scientific practices.

6.4  The student can *make claims and predictions about natural phenomena* based on scientific theories and models.

**Science Practice 7:** The student is able to connect and relate knowledge across various scales, concepts, and representations in and across domains.

7.1  The student can *connect phenomena and models* across spatial and temporal scales.

7.2  The student can *connect concepts* in and across domain(s) to generalize or extrapolate in and/or across enduring understandings and/or big ideas.

## Concepts and Vocabulary to Review:

Section 5.3

# The Simple Gas Laws: Boyle's Law, Charles's Law, and Avogadro's Law

Gases take up and fill the space of the container they are in and are readily compressible if the container changes its volume. Measurements can be taken of their pressure, temperature, volume, and the number of gas particles present. Changes in these parameters affect the other gas parameters. Each simple gas law shows a relationship between two of these variables. It is not important to know the names of the laws, but it is important to understand and be able to explain the concepts behind them, as well as perform calculations using them. For each simple law, be able to draw a graphical relationship, explain what the relationship is, and using a model of an ideal gas, explain why the relationship exists.

Handling quantitative problems about gases involves having a good understanding of the different units used, and their interrelationships. In AP, the pressure ($P$) units used can be measured in atm, mmHg, and torr. Temperatures ($T$) may be given in °C or K but must always be in K when solving numerical gas problems, volumes ($V$) may be given in mL, $cm^3$, or L, but should be in liters when performing calculations such as the Ideal Gas Law, and the amount of gas should be expressed in moles ($n$).

Historically, scientists studied the effects of changing one variable on another and their conclusions have become known as the *gas laws*. Each can be represented by a graph and/or an equation of change comparing one set of conditions to another. However, eventually it was realized these individual laws could be combined under most conditions into a single statement that became known as the Ideal Gas Law. Remember that in each of the following "single laws," only TWO variables are considered at a time. This means all the other variables must remain constant, or the law does not hold. The ideal gas law does allow more than one variable changing at once.

**Boyle's Law** states the inverse relationship between pressure and volume when the other variables are held constant. When either $P$ or $V$ goes up, the other goes down. If you push down on a capped off syringe with a gas inside, the pressure on the gas goes up, while the volume occupied by the gas decreases. If you pull on the syringe, the gas volume will go up, but its pressure will go down. This is evidence of the inverse relationship. Only by plotting the INVERSE of one variable on a graph will a straight-line relationship appear.

The mathematical formula for Boyle's Law is: $P_1V_1 = P_2V_2$

**Charles's Law** states the direct relationship between temperature and volume, while the other variables are held constant. The evidence of the direct relationship is when either temperature or volume changes the other has the same degree of change. In a graph, this will appear as a linear relationship. If the temperature ($T$) in Kelvin doubles, the volume ($V$) will correspondingly double. Note that the simple numerical relationship only works for Kelvin temperature units, which are based on Charles's

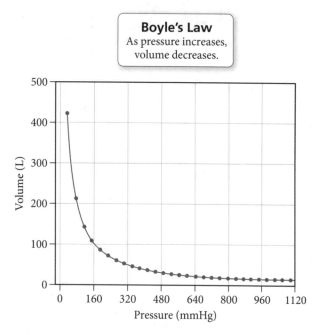

**Boyle's Law**
As pressure increases,
volume decreases.

**Figure 5.1  Volume versus Pressure**   A plot of the volume of a gas sample—as measured in a J-tube—versus pressure. The plot shows that volume and pressure are inversely related.

results. This explains why warm air rises. As the gases temperature increases, the volume expands, which in turn lowers the density of the gas. Remember density is mass per unit volume, so this assumes the mass of the gas in the air remains constant. The less dense gas rises.

The mathematical formula for Charles's Law is: $\dfrac{V_1}{T_1} = \dfrac{V_2}{T_2}$

**Avogadro's Law** explains the direct relationship between volume and the number of moles ($n$) of a gas present when the other variables are held constant. As a direct relationship, when the volume and number of moles (not mass in grams) are plotted in a graph, the graph will appear linear Indicating when the number of moles or the volume increases or decreases, so does the other.

The mathematical formula for Avogadro's Law is: $\dfrac{V_1}{n_1} = \dfrac{V_2}{n_2}$

Another simple gas law, Gay-Lussac's Law, will be covered in Section 5.4.

A simplification of Boyle's, Charles's, Avogadro's, and Gay-Lussac (mentioned below in section 5.4) laws is the combined gas law where $\dfrac{P_1 V_1}{n_1 T_1} = \dfrac{P_2 V_2}{n_2 T_2}$. This is useful as only one equation is worked with instead of four. Each law can be seen by removing the variables held constant.

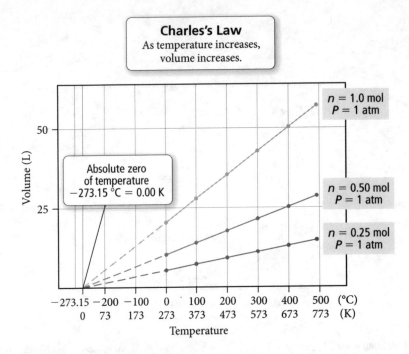

Figure 5.2  **Volume versus Temperature**   The volume of a fixed amount of gas at a constant pressure increases linearly with increasing temperature in kelvins. (The extrapolated lines cannot be measured experimentally because all gases condense into liquids before −273.15 °C is reached.)

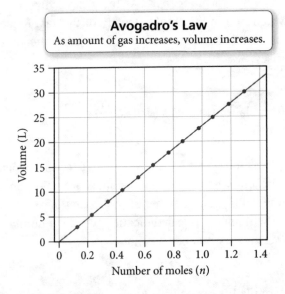

Figure 5.3  **Volume versus Number of Moles**   The volume of a gas sample increases linearly with the number of moles of gas in the sample.

## Section 5.4    The Ideal Gas Law

The laws above can be combined into a single law/equation. Combining Boyle's Law, Charles's Law, and Avogadro's law results in the **ideal gas law equation**, $PV = nRT$, where $R$ is called the gas constant. The units of pressure will dictate the value of

$R$ used in solving any numerical problem, but as previously noted, $T$ is always in

Kelvin, $V$ is in liters, and $n$ is always numbers of moles. $R$ can be $0.0821 \dfrac{\text{L} \cdot \text{atm}}{\text{K} \cdot \text{mol}}$ or

another value provided on the AP test is $62.4 \dfrac{\text{L} \cdot \text{mmHg}}{\text{K} \cdot \text{mol}}$. Notice that K stands in for $T$ in kelvin units.

Another gas law is **Gay-Lussac's Law,** which describes the direct relationship between pressure and temperature, while the other variables are held constant. This direct relationship when graphed results in a linear relationship where if one increases, so does the other. This explains why an aerosol can explodes upon heating. If the temperature increases, the pressure increases until the can "blows."

$$\frac{P_1}{T_1} = \frac{P_2}{T_2}$$

## Applications of the Ideal Gas Law: Molar Volume, Density, and Molar Mass of a Gas                Section 5.5

### Key definitions to know:

**STP** (standard temperature and pressure) are the conditions of $0\,°C$ or 273 K (standard temperature) and 1.00 atm (standard pressure).

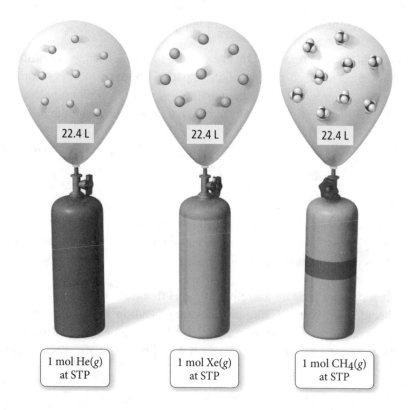

1 mol He(g) at STP

1 mol Xe(g) at STP

1 mol $CH_4$(g) at STP

**Molar volume** is the volume occupied by one mole of gas. If one mole of gas is present ($n = 1$) and the conditions of STP are substituted into the ideal gas law equation $PV = nRT$ and rearranged to solve for the volume, $V = \dfrac{nRT}{P}$, the resulting volume is 22.4 liters. This is true regardless of the gas present. Watch for these conditions!

**Gas density:** At STP, the density of a gas equation becomes $d = \dfrac{M}{22.4\frac{g}{L}}$ or $\dfrac{\text{Molar mass}}{\text{Molar volume}}$. When comparing 1 mole of gases at STP, the density of a gas is directly proportional to the molar mass; therefore, the larger the molar mass, the more dense the gas. If the conditions are not at STP, the equation to use for density of a gas is $d = \dfrac{PM}{RT}$. This is derived from substituting $\dfrac{m}{M}\left(\dfrac{\text{mass in grams}}{\text{molar mass}}\right)$ *for n* and rearranging the ideal gas equation to $\dfrac{m}{V} = \dfrac{PM}{RT}$. This same equation can be rearranged to solve for the molar mass of a gas: $M = \dfrac{mRT}{PV}$, which can also be written as $M = \dfrac{dRT}{P}$.

## Section 5.6    Mixtures of Gases and Partial Pressures

In earlier gas laws, it was assumed a single gas was present. Dalton showed several gases can be present and the gas laws still apply.

**Dalton's Law of Partial Pressures**: In any mixture of gases, each gas contributes to the total pressure present. Each gas contributes a **partial pressure** and when combined add up to the total gas pressure in the container. This relationship is represented by the equation $P_{\text{total}} = P_a + P_b + P_c + \ldots$ where $a$, $b$, and $c$ represent the different gases.

The **mole fraction** of any gas (moles of a gas present compared to the total moles of gas present or $\dfrac{X_a}{X_{\text{total}}}$) can also be used to determine the partial pressure. For gas $a$ this would be $P_a = X_a P_{\text{total}}$. In other words, the part that the gas is of the total moles, it is the same part total pressure. If the gas is half of the moles present, it will be half of the pressure present. This comes about because each gas independently follows the combined gas equation as reviewed in the previous section.

Often in reactions to prepare a sample of a gas that does not dissolve in water, the gas is collected over water. Using the concept of Dalton's Law of Partial Pressure, the total pressure is the sum of the gas collected and the pressure of the water vapor present. Water vapor pressure in equilibrium with liquid water can be determined by

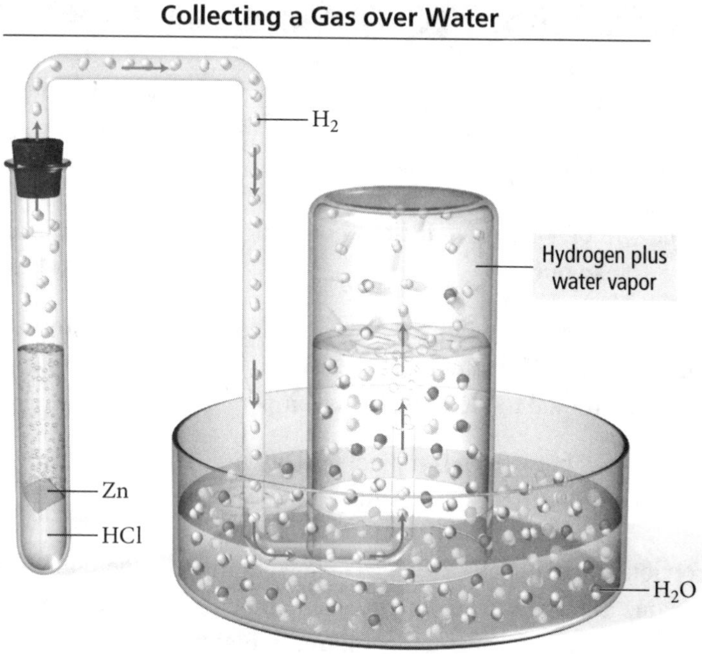

## Collecting a Gas over Water

**Figure 5.4  Collecting a Gas over Water**   When the gaseous product of a chemical reaction is collected over water, the product molecules (in this case $H_2$) are mixed with water molecules. The pressure of water in the final mixture is equal to the vapor pressure of water at the temperature at which the gas is collected. The partial pressure of the product is the total pressure minus the partial pressure of water.

knowing the temperature of the water and looking at a table of water vapor pressures in a handbook or in an online table. In normal lab conditions, the temperature of the water is room temperature and total pressure is local atmospheric pressure. The water vapor pressure is subtracted from the total pressure to determine the pressure of the gas.

**Table 5.1**   Vapor Pressure of Water versus Temperature

| Temperature (°C) | Pressure (mmHg) | Temperature (°C) | Pressure (mmHg) |
|---|---|---|---|
| 0 | 4.58 | 55 | 118.2 |
| 5 | 6.54 | 60 | 149.6 |
| 10 | 9.21 | 65 | 187.5 |
| 15 | 12.79 | 70 | 233.7 |
| 20 | 17.55 | 75 | 289.1 |
| 25 | 23.78 | 80 | 355.1 |
| 30 | 31.86 | 85 | 433.6 |
| 35 | 42.23 | 90 | 525.8 |
| 40 | 55.40 | 95 | 633.9 |
| 45 | 71.97 | 100 | 760.0 |
| 50 | 92.6 | | |

Section 5.8    **Kinetic Molecular Theory (KMT): A Model for Gases**

**Kinetic Molecular Theory** is a model used to explain how gases behave under varying conditions. It can be used to explain all the gas laws. The model is based on three assumptions:

1. The size of a gas particle does not matter since gas particles are tiny and are spread out.

2. The average kinetic energy (KE) of a gas particle is proportional to its temperature. The total kinetic energy of all the gas particles in a sample is proportional to the overall gas temperature.

3. Collisions between gas molecules (or within container walls) are totally elastic (no energy is lost as they collide).

One misconception is that all gas molecules in any gas move at the same speed because they have the same average kinetic energy. Remember, gases with the same average kinetic energy must be at the same temperature. In reality, the higher the molar mass of a gas is, the slower its velocity or speed will be. In addition, there is a distribution of velocities within a gas sample known as a Maxwell–Boltzmann distribution.

KMT explanation of Boyle's Law: As the volume of a gas decreases, the gas molecules will hit the sides of a container more often creating a greater pressure. More hits in the same time means more force is transferred to an area of the container surface. (Remember temperature and the number of gas particles are held constant.)

KMT explanation of Charles's Law: As the temperature increases, the average kinetic energy of the gas increases. This indicates the gas particles are moving at a higher average velocity so the collisions with the sides of the container are more frequent, creating a higher pressure. This increased pressure of a non-rigid container causes the volume to increase to keep pressure constant. (Remember the variables of pressure and the number of gas particles are held constant.)

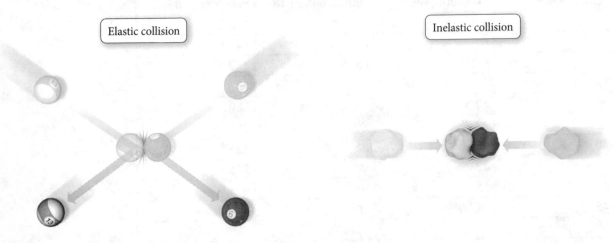

**Figure 5.5  Elastic versus Inelastic Collisions**    When two billiard balls collide, the collision is elastic—the total kinetic energy of the colliding bodies is the same before and after the collision. When two lumps of clay collide, the collision is inelastic—the kinetic energy of the colliding bodies dissipates in the form of heat during the collision.

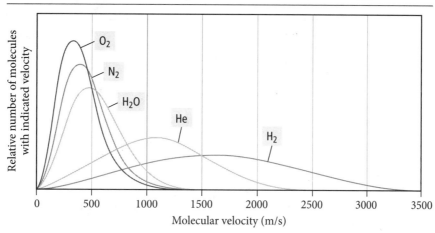

**Figure 5.6  Velocity Distribution for Several Gases at 25 °C**    At a given temperature, there is a distribution of velocities among the particles in a sample of gas. The exact shape and peak of the distribution varies with the molar mass of the gas.

KMT explanation of Avogadro's Law: If the number of gas molecules increases in the same volume of a non-rigid container, there will be more collisions with the sides of the container, increasing the volume to maintain the same pressure. (Remember the variables of pressure and temperature are held constant.)

KMT explanation of Dalton's Law: Because all gas molecules present have the same average kinetic energy (they are at the same temperature), all the molecules will exert the same force. The partial forces will add up to give the total pressure, so the fraction of particles of each type (mole fraction) will determine each gas's contribution to that total. Total pressure will be the partial pressure of all the gases added together.

At any temperature, lighter gases travel faster *on average* than heavier gases. Some gas molecules will be faster and some will be slower and in fact, the rate of movement of a gas is inversely proportional to its molar mass. The root mean square speed ($u_{rms}$) of a gas is represented by the equation $u_{rms} = \sqrt{\dfrac{3RT}{M}}$. The variations of velocities can be seen in a velocity graph at the same temperature of different gases.

## Real Gases: The Effects of Size and Intermolecular Forces    Section 5.10

Do gases always behave ideally? No! Remember KMT is based on three assumptions. If any of these are not true, then we would expect deviations.

If the gas particles are forced close enough together, the size of the gas particle does matter. As the particles move more slowly, the collisions may be less elastic and more inelastic. The conditions causing this to happen are high pressure and/or low temperatures. Johannes van der Waals explained this by adding terms to the ideal gas equation for all gases at any condition. His equation is

**The Behavior of Real Gases**

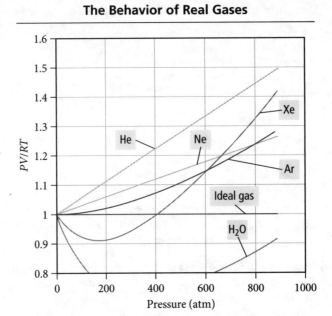

**Figure 5.7  Real versus Ideal Behavior**    For 1 mol of an ideal gas, $PV/RT$ is equal to 1. The combined effects of the volume of gas particles and the interactions among them cause each real gas to deviate from ideal behavior in a slightly different way. These curves were calculated at a temperature of 500 K.

$$\left[P + a\left(\frac{n}{V}\right)^2\right] \times \left[V - nb\right] = nRT$$ where $a$ is a correction value for the attraction between gas particles (leading to nonelastic collisions) and $b$ is the correction value for the volume of the gas particles. The numerical values for $a$ and $b$ are unique to each gas. If collisions are not elastic, fewer collisions will occur; the resulting pressure will be less than predicted by the ideal gas law, so the correction is added. If the container volume decreases enough, the space occupied by the actual gas particles becomes significant compared to the actual "empty space"; the volume used in the ideal gas law is too high, so the correction is subtracted. The size of gas particles and attractive forces between gas particles can be compared to an ideal gas in the above graph.

Each gas is slightly different due to the combination of factors, including intermolecular forces. Helium has little attraction and a small atomic size compared to water vapor with high attractions and a much larger molecular size.

## Additional Practice

*Self-Assessment Quiz Questions Q1, Q2, Q3, Q4, Q5, Q6, Q7 Q8, Q9, Q10, Q11, Q12, Q13, Q14, and Q15*
*Problems 29, 31, 33, 35, 37, 44, 45, 49, 51, 53, 57, 61, 65, 67, 71, 77, 81, 82, 86, 87, 89, 90, 97, 102, 107, 139, 143, 144, and 145*

## Practice AP® Test Questions

1. If a 600.0 mL volume of a sample gas has a mass of 1.60 grams at 2.00 atm and 27.00 °C, which of the following gases could it be?

   A) $NH_3$

   B) $O_2$

   C) $SO_2$

   D) Kr

2. What will happen to the volume of helium gas in a sealed weather balloon if the gas starts at 27.0 °C and 1.00 atm and rises to a height where the pressure is 0.333 atm and a temperature of −73.0 °C?

   A) The volume of gas will decrease by a factor of two.

   B) The volume of gas will remain the same.

   C) The volume of gas will increase by a factor of two.

   D) The volume of gas will increase by a factor of four.

3. The diagram below represents a ratio of a mixture of gases at the molecule level in a small volume of gas within a sealed container, X. Oxygen molecules are represented by two joined grey spheres, helium atoms by unshaded spheres, and neon atoms by black spheres.

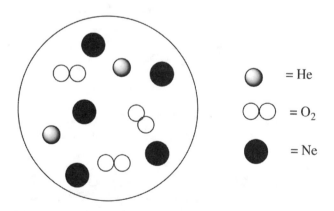

If the total pressure of the gases in sealed container, X, is 450 mmHg, what is the partial pressure of helium?

A) 45 mmHg

B) 90.0 mmHg

C) 135 mmHg

D) 225 mmHg

4. When 7.50 g of zinc metal reacts with excess HCl, how many liters of $H_2$ gas can form at STP?

A) 0.114 L

B) 0.229 L

C) 2.57 L

D) 5.15 L

5. If 1.00 mole of $O_2$ and Xe gases are allowed to effuse through a small hole under identical conditions of pressure and temperature, the rate of effusion of oxygen gas will be _____ times faster compared to xenon gas.

A) 0.25

B) 0.50

C) 2

D) 4

# THERMOCHEMISTRY

In the AP Curriculum, the concepts of thermochemistry are enveloped in Big Idea 5. The first part of the chapter reviews types of energy and energy units. The units used on the AP chemistry exam will be joules or kilojoules. Section 6.5 on constant-volume calorimetry is not directly tested in the AP curriculum, but it is the source of most heat of reaction data, important, for example, to the food industry.

The most important sections to review are:

6.3 **The First Law of Thermodynamics: There is No Free Lunch**

6.4 **Quantifying Heat and Work**

6.6 **Enthalpy: The Heat Evolved in a Chemical Reaction at Constant Pressure**

6.7 **Constant-Pressure Calorimetry: Measuring** $\Delta H_{rxn}$

6.8 **Relationships Involving** $\Delta H_{rxn}$

6.9 **Determining Enthalpies of Reaction from Standard Enthalpies of Formation**

## Specific Learning Objectives Addressed in This Chapter:

**Learning objective 3.11** The student is able to interpret observations regarding macroscopic energy changes associated with a reaction or process to generate a relevant symbolic and/or graphical representation of the energy changes. [*See* **SP 1.5, 4.4**]

**Learning objective 5.2** The student is able to relate temperature to the motions of particles, either via particulate representations, such as drawings of particles with arrows indicating velocities, and/or via representations of average kinetic energy and distribution of kinetic energies of the particles, such as plots of the Maxwell-Boltzmann distribution. [*See* **SP 1.1, 1.4, 7.1**]

**Learning objective 5.3** The student can generate explanations or make predictions about the transfer of thermal energy between systems based on this transfer being due to a kinetic energy transfer between systems arising from molecular collisions. [*See* **SP 7.1**]

**Learning objective 5.4** The student is able to use conservation of energy to relate the magnitudes of the energy changes occurring in two or more interacting systems, including identification of the systems, the type (heat versus work), or the direction of energy flow. [*See* **SP 1.4, 2.2**]

**Learning objective 5.5** The student is able to use conservation of energy to relate the magnitudes of the energy changes when two nonreacting substances are mixed or brought into contact with one another. [*See* **SP 2.2**]

**Learning objective 5.6** The student is able to use calculations or estimations to relate energy changes associated with heating/cooling a substance to the heat capacity, relate energy changes associated with a phase transition to the enthalpy of fusion/vaporization, relate energy changes associated with a chemical reaction to the enthalpy of the reaction, and relate energy changes to $P\Delta V$ work. [*See* **SP 2.2, 2.3**]

**Learning objective 5.7** The student is able to design and/or interpret the results of an experiment in which calorimetry is used to determine the change in enthalpy of a chemical process (heating/cooling, phase transition, or chemical reaction) at constant pressure. [*See* **SP 4.2, 5.1**]

**Learning objective 5.8** The student is able to draw qualitative and quantitative connections between the reaction enthalpy and the energies involved in the breaking and formation of chemical bonds. [*See* **SP 2.3, 7.1, 7.2**]

## Specific Science Practices Addressed in This Chapter:

**Science Practice1:** The student can use representations and models to communicate scientific phenomena and solve scientific problems.

    1.1    The student can *create representations and models* of natural or man-made phenomena and systems in the domain.

    1.4    The student can *use representations and models* to analyze situations or solve problems qualitatively and quantitatively.

    1.5    The student can *re-express key elements* of natural phenomena across multiple representations in the domain.

**Science Practice 2:** The student can use mathematics appropriately.

    2.2    The student can *apply mathematical routines* to quantities that describe natural phenomena.

    2.3    The student can *estimate numerically* quantities that describe natural phenomena.

**Science Practice 4:** The student can plan and implement data collection strategies in relation to a particular scientific question.

    4.2    The student can *design a plan* for collecting data to answer a particular scientific question.

4.4  The student can *evaluate sources of data* to answer a particular scientific question.

**Science Practice 5:** The student can perform data analysis and evaluation of evidence.

5.1  The student can *analyze data* to identify patterns or relationships.

**Science Practice 7:** The student is able to connect and relate knowledge across various scales, concepts, and representations in and across domains.

7.1  The student can *connect phenomena and models* across spatial and temporal scales.

7.2  The student can *connect concepts* in and across domain(s) to generalize or extrapolate in and/or across enduring understandings and/or big ideas.

## Concepts and Vocabulary to Review:

## The First Law of Thermodynamics: There is No Free Lunch     Section 6.3

In the field of thermodynamics, scientists realized it was very important to carefully define what was being measured or studied. Everything in the universe is to be included, but a small part called the *system* will be studied. Everything outside the *system* is the *surroundings*. We could write an equation:

Universe = SYSTEM + SURROUNDINGS.

Each law is a general finding (meaning nothing has ever been identified as not following the rule) about the relationships with a system and/or its surroundings. Many general misconceptions arise from misunderstanding the concept of the system. Thermodynamics is full of definitions of quantities and terms that must be precisely understood and applied. Remember the terms were defined for convenience for communication among scientists trying to understand how nature works. Nature proceeds by its own rules without having to learn the definitions.

The first law of thermodynamics is: The total of energy in the universe is constant.

In other words, energy lost by a system must be equal to what is gained by its surroundings. This is represented as change in internal energy equals the sum of heat and work: $\Delta E = q + w$.

A *state function* is a defined property of a system. State functions depend only on the beginning and ending conditions of the system and not the path of the reaction or change. You can travel from Chicago to New York by several different routes, but Chicago and New York look just the same no matter which route you take! The same is true with state functions and chemical or physical change. *Internal energy*, the

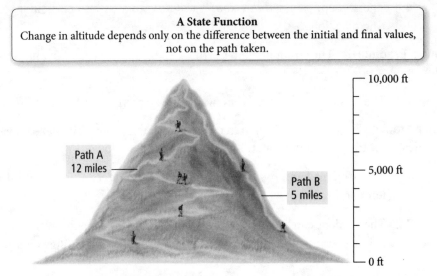

**A State Function**
Change in altitude depends only on the difference between the initial and final values, not on the path taken.

**Figure 6.1  Altitude as a State Function**   The change in altitude during a climb depends only on the difference between the final and initial altitudes, not on the route traveled.

sum of kinetic and potential energies in a system, is a state function. Work and heat are not state functions as they depend on the pathway of the change.

In chemical and physical change measurements, the focus is on what happens to the system. In chemical reactions, the system is all the chemicals in the reaction. The container is part of the surroundings although it is up to the scientist doing the experiment to define the system and the surroundings. As long as accurate accounting of thermal energy changes is done, it all works out. If the internal energy is higher in the reactants than the products, energy will be given off by the reaction. When energy is released by a reaction, the sign of the energy change is defined as negative since the system loses energy to the surroundings. If the internal energy in reactants is lower than the products, energy must be absorbed by the system's products from its surroundings, so the sign of the energy change is positive.

**Table 6.1**    Sign Conventions for $q$, $w$, and $\Delta E$

| $q$ (heat) | + system *gains* thermal energy | − system *loses* thermal energy |
|---|---|---|
| $w$ (work) | + work done *on* the system | − work done *by* the system |
| $\Delta E$ (change in internal energy) | + energy flows *into* the system | − energy flows *out* of the system |

## Section 6.4     Quantifying Heat and Work

Many students have a misunderstanding of temperature and heat. *Temperature* is a measure of thermal energy within a sample of matter. *Heat* is thermal energy being transferred. All around us, we can observe when objects with different temperatures come into contact with each other. Thermal energy will transfer until both objects have the same thermal energy (temperature). When the same temperature is reached, thermal equilibrium is reached. We also observe this transfer from the object with the higher temperature to the object with the lower temperature, so this was established as the conventional direction for thermal energy transfer.

Different materials have a different capacity to absorb heat because they have different ways of distributing the energy internally. This is called *heat capacity* (*C*) and is defined in the equation $C = \dfrac{q}{\Delta T}$ where, *C* is the heat capacity, *q* is heat transferred, and $\Delta T$ is the change in temperature. The amount of heat needed to change the temperature of a substance by one degree is dependent on the amount of substance present. A small amount of water requires less energy to raise its temperature than a large amount of water for the number of degrees of change. This means heat capacity is an extensive property.

Often, it is more convenient to compare the amount of heat necessary to raise the temperature 1°C for different substances. This task involves comparing the heat needed to raise similar masses of the different substances. *Specific heat capacity* is defined as the amount of heat needed to raise the temperature of 1.0 g by 1°C. Because specific heat capacity is based on a fixed amount of mass (1.0 g), it becomes an intensive property. Another intensive property is created by comparing the heat required to raise a mole of substance by 1°C; this is called *molar heat capacity*. The specific heat equation used in this book is $q = m \times C_s \times \Delta T$ where the subscript *s* distinguishes it as the specific heat, rather than heat capacity. On the AP test equation pages, the equation given is $q = mc\Delta T$. The specific heat is equal to the heat capacity, divided by the number of grams present; $\dfrac{C}{m} = C_s \, or \, c$. Pay attention to the units given to know whether *c* is specific heat capacity (J/g · °C), or molar heat capacity (J/mol · °C) When a hot object, like a hot piece of metal, is placed in cold water, the hot metal will lose heat while the water gains heat until thermal equilibrium is established. The amount of energy lost by the metal is equal in magnitude, but opposite in sign: $q_{metal} = -q_{water}$ as long as the metal-water is the system and no energy is lost to the surroundings. This concept allows us to write the equation: $m_1 c_1 \Delta T_1 = -m_2 c_2 \Delta T_2$. This equation is not listed on the AP test equation pages. It is expected that you know the specific heat of water is 4.18 J/g°C. Although the AP curriculum focuses on joules, one should know 1 calorie = 4.18 joules. Besides water, there are no other specific heat values you must know. Be able to solve problems for the final temperature when two objects are placed together, problems involving calculation of a specific heat, and problems solving for a mass of a substance, given the temperature changes and circumstances.

If a reaction occurs in a confined cylinder such as gasoline combustion in an automobile, the gases expand with the increased temperature and cause the cylinders to push a piston upward. This mechanical work is defined in physics as force x distance, which in this case is equal to pressure x volume change so $W = -P\Delta V$, where *P* is the pressure in atmospheres and $\Delta V$ is the change in volume in liters. The negative sign results as work is done by the system on the surroundings, so is counted as a loss to the system. This results in work having the unit of L · atm. To convert to the energy unit of joules the L · atm answer must be multiplied by $\frac{101.3\,J}{1\,L\cdot atm}$.

## Enthalpy: The Heat Evolved in a Chemical Reaction at Constant Pressure

*Enthalpy* (*H*) is defined as the sum of internal energy and the product of pressure and volume for a system. $\Delta H$, or the change in enthalpy of a system, is the heat transferred under constant pressure. The change of enthalpy can be positive or negative for the system, and the opposite sign for the surroundings.

In a chemical reaction, if the system takes in energy from its surroundings, the reaction is endothermic and the sign of $\Delta H$ is positive. As reactant bonds break and new product bonds form, thermal energy is needed that must come from the surroundings, so the surroundings temperature decreases. If the reaction is exothermic, then the sign of $\Delta H$ is negative. In this case thermal energy is released to the surroundings and the surroundings temperature will increase. This is happening in the hand warmer where your hand is part of the surroundings. The relationship between the energies of bonds breaking and bonds forming in chemical reactions will be covered in Chapter 9.

Thermochemical equations include information about enthalpy. The enthalpy is specific to the reaction written with its stoichiometric coefficients and is therefore written as: $\Delta H_{rxn}$. The values will have a sign to indicate if the reaction is endothermic or exothermic as it proceeds in the conventional manner—from left to right.

$$C_3H_8(g) + 5\,O_2(g) \rightarrow 3\,CO_2(g) + 4\,H_2O(g) \quad \Delta H_{rxn} \;\; -2044\,kJ$$

In this reaction equation, the reaction is exothermic, hence the negative sign. The values can be used in ratios to determine the amount of heat with a different amount of reactant. For example $\frac{-2044\,kJ}{1\,mol\,C_2H_2}$ is one ratio that can be used. It also can be expressed as $-2044\,kJ/3\,mol\,CO_2$ produced.

## Constant-Pressure Calorimetry: Measuring $\Delta H_{rxn}$

Using a coffee-cup calorimeter is a common laboratory method to find the $\Delta H_{rxn}$. During the reaction, energy of reaction will result in a temperature rise of a known amount of water in which the reactants are dissolved; by taking temperature measurements of the system before and after, the amount of heat (thermal energy transferred) can be determined. This assumes the calorimeter is well insulated so no heat

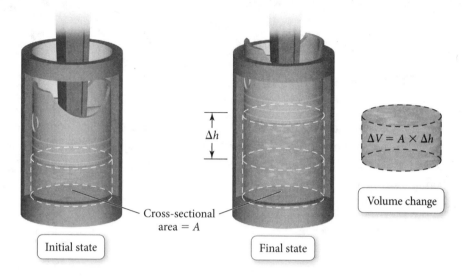

**Figure 6.2 Piston Moving within a Cylinder against an External Pressure.**

is lost to the calorimeter or other parts of its surroundings. In other words, the system is the reacting chemicals and the water. This is especially easy to see if the reaction is the result of mixing two solutions, for instance an acid with a base. The heat of reaction increases the temperature of the combined solution system, which are assumed to have the same specific heat as pure water. This assumption usually introduces only a very small error.

A measured amount of solution will be in the calorimeter. The heat of the solution is calculated using the equation $q_{soln} = m_{sol}c_{sol}\Delta T$ or $q = mc\Delta T$. The $q_{rxn}$ will have the same value but opposite sign compared to $q_{soln}$. Usually, the solution is water and so the heat capacity ($c$) is 4.18 J/g·°C. To determine the $\Delta H_{rxn}$, a balanced equation will be needed. Then a calculation can be set up to determine the amount that would be released or absorbed per mole. This is one of labs specified in the AP curriculum.

## Relationships Involving $\Delta H_{rxn}$     Section 6.8

Remember $\Delta H_{rxn}$ is for a particular reaction and a particular number of moles. If the reaction is multiplied by a factor such as 2, the $\Delta H_{rxn}$ is also multiplied by the same factor. If the reaction is reversed, then the numerical value $\Delta H_{rxn}$ is the same, but the sign reverses. If the reaction is endothermic in the forward direction, it will be exothermic in the reverse direction.

Another relationship used to find $\Delta H_{rxn}$ is called Hess's Law. If a series of chemical equations can be added or subtracted to get a final desired equation, the net sum of the $\Delta Hs$ of each reaction will sum to the overall $\Delta H_{rxn}$ of the desired equation. In other words $\Delta H_1 + \Delta H_2 + \Delta H_3 = \Delta H_{rxn}$. It is vital to retain proper signs for the $\Delta H$ values during this procedure.

For instance, given the following two equations:

$$Ca(s) + CO_2(g) + 1/2O_2(g) \rightarrow CaCO_3(s) \quad \Delta H = -812.8 \text{ kJ}$$

$$2Ca(s) + O_2(g) \rightarrow 2CaO(s) \qquad\qquad \Delta H = -1269.8 \text{ kJ}$$

Find the $\Delta H_{rxn}$ for the equation $CaO(s) + CO_2(g) \rightarrow CaCO_3(s)$. The product in the first reaction is the product wanted in the desired reaction, so it remains. The second equation needs the product as a reactant, so the equation needs to be reversed, remembering to reverse the sign of $\Delta H$. It also needs to be cut in half as only one mole of CaO is needed, not two. These will now add to the desired equation. Using Hess's Law, the $\Delta H_{rxn}$ is $-812.8 \text{ kJ} + \dfrac{1269.8 \text{ kJ}}{2}$ or $-177.9 \text{ kJ}$.

## Section 6.9    Determining Enthalpies of Reaction from Standard Enthalpies of Formation

Earlier chemists realized that when a compound is synthesized from its elements, a specific amount of enthalpy is used or released. Thus, it was convenient to define this quantity as *standard enthalpy of formation* when carried out under specified conditions. This was made more useful when it was realized only enthalpy changes were being considered. It was possible to define the starting point as the system including the required amounts (moles) of elements required to form the compound and it was possible to define each element's contribution to the enthalpy when in their "standard state" of zero. Thus, a set of values for standard enthalpies of formation can be determined and published in a table.

Standard enthalpies of formation from tables provide a very convenient way to determine $\Delta H_{rxn}$, because these, like other thermodynamic quantities, are additive as seen in Hess's Law. Note the following equation is slightly different than the one appearing in the textbook, but this one is the equation given on the AP test equation pages.

$$\Delta H° = \sum \Delta H_f° \text{ products} - \sum \Delta H_f° \text{ reactants}$$

Note the degree sign indicates standard state. The (algebraic) sum of standard enthalpies of formation of all products minus the (algebraic) sum of the standard enthalpies of formation of all reactants will give the overall standard enthalpy *change* for the reaction. The standard values will be provided in a table, but you should know that the tables assume that the standard heat of formation of any element in its standard state is 0 or $\Delta H_f° = 0$. It is also vital to find the correct physical state for each substance in a provided table as the solid, liquid, and gaseous states will differ in their values for $\Delta H_f°$.

More of thermodynamics will be covered in a later chapter.

**Table 6.2**  Standard Enthalpies (or Heats) of Formation, $\Delta H^\circ_f$, at 298 K

| Formula | $\Delta H^\circ_f$ (kJ/mol) | Formula | $\Delta H^\circ_f$ (kJ/mol) | Formula | $\Delta H^\circ_f$ (kJ/mol) |
|---|---|---|---|---|---|
| *Bromine* | | $C_3H_8O(l$, isopropanol$)$ | −318.1 | *Oxygen* | |
| $Br(g)$ | 111.9 | $C_6H_6(l)$ | 49.1 | $O_2(g)$ | 0 |
| $Br_2(l)$ | 0 | $C_6H_{12}O_6(s$, glucose$)$ | −1273.3 | $O_3(g)$ | 142.7 |
| $HBr(g)$ | −36.3 | $C_{12}H_{22}O_{11}(s$, sucrose$)$ | 2226.1 | $H_2O(g)$ | −241.8 |
| *Calcium* | | *Chlorine* | | $H_2O(l)$ | −285.8 |
| $Ca(s)$ | 0 | $Cl(g)$ | 121.3 | *Silver* | |
| $CaO(s)$ | −634.9 | $Cl_2(g)$ | 0 | $Ag(s)$ | 0 |
| $CaCO^3(s)$ | −1207.6 | $HCl(g)$ | −92.3 | $AgCl(s)$ | −127.0 |
| *Carbon* | | *Fluorine* | | *Sodium* | |
| $C(s$, graphite$)$ | 0 | $F(g)$ | 79.38 | $Na(s)$ | 0 |
| $C(s$, diamond$)$ | 1.88 | $F_2(g)$ | 0 | $Na(g)$ | 107.5 |
| $CO(g)$ | −110.5 | $HF(g)$ | −273.3 | $NaCl(s)$ | −411.2 |
| $CO_2(g)$ | −393.5 | *Hydrogen* | | $Na_2CO_3(s)$ | −1130.7 |
| $CH_4(g)$ | −74.6 | $H(g)$ | 218.0 | $NaHCO_3(s)$ | −950.8 |
| $CH_3OH(l)$ | −238.6 | $H_2(g)$ | 0 | *Sulfur* | |
| $C_2H_2(g)$ | 227.4 | *Nitrogen* | | $S_8(s$, rhombic$)$ | 0 |
| $C_2H_4(g)$ | 52.4 | $N_2(g)$ | 0 | $S_8(s$, monoclinic$)$ | 0.3 |
| $C_2H_6(g)$ | −84.68 | $NH_3(g)$ | −45.9 | $SO_2(g)$ | −296.8 |
| $C_2H_5OH(l)$ | −277.6 | $NH_4NO_3(s)$ | −365.6 | $SO_3(g)$ | −395.7 |
| $C_3H_8(g)$ | −103.85 | $NO(g)$ | 91.3 | $H_2SO_4(l)$ | −814.0 |
| $C_3H_6O(l$, acetone$)$ | −248.4 | $N_2O(g)$ | 81.6 | | |

## Additional Practice

*Self-Assessment Quiz Questions Q1, Q2, Q3, Q4, Q5, Q6, Q7, Q8, Q9, Q10, Q11, Q12, Q13, Q14, and Q15*

*Problems 8, 10, 11, 12, 14, 15, 21, 23, 25, 33, 37, 41, 45, 47, 49, 55, 57, 58, 60, 65, 76, 77, 78, 79, 83, 87, 99, 114, 123, 128, 131, 136, and 138*

## Practice AP® Test Questions

1. Nutrition scientists recommend cooking with vegetable oils instead of animal fats to lower the risk of heart disease. Olive oil is often used in cooking. One of the main compounds in olive oil is oleic acid ($C_{18}H_{24}O_2$). The equation (not balanced) for the combustion of olive oil is:

$$\_\_ C_{18}H_{24}O_2 \,(l) + \_\_ O_2 \,(g) \rightarrow \_\_ CO_2 \,(g) + \_\_ H_2O(g) \; \Delta H$$
$$= -1.11 \times 10^4 \, kJ/mole$$

   Use the data in the table below and calculate the change in enthalpy of formation for oleic acid.

| Substance | $\Delta H_f^\circ$ Standard enthalpy of formation (kJ/mol) |
|---|---|
| $C_{18}H_{24}O_2 \,(l)$ | ? |
| $CO_2 \,(g)$ | $-393.5$ |
| $H_2O(g)$ | $-241.8$ |

   A)  $-2026$ kJ

   B)  $-1115$ kJ

   C)  $+1115$ kJ

   D)  $+2026$ kJ

2. Vegetable oils can also be used as fuel for car or truck engines. These engines have moving pistons. When the combustion reaction in the previous problem occurs in an insulated container with a movable piston under a constant pressure of 12.00 atm, what will happen to the volume of the container and what is the work performed?

   A)  The volume will decrease and work will be done on the system.

   B)  The volume will decrease and work will be done by the system.

   C)  The volume will increase and work will be done on the system.

   D)  The volume will increase and work will be done by the system.

3. $NO_2$ gas is formed in automotive engines as a byproduct and contributes to atmospheric pollution. Given the following equations:

$$N_2\,(g) + O_2\,(g) \rightarrow 2NO(g) \qquad \Delta H = +180.8 \text{ kJ}$$
$$NO(g) + 1/2\,O_2\,(g) \rightarrow NO_2\,(g) \qquad \Delta H = -56.0 \text{ kJ}$$

Calculate the heat of formation of $NO_2$ gas.

A) $-68$ kJ

B) $+68$ kJ

C) $+124.8$ kJ

D) $+236.8$ kJ

4. In a coffee-cup calorimeter, 50.0 mL of 0.800 M calcium nitrate are added to 50.0 mL of 1.600 M sodium fluoride, and a precipitate forms. The initial temperature of both solutions is 20.00°C. Assume the specific heat of the resulting solution is 4.18 J/(g·°C) and the density is 1.00 g/mL. Calculate the final temperature of the solution.

$$Ca^{2+}\,(aq) + 2\,F^-(aq) \rightarrow CaF_2\,(s)\ \Delta H° = -11.5 \text{ kJ}$$

A) 18.1°C

B) 20.55°C

C) 21.10°C

D) 22.55°C

5. Refer to the previous problem (4) and identify the heat transfer.

A) The reactants transfer heat to the products.

B) The reactants transfer heat to the water.

C) The chemical reaction gets hotter.

D) The chemical reaction releases heat to the solution.

# THE QUANTUM-MECHANICAL MODEL OF THE ATOM

This chapter discusses the electron and its behavior in atoms. Chemistry is fundamentally determined by the behavior of electrons in and between atoms, so understanding this concept helps to understand the atom, including models such as the quantum-mechanical model and interactions in chemical bonding and structure. The most important sections to review are as follows:

7.2 **The Nature of Light**

7.3 **Atomic Spectroscopy and the Bohr Model**

7.4 **The Wave Nature of Matter: The de Broglie Wavelength, the Uncertainty Principle, and Indeterminacy**

Some other relevant review concepts are how electrons exist in orbitals, how they "transition" between orbitals, how this transition may release or absorb energy, and how to determine the number of orbitals present as well as the number of electrons present in them.

## Specific Learning Objectives Addressed in This Chapter:

**Learning objective 1.6** The student is able to analyze data relating to electron energies for patterns and relationships. [*See* **SP 5.1**]

**Learning objective 1.9** The student is able to predict and/or justify trends in atomic properties based on location on the periodic table and/or the shell model. [*See* **SP 6.4**]

**Learning objective 1.10** Students can justify with evidence the arrangement of the periodic table and can apply periodic properties to chemical reactivity. [*See* **SP 6.1**]

**Learning objective 1.12** The student is able to explain why a given set of data suggests, or does not suggest, the need to refine the atomic model from a classical shell model with the quantum mechanical model. [*See* **SP 6.3**]

**Learning objective 1.13** Given information about a particular model of the atom, the student is able to determine if the model is consistent with specified evidence. [*See* **SP 5.3**]

**Learning objective 1.15** The student can justify the selection of a particular type of spectroscopy to measure properties associated with vibrational or electronic motions of molecules. [*See* **SP 4.1**]

## Specific Science Practices Addressed in This Chapter:

**Science Practice 4:** The student can plan and implement data collection strategies in relation to a particular scientific question.

> 4.1 The student can *justify the selection of the kind of data* needed to answer a particular scientific question.

**Science Practice 5:** The student can perform data analysis and evaluation of evidence.

> 5.1 The student can *analyze data* to identify patterns or relationships.

> 5.3 The student can *evaluate the evidence provided by data sets* in relation to a particular scientific question.

**Science Practice 6:** The student can work with scientific explanations and theories.

> 6.1 The student can *justify claims with evidence*.

> 6.4 The student can *make claims and predictions about natural phenomena* based on scientific theories and models.

> 6.5 The student can *evaluate alternative scientific explanations*.

## Concepts and Vocabulary to Review:

## The Nature of Light    Section 7.2

Light is a transverse wave—the variations occur perpendicular to its motion. Such waves can be described based on amplitude, wavelength, and frequency. The height or depth of a wave is its *amplitude*. The *wavelength* is the distance between analogous points of two waves. The most energetic waves have shortest wavelengths. *Frequency* is the number of variations (vibrations) of the wave passing a certain point in a second. A hertz (Hz) is one cycle per second. The higher the frequency, the more energy the light wave has and the shorter the waves. Since all light travels at the same speed in vacuum, there is an inverse relationship between wavelength and frequency. Wavelengths ($\lambda$) can be calculated by knowing the speed of light ($c$) and the frequency ($v$) of the wave using the equation: $\lambda = \dfrac{c}{v}$. The energy of a photon can be calculated using the equation $E = \dfrac{hc}{\lambda}$, where $h$ is $6.626 \times 10^{-34}$ J·s. This proportionality constant is called Plank's constant.

## The Electromagnetic Spectrum

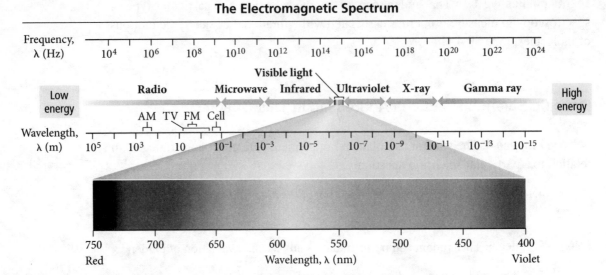

**Figure 7.1 The Electromagnetic Spectrum**   The right side of the spectrum consists of high-energy, high-frequency, short-wavelength radiation. The left side consists of low-energy, low-frequency, long-wavelength radiation. Visible light constitutes a small segment in the middle.

In the visible light range, red light has the longest wavelength and lowest energy, whereas violet light has the shortest wavelength and highest energy.

The color we see when we observe an object corresponds to the wavelength reflected by the object. The other wavelengths of white light are absorbed.

The full electromagnetic spectrum is shown above.

Some high energy waves such as gamma rays, UV, and X-rays can damage biological molecules. They do this by creating ions from neutral atoms or molecules. Radio waves are the longest waves and the least damaging.

The explanation of the photoelectric effect helped to explain more about light and electrons in atoms. The data showed that it took a threshold frequency to dislodge an electron from a metal surface. Light not meeting the threshold energy will not dislodge an electron no matter how long or how brightly the light shines on the metal. Even if the intensity is low, if the light meets the threshold frequency, electrons will be ejected. Albert Einstein explained this as light energy comes in packets called *photons*. If the light has energy beyond the threshold (called the *electron binding energy*), the extra energy is transferred to the electron as kinetic energy. More recently photoelectron spectroscopy (PES) has been used to measure accurately the energies of all electrons in atoms.

It is frequently more convenient to think of light (and all other electromagnetic waves), as photons rather than as waves (see Section 7.4 below). When the photon

**The Photoelectric Effect**

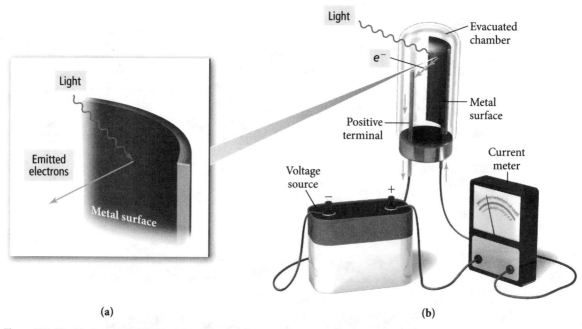

**Figure 7.2  The Photoelectric Effect**    (a) When sufficiently energetic light shines on a metal surface, the surface emits electrons. (b) The emitted electrons can be measured as an electrical current.

interacts with an electron in a photoelectric effect, the photon's energy is transferred to the electron, the photon disappears and the electron gains all the photon energy. A high energy photon is thus able to transfer sufficient energy for the electron to break away from the atom. Therefore, energy conservation is:

$$e_{photon} = e_{(electron\ binding)} + e_{(electron\ kinetic)}.$$

## Atomic Spectroscopy and the Bohr Model    Section 7.3

*Atomic spectroscopy* is the study of electromagnetic radiation being absorbed or emitted by atoms. Atoms in the gas state can be uniquely identified by the emission spectrum given off when the atoms are excited with electrical energy.

This is also reflected by an element's characteristic color in flame tests.

The color observed in a flame test derives from the brightest line in the atom's emission spectra.

When an electron makes a transition to another energy state, it absorbs energy to go to a higher energy level and emits, when the transition is downward, to a lower energy state. These transitions were explained by Neils Bohr, although he was incorrect in stating electrons circled the atom in orbits like planets around the sun.

## Emission Spectra

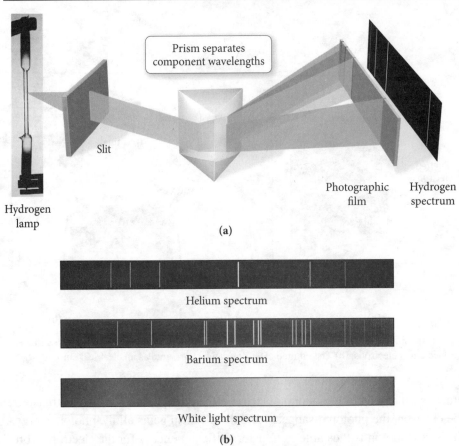

**(a)**

Prism separates component wavelengths

Slit

Hydrogen lamp

Photographic film

Hydrogen spectrum

Helium spectrum

Barium spectrum

White light spectrum

**(b)**

**Figure 7.3 Emission Spectra**    (a) The light emitted from a hydrogen, helium, or barium lamp consists of specific wavelengths that can be separated by passing the light through a prism. (b) The resulting bright lines constitute an emission spectrum characteristic of the element that produced it.

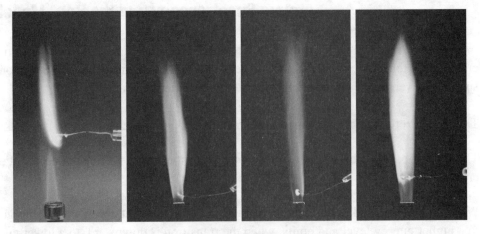

**Figure 7.4 Flame Tests (from left to right) for Sodium, Potassium, Lithium, and Barium**    We can identify elements by the characteristic color of the light they produce when heated. The colors derive from especially bright lines in their emission spectra.

# The Wave Nature of Matter: The de Broglie Wavelength, the Uncertainty Principle, and Indeterminacy

Section 7.4

Like an electromagnetic wave and a photon (see above), an electron can behave both as a particle and as a wave. However, the wave characteristics and particle characteristics cannot be observed at the same time. On a very small scale, we cannot know position and velocity at the same time of any part of matter. The more known about position, the less is known about velocity (or energy). Heisenberg established this rule, called the Heisenberg uncertainty principle.

In an atom, the strong coulombic force of attraction between the electron and the positive nucleus causes the electron to stay in the atom, the question is where it "stays." The electron location can be described according to a probability map. This is a theoretically calculated statistical representation of where an electron might be located. These are created using mathematical derivations from the Schrodinger wave equation and can demonstrate the shape and energy of an electron in an atom, called an orbital. They are a human's best guess at what an atom really looks like inside. Detailed models of the electron orbitals in atoms and molecules with lots of electrons are still an area of research by theoretical chemists. The nature of the chemical bonding and the shapes of molecules can, however, be predicted fairly accurately using elaborate models based on these principles. The electron orbitals described by the models cluster into shells and subshells based on energies. These explain the chemical properties and the periodicity found in the periodic table remarkably well. This is explored in the following chapter.

### Additional Practice

*Self-Assessment Quiz Questions Q1, Q2, Q3, Q4, Q5, Q6, Q7, Q8, Q9, and Q10*
*Problems 6, 7, 10, 11, 14, 23, 45, 51, 57, 69, 70, 80, 85, 103, and 104*

### Practice AP® Test Questions

1. The electric field vectors for two different electromagnetic radiations (X and Y) are represented in the graphs below.

Wave X has:

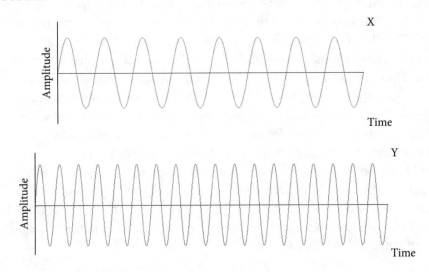

A) A longer wavelength and higher energy compared to Y

B) The same wavelength and same energy as Y

C) A shorter wavelength and a lower energy compared to Y

D) A shorter wavelength and a higher energy compared to Y

2. Calculate the frequency of electromagnetic radiation having a wavelength of 60.0 nm. The speed of light is $3.00 \times 10^8$ m/s.

A) $5.00 \times 10^6 \, \text{s}^{-1}$

B) $5.00 \times 10^{15} \, \text{s}^{-1}$

C) $2.00 \times 10^{-16} \, \text{s}^{-1}$

D) $200. \, \text{s}^{-1}$

3. Results from several photoelectric effect experiments provided evidence for which of the following claims:

A) Electrons in atoms have quantized energies.

B) Electromagnetic radiation has characteristics of wave behavior.

C) Electromagnetic energy has characteristics of particle behavior.

D) Electrons in atoms exhibit properties characteristic of waves.

4. What is the minimum wavelength of a photon of electromagnetic radiation that can be absorbed by an electron in a hydrogen atom to cause it to undergo a transition from the $n = 2$ energy level to the $n = 4$ energy level?

A) 500 nm

B) 600 nm

C) 700 nm

D) 800 nm

5. Calculate the de Broglie wavelength (in m) of an electron (mass = $9.11 \times 10^{-31}$ kg) traveling at a speed of $7.45 \times 10^6$ m/s. (h = $6.6 \times 10^{-34}$ J s)

A) Greater than $1 \times 10^{-5}$

B) Between $10^{-5}$ and $10^{-7}$

C) Between $10^{-7}$ and $10^{-9}$

D) Less than $1 \times 10^{-10}$

1. D); 2. B); 3. C); 4. A); 5. D)

**Answers**

# CHAPTER 8

# PERIODIC PROPERTIES OF THE ELEMENTS

This chapter explores the reasons for periodicity. A brief history is covered in Section 8.2: The Development of the Periodic Table. Although the history is fascinating, it is not a major concept in the AP Chemistry Curriculum. More important concepts include how to write electron configurations for atoms and ions and understand the trends in outer configurations (valence electrons) and how they relate to periodic trends in size of atoms, ionic radii, ionization energies, and electron affinities. The trends are explained using effective nuclear charge, Coulomb's law, and shielding. Trends can be observed both across the table (periods) or down the table (families or groups). The trends of properties in families can be addressed by looking at electron configurations within families. This chapter addresses several Learning Objectives in the AP Chemistry Curriculum. Although Section 8.9 has excellent examples from the alkali metals, halogens, and the noble gases to review, the most important sections are as follows:

8.3 **Electron Configurations: How Electrons Occupy Orbitals**

8.4 **Electron Configurations, Valence Electrons, and the Periodic Table**

8.6 **Periodic Trends in the Size of Atoms and Effective Nuclear Charge**

8.7 **Ions: Electron Configurations, Magnetic Properties, Ionic Radii, and Ionization Energy**

## Specific Learning Objectives Addressed in This Chapter:

**Learning objective 1.6**    The student is able to analyze data relating to electron energies for patterns and relationships. [*See* **SP 5.1**]

**Learning objective 1.7**    The student is able to describe the electronic structure of the atom using PES data, ionization energy data, and/or Coulomb's Law to construct explanations of how the energies of electrons within shells in atoms vary. [*See* **SP 5.1**, **6.2**]

**Learning objective 1.8**    The student is able to explain the distribution of electrons using Coulomb's Law to analyze measured energies. [*See* **SP 6.2**]

**Learning objective 1.9**    The student is able to predict and/or justify trends in atomic properties based on location on the periodic table and/or the shell model. [*See* **SP 6.4**]

**Learning objective 1.10**  Students can justify with evidence the arrangement of the periodic table and can apply periodic properties to chemical reactivity. [*See* **SP 6.1**]

**Learning objective 1.11**  The student can analyze data, based on periodicity and the properties of binary compounds, to identify patterns and generate hypotheses related to the molecular design of compounds for which data are not supplied. [*See* **SP 3.1, 5.1**]

**Learning objective 1.12**  The student is able to explain why a given set of data suggests, or does not suggest, the need to refine the atomic model from a classical shell model with the quantum mechanical model. [*See* **SP 6.3**]

**Learning objective 1.13**  Given information about a particular model of the atom, the student is able to determine if the model is consistent with specified evidence. [*See* **SP 5.3**]

**Learning objective 2.14**  The student is able to apply Coulomb's Law qualitatively (including using representations) to describe the interactions of ions, and the attractions between ions and solvents to explain the factors that contribute to the solubility of ionic compounds. [*See* **SP 1.4, 6.4**]

**Learning objective 2.23**  The student can create a representation of an ionic solid that shows essential characteristics of the structure and interactions present in the substance. [*See* **SP 1.1**]

**Learning objective 2.24**  The student is able to explain a representation that connects properties of an ionic solid to its structural attributes and to the interactions present at the atomic level. [*See* **SP 1.1, 6.2, 7.1**]

**Learning objective 5.1**   The student is able to create or use graphical representations in order to connect the dependence of potential energy to the distance between atoms and factors, such as bond order (for covalent interactions) and polarity (for intermolecular interactions), which influence the interaction strength. [*See* **SP 1.1, 1.4, 7.2**]

**Learning objective 5.8**   The student is able to draw qualitative and quantitative connections between the reaction enthalpy and the energies involved in the breaking and formation of chemical bonds. [*See* **SP 2.3, 7.1, 7.2**]

## Specific Science Practices Addressed in This Chapter:

**Science Practice 1:** The student can use representations and models to communicate scientific phenomena and solve scientific problems.

> 1.1  The student can *create representations and models* of natural or man-made phenomena and systems in the domain.

> 1.4  The student can *use representations and models* to analyze situations or solve problems qualitatively and quantitatively.

**Science Practice 2:** The student can use mathematics appropriately.

> 2.3  The student can *estimate numerically* quantities that describe natural phenomena.

**Science Practice 3:** The student can engage in scientific questioning to extend thinking or to guide investigations within the context of the AP course.

    3.1  The student can *pose scientific questions*.

**Science Practice 5:** The student can perform data analysis and evaluation of evidence.

    5.1  The student can *analyze data* to identify patterns or relationships.

    5.3  The student can *evaluate the evidence provided by data sets* in relation to a particular scientific question.

**Science Practice 6:** The student can work with scientific explanations and theories.

    6.1  The student can *justify claims with evidence*.

    6.2  The student can *construct explanations of phenomena based on evidence* produced through scientific practices.

    6.3  The student can *articulate the reasons that scientific explanations and theories are refined or replaced*.

    6.4  The student can *make claims and predictions about natural phenomena* based on scientific theories and models.

**Science Practice 7:** The student is able to connect and relate knowledge across various scales, concepts, and representations in and across domains.

    7.1  The student can *connect phenomena and models* across spatial and temporal scales.

    7.2  The student can *connect concepts* in and across domain(s) to generalize or extrapolate in and/or across enduring understandings and/or big ideas.

### Concepts and Vocabulary to Review:

## Section 8.3   Electron Configurations: How Electrons Occupy Orbitals

When all of the electrons in an atom are in their lowest possible energy state, the atom is said to be in its "ground state". Electron configurations are written to show how, according to the quantum model, the electrons occupy orbitals (defined energies and shapes calculated from mathematical models) in the atom. It is the arrangement of electrons that determines the chemical properties of an atom. Although orbitals generally do not exist in the absence of an electron, chemists often talk about them as if they do, using terms like *hold* or *occupy,* or even *unoccupied*. Any single orbital can be occupied by two electrons at the most (they must have opposite spins), but the different types of orbital sublevels can cluster to hold different maximum numbers of electrons. The *s* orbital can hold up to two electrons, the *p* orbital, with three sublevels, can hold up to six electrons (two in each sublevel), the *d* orbital, with five sublevels, can hold up to ten electrons, and the *f* orbital, with seven sublevels, can hold up to fourteen electrons.

While the skill of writing an atom's electron configuration and determining the number of valence electrons is important, students need to understand and be able to explain how trends in chemical properties of families and periods can be explained as a result of the changes in configurations.

| Orbital | Number of Sublevels | Maximum Number of Electrons |
|---------|---------------------|-----------------------------|
| *s* | 1 | 2 |
| *p* | 3 | 6 |
| *d* | 5 | 10 |
| *f* | 7 | 14 |

Electron configurations indicate the energy level and orbital of all the electrons in an atom. For instance, the atom boron has the configuration $1s^2 2s^2 2p^1$. The numbers in front of each orbital designation is the energy level or primary "shell". The orbitals, or *subshells*, are indicated by *s*, *p*, *d*, and *f*. The number of electrons present in each orbital is indicated by the superscript. If the superscripts are added together, this must equal the total number of electrons. If this is a neutral atom, this number will equal the proton number and hence the atomic number.

The Pauli exclusion principle indicates no two electrons can be in the same atom with the same set of four quantum numbers. Although AP Chemistry students will not be assessed on assigning quantum numbers to electrons, they need to understand how quantum numbers serves as the basis for orbital diagrams. Orbital diagrams can be used to indicate if electrons are paired or unpaired in their orbitals. The Pauli exclusion principle states when there are two electrons in the same orbital, they must have opposite spins.

Another factor affecting how electrons fill orbitals is Hund's rule regarding sublevel energy splitting. When electrons fill sublevels of orbitals, such as $2p$ ($2p_x$, $2p_y$, and $2p_z$), the electrons will put one electron in each of the three $2p$ orbitals before the second electron of opposite spin is added to each of the orbitals. When looking at orbital diagrams of the atoms of boron, carbon, nitrogen, and oxygen, you can see this—parallel spins in equal energy orbitals are entered before pairing. Why? The electrons can spread out farther from each other reducing the repulsion.

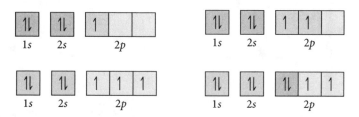

**The orbital diagrams of boron, carbon, nitrogen, and oxygen.**

If the first electron in an orbital has an up spin, each sublevel of 2*p* has an up spin, then the next electron will be a down spin. Note that "up" and "down" are arbitrary indications, they just have to be opposites.

Coulomb's law states $E = \dfrac{q_1 q_2}{r}$ and this shows how the potential energy of two charged species depends on their charges ($q_1 q_2$) and on the distance between them (*r*). Note that q$_1$ and q$_2$ keep their signs as well as their value. For opposite charges, the potential energy is negative and becomes more negative as the particles get closer together. This means opposite charges attract each other. For like charges, the potential energy is positive and decreases as the electrons inhabit orbitals, on average, farther from the nucleus. This means when comparing two atoms within the same column (family) and with the same charge, the potential energy of the outermost electron decreases as the atoms get larger due to an increase in the average distance of the electron from the proton containing nucleus.

The magnitude of the interaction between charged particles increases as the charge increases. Charges of $+2$ and $-2$ are more attracted to each other than charges of $+1$ and $-1$. Of course, *r* may not be the same so the value may not increase as much as expected.

What affects the pull of the positively charged nucleus on the valence (outermost) electrons? Other than the distance described above, an additional factor is shielding. The more inner energy level orbitals between the outer electrons and the nucleus, the less pull from the nucleus will be on the outermost electrons. As you go down a family in the periodic table, the number of outer valence electrons is the same, but the number of lower energy levels between the nucleus and valence electrons

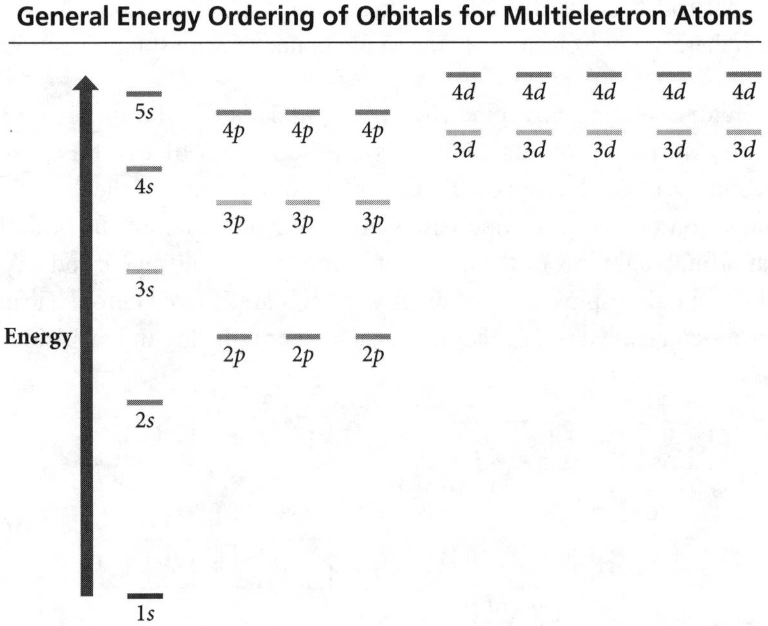

**General Energy Ordering of Orbitals for Multielectron Atoms**

**Figure 8.1  General Energy Ordering of Orbitals for Multielectron Atoms.**

increases. The inner core electrons occupy inner space, but also shield the valence electrons from nuclear charge. Thus, the nuclear charge the outer electrons experience is reduced, and this is called the *effective nuclear charge* ($Z_{eff}$). The end result is a general ordering of how electrons fill orbitals by energy (strongest forces—most negative energy first) and this pattern is known as the aufbau principle. Students should be able to take an element of the periodic table and indicate its configuration without memorizing the order of filling. Detailed energy considerations lead to a few irregularities in filling order, but they are not part of the AP curriculum.

## Electron Configurations, Valence Electrons, and the Periodic Table

Section 8.4

There are two ways to write electron configurations. They can be written in the order in which orbitals fill using the aufbau principle or they can be written by energy level. What is the difference? There is none when looking at atoms without *d* and *f* orbitals. For instance, sodium would have the same configuration either way: $1s^2 2s^2 2p^6 3s^1$. However, if zinc is compared, they are different. In order of filling, zinc's configuration is $1s^2 2s^2 2p^6 3s^2 3p^6 4s^2 3d^{10}$. However, in order of decreasing energy level, the configuration is $1s^2 2s^2 2p^6 3s^2 3p^6 3d^{10} 4s^2$. Why would this be helpful? When electrons are removed from an atom, they are removed from the highest (least bound) energy level first. The first electron removed from the zinc would be a 4*s* electron not a 3*d* electron. This also helps to identify core and valence electrons easily because the valence electrons are at the end of the configuration. On the AP exam, students should expect to see either method of writing configurations. Also, students will be notified when *complete configurations are asked for*, electron configurations must start with 1*s*. An abbreviated configuration starting with a noble gas such as $[Ar]4s^1$ for potassium is not acceptable as a *complete* electron configuration.

If all elements' electron configurations are put in sequence on the periodic table, patterns of arrangement emerge. Atoms in the same column (family) all have the same number of valence electrons (outer) in the same type of orbital. For instance, all of column one are the alkali metals, which all end in an $s^1$ configuration. The difference is the energy level, *n*. When comparing three alkali metal electron configurations, we can observe lithium ends in $2s^1$, sodium ends in $3s^1$, and potassium ends in $4s^1$.

Notice on the periodic table the sequence in *s, p, d,* and *f* filling is apparent. From knowing the location of atoms ending in an *s, p, d,* or *f* orbital, a student should be able to determine a complete configuration of any atom by simply following the table. For instance, on the table, the first orbital is 1*s*, the next orbital is 2*s*, and then 2*p*. When considering atoms with *d* and *f* orbitals, the *d* orbital number is one behind the row number and the *f* orbital number is two behind the row number. Looking at the periodic table, 4*s* is followed by 3*d*, 5*s* is followed by 4*d*, 6*s* is followed by 4*f*, and then 5*d*, whereas 7*s* is followed by 5*s* and then 6*d*. As noted above, any exceptions in filling, such as chromium and copper, need not be memorized but students may be asked to explain why the exception occurs.

**Orbital Blocks of the Periodic Table**

| Groups | | | | | | | | | | | | | | | | | |
|---|---|---|---|---|---|---|---|---|---|---|---|---|---|---|---|---|---|
| 1 1A | 2 2A | | | | | | | | | | | 13 3A | 14 4A | 15 5A | 16 6A | 17 7A | 18 8A |

s-block elements   p-block elements
d-block elements   f-block elements

| Periods | | | | | | | | | | | | | | | | | |
|---|---|---|---|---|---|---|---|---|---|---|---|---|---|---|---|---|---|
| **1** H $1s^1$ | 2 2A | | | | | | | | | | | | | | | | **2** He $1s^2$ |
| **3** Li $2s^1$ | **4** Be $2s^2$ | 3 3B | 4 4B | 5 5B | 6 6B | 7 7B | 8 | 9 8B | 10 | 11 1B | 12 2B | **5** B $2s^2 2p^1$ | **6** C $2s^2 2p^2$ | **7** N $2s^2 2p^3$ | **8** O $2s^2 2p^4$ | **9** F $2s^2 2p^5$ | **10** Ne $2s^2 2p^6$ |
| **11** Na $3s^1$ | **12** Mg $3s^2$ | | | | | | | | | | | **13** Al $3s^2 3p^1$ | **14** Si $3s^2 3p^2$ | **15** P $3s^2 3p^3$ | **16** S $3s^2 3p^4$ | **17** Cl $3s^2 3p^5$ | **18** Ar $3s^2 3p^6$ |
| **19** K $4s^1$ | **20** Ca $4s^2$ | **21** Sc $4s^2 3d^1$ | **22** Ti $4s^2 3d^2$ | **23** V $4s^2 3d^3$ | **24** Cr $4s^1 3d^5$ | **25** Mn $4s^2 3d^5$ | **26** Fe $4s^2 3d^6$ | **27** Co $4s^2 3d^7$ | **28** Ni $4s^2 3d^8$ | **29** Cu $4s^1 3d^{10}$ | **30** Zn $4s^2 3d^{10}$ | **31** Ga $4s^2 4p^1$ | **32** Ge $4s^2 4p^2$ | **33** As $4s^2 4p^3$ | **34** Se $4s^2 4p^4$ | **35** Br $4s^2 4p^5$ | **36** Kr $4s^2 4p^6$ |
| **37** Rb $5s^1$ | **38** Sr $5s^2$ | **39** Y $5s^2 4d^1$ | **40** Zr $5s^2 4d^2$ | **41** Nb $5s^1 4d^4$ | **42** Mo $5s^1 4d^5$ | **43** Tc $5s^2 4d^5$ | **44** Ru $5s^1 4d^7$ | **45** Rh $5s^1 4d^8$ | **46** Pd $4d^{10}$ | **47** Ag $5s^1 4d^{10}$ | **48** Cd $5s^2 4d^{10}$ | **49** In $5s^2 5p^1$ | **50** Sn $5s^2 5p^2$ | **51** Sb $5s^2 5p^3$ | **52** Te $5s^2 5p^4$ | **53** I $5s^2 5p^5$ | **54** Xe $5s^2 5p^6$ |
| **55** Cs $6s^1$ | **56** Ba $6s^2$ | **57** La $6s^2 5d^1$ | **72** Hf $6s^2 5d^2$ | **73** Ta $6s^2 5d^3$ | **74** W $6s^2 5d^4$ | **75** Re $6s^2 5d^5$ | **76** Os $6s^2 5d^6$ | **77** Ir $6s^2 5d^7$ | **78** Pt $6s^1 5d^9$ | **79** Au $6s^1 5d^{10}$ | **80** Hg $6s^2 5d^{10}$ | **81** Tl $6s^2 6p^1$ | **82** Pb $6s^2 6p^2$ | **83** Bi $6s^2 6p^3$ | **84** Po $6s^2 6p^4$ | **85** At $6s^2 6p^5$ | **86** Rn $6s^2 6p^6$ |
| **87** Fr $7s^1$ | **88** Ra $7s^2$ | **89** Ac $7s^2 6d^1$ | **104** Rf $7s^2 6d^2$ | **105** Db $7s^2 6d^3$ | **106** Sg $7s^2 6d^4$ | **107** Bh | **108** Hs | **109** Mt | **110** Ds | **111** Rg | **112** Cn | **113** ** | **114** Fl | **115** ** | **116** Lv | **117** ** | **118** ** |

| Lanthanides | | | | | | | | | | | | | |
|---|---|---|---|---|---|---|---|---|---|---|---|---|---|
| **58** Ce $6s^2 4f^1 5d^1$ | **59** Pr $6s^2 4f^3$ | **60** Nd $6s^2 4f^4$ | **61** Pm $6s^2 4f^5$ | **62** Sm $6s^2 4f^6$ | **63** Eu $6s^2 4f^7$ | **64** Gd $6s^2 4f^7 5d^1$ | **65** Tb $6s^2 4f^9$ | **66** Dy $6s^2 4f^{10}$ | **67** Ho $6s^2 4f^{11}$ | **68** Er $6s^2 4f^{12}$ | **69** Tm $6s^2 4f^{13}$ | **70** Yb $6s^2 4f^{14}$ | **71** Lu $6s^2 4f^{14} 6d^1$ |

| Actinides | | | | | | | | | | | | | |
|---|---|---|---|---|---|---|---|---|---|---|---|---|---|
| **90** Th $7s^2 6d^2$ | **91** Pa $7s^2 5f^2 6d^1$ | **92** U $7s^2 5f^3 6d^1$ | **93** Np $7s^2 5f^4 6d^1$ | **94** Pu $7s^2 5f^6$ | **95** Am $7s^2 5f^7$ | **96** Cm $7s^2 5f^7 6d^1$ | **97** Bk $7s^2 5f^9$ | **98** Cf $7s^2 5f^{10}$ | **99** Es $7s^2 5f^{11}$ | **100** Fm $7s^2 5f^{12}$ | **101** Md $7s^2 5f^{13}$ | **102** No $7s^2 5f^{14}$ | **103** Lr $7s^2 5f^{14} 6d^1$ |

**Figure 8.2  The s, p, d, and f Blocks of the Periodic Table**

## Section 8.6  Periodic Trends in the Size of Atoms and Effective Nuclear Charge

To determine the radius of an atom, the distance between two nonbonded atoms is measured. Half this distance is the radius. This is called *van der Waals radius*.

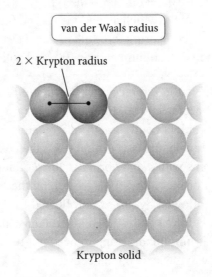

van der Waals radius

2 × Krypton radius

Krypton solid

If atoms are chemically bonded, then the radius has a different value and is found to be different in nonmetals and metals. In nonmetals, it is half the distance between the nuclei of the two atoms bonded together, whereas in metals it is half the distance between the nuclei of two atoms in a crystal of the metal. When an atom bonds to another atom, the radius is always less than the van der Waals radius of the atom. How the radius is determined is not tested by AP.

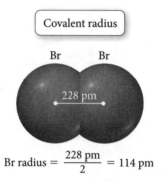

$$\text{Br radius} = \frac{228 \text{ pm}}{2} = 114 \text{ pm}$$

When comparing atoms in families and periods, trends in the radii can be observed.

When students are asked to explain these trends, they need to use the concepts of shielding and effective nuclear charge, depending on the atoms being compared. An explanation of why the potassium atom is larger than the sodium atom is NOT

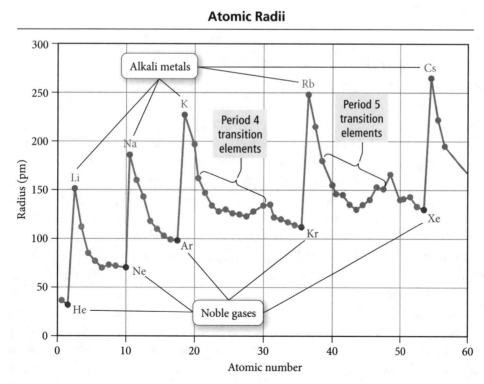

**Figure 8.3 Atomic Radius versus Atomic Number**   Notice the periodic trend in atomic radius, starting at a peak with each alkali metal and falling to a minimum with each noble gas.

**Trends in Atomic Radius**

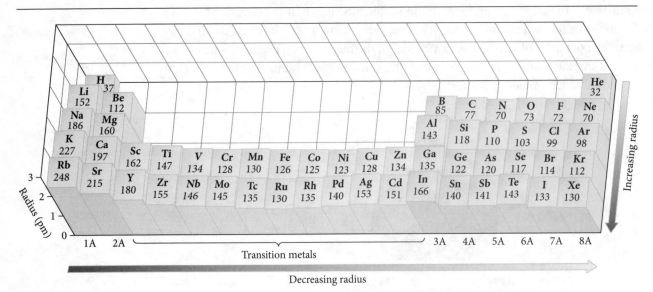

**Figure 8.4 Trends in Atomic Radius**    In general, atomic radii increase as we move down a column and decrease as we move to the right across a period in the periodic table.

the trend is atoms get larger going down a column. This may be the trend, but is NOT the explanation for the trend. To get credit for their answer the student is expected to explain the additional energy level and increased shielding of the outer valence electrons in potassium with $1s^22s^22p^63s^23p^64s^1$ compared to sodium with $1s^22s^22p^63s^1$.

## Section 8.7    Ions: Electron Configurations, Magnetic Properties, Ionic Radii, and Ionization Energy

While writing electron configurations is not going to be tested on the AP exam, it is important to understand them to explain periodic properties and/or explain trends in atomic properties based on their location on the periodic table. When writing an electron configuration of an ion, it is important to understand the difference between anions and cations. Anions add electrons to form a negatively charged species whereas cations have lost one or more electrons to form a positively charged species. When subtracting electrons, students must understand they are removed from the outermost (lowest) energy level first, which is not necessarily the last orbital filled in the periodic table sequence. This is true for the nonrepresentative elements. For instance, zinc has the configuration $1s^22s^22p^63s^23p^64s^23d^{10}$, but when the zinc forms its $+2$ cation, the configuration becomes $1s^22s^22p^63s^23p^63d^{10}$. The entire $4s$ orbital is not present. This was explained as a result of energy levels, not filling order in a previous section. Cations have smaller radii than their atoms because the number of protons in the nucleus has not changed, however, there are fewer electrons, so the protons have an increased pull on the electrons.

## Radii of Atoms and Their Cations (pm)

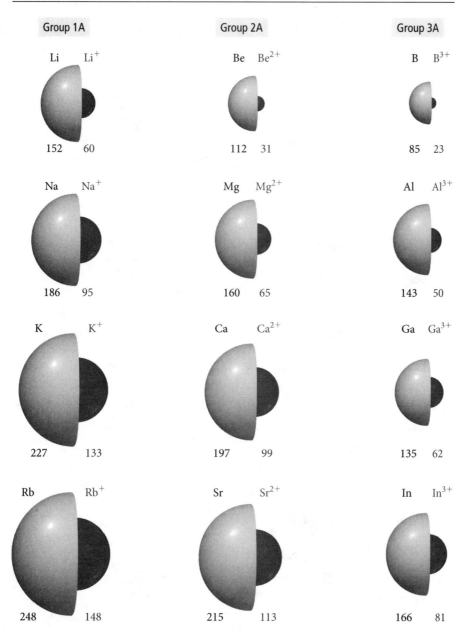

| Group 1A | Group 2A | Group 3A |

Li   Li$^+$
152   60

Na   Na$^+$
186   95

K   K$^+$
227   133

Rb   Rb$^+$
248   148

Be   Be$^{2+}$
112   31

Mg   Mg$^{2+}$
160   65

Ca   Ca$^{2+}$
197   99

Sr   Sr$^{2+}$
215   113

B   B$^{3+}$
85   23

Al   Al$^{3+}$
143   50

Ga   Ga$^{3+}$
135   62

In   In$^{3+}$
166   81

**Figure 8.5  Sizes of Atoms and Their Cations**    Atomic and ionic radii (pm) for the first three columns of main-group elements.

For anions, the additional electrons have a lower effective nuclear charge because the proton number has not changed, so the anion is larger than the neutral atom. When looking at electron configurations of atoms or ions, if the orbital diagram shows unpaired electrons, the species will be paramagnetic. The unpaired electron(s) generates a magnetic field and is attracted to an external magnetic field. If all the electrons in a species are paired, the species will not be attracted to a magnetic field. This is called *diamagnetic*.

## Radii of Atoms and Their Anions (pm)

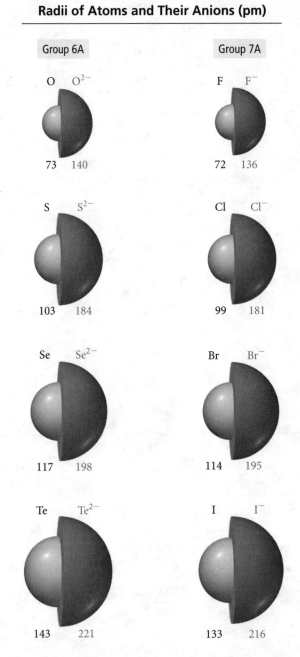

**Figure 8.6  Sizes of Atoms and Their Anions**    Atomic and ionic radii for groups 6A and 7A in the periodic table.

**Ionization energy (IE)** is defined as the energy required to remove an electron from an atom or ion in its gaseous state. The energy required to remove an electron is always defined as positive because an input in energy is required.

The ionization energies do not consistently increase across a period. Why? The pattern of electron configurations provides part of the answer. Between beryllium (Be) and boron (B), there is a drop in the first IE. Be is losing a $2s$ electron, whereas B is losing a $2p$ electron. The $2p$ electron is higher in energy and easier to remove.

## First Ionization Energies

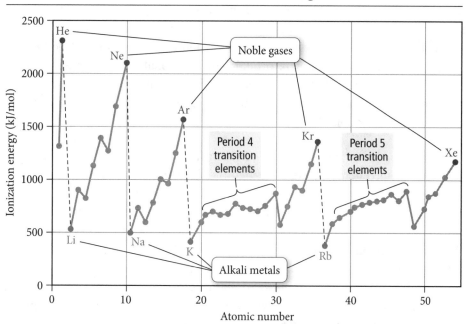

**Figure 8.7  First Ionization Energy versus Atomic Number for the Elements through Xenon**
Ionization starts at a minimum with each alkali metal and rises to a peak with each noble gas.

## Trends in First Ionization Energy

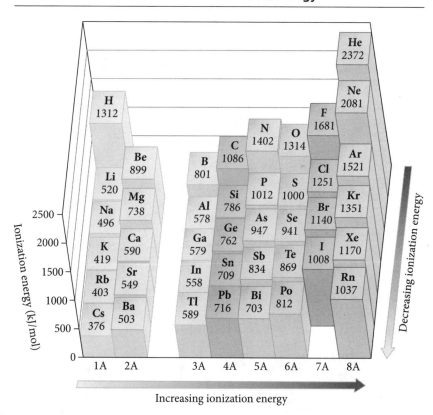

**Figure 8.8  Trends in Ionization Energy**    Ionization energy increases as we move to the right across a period and decreases as we move down a column in the periodic table.

Although the atoms following are also losing *p* electrons, this still needs more energy than the 2*s* of Be. Between nitrogen and oxygen, there is also a drop in IE. This can be understood by looking at orbital diagrams. The nitrogen family has parallel spins in the outer *p* orbitals. In the oxygen family, an additional electron is added, indicating a pairing of electrons in the $p_x$ orbital. The additional electron causes repulsion among the two pairing electrons, making it easier to remove the electron. When all the outer *p* orbitals have parallel spins, there is reduced repulsion (Hund's rule) and the species is more stable.

The energy needed to remove a second electron is called the second IE, and for a third electron the energy needed is called the third IE. Subsequent IEs are always larger than the one before, i.e., $3^{rd} > 2^{nd} > 1^{st}$. Note—you cannot remove more electrons than a species has, so hydrogen only has one IE because it only has one electron to remove. As electrons are removed, the amount of energy to remove the next electron increases due to the increased effective nuclear charge on the remaining electrons. The number of protons in the species has not changed and they are pulling on fewer electrons as additional electrons are removed. If an orbital shell is also lost, the remaining outer electrons will be much closer to the nucleus and will experience a greater attractive force as a result of the nuclear charge. Note the nuclear charge itself has remained the same. If enough electrons are removed to be isoelectronic to a noble gas configuration, the next electron to be removed will require a larger amount in energy.

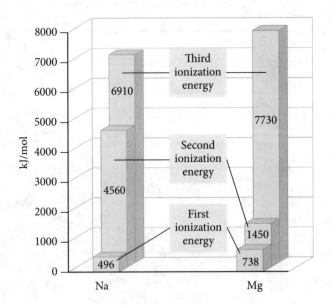

## Additional Practice

*Self-Assessment Quiz Questions Q1, Q2, Q3, Q4, Q5, Q6, Q7, Q8, Q9, Q10, Q11, Q12, Q13, Q14, and Q15*

*Problems 8, 9, 17, 20, 21, 25, 27, 28, 30, 31, 35, 36, 41, 43, 50, 55, 65, 67, 78, 85, 87, 88, 89, 90, 91, and 131*

## Practice AP® Test Questions

1. An element from Group 2, *X*, reacts with chlorine gas. What is the formula of the most likely product formed?

    A) $XCl$

    B) $XCl_2$

    C) $XCl_3$

    D) $X_2Cl_2$

2. When an active metal, *M*, reacts with water, which substance is always one of the products produced?

    A) $H_2O$

    B) $O_2$

    C) $H_2$

    D) $MOH$

3. Which of the following atoms has the largest atomic radius?

    A) Ca

    B) V

    C) Cr

    D) Ni

4. A $Na^+$ cation is smaller than a Na atom because:

    A) The sodium cation has more protons than electrons and the effective nuclear charge on the outer electrons is larger compared to the Na atom

    B) The distance of the outer electrons to the nucleus is shorter compared to the distance of the outer electron in $Na^+$

    C) Coulombic forces between the protons in the sodium cation are greater than Coulombic forces between the sodium atom's proton and outer electrons

    D) The sodium cation has one less electron compared to the sodium atom. Fewer electrons in the sodium cation occupy less space compared to the electrons in the sodium atom.

5. Which atom has the largest first ionization energy in units of kJ/mol?

   A) Na

   B) Rb

   C) Mg

   D) Sr

# CHEMICAL BONDING 1: THE LEWIS MODEL

The majority of this chapter is covered in the AP Chemistry curriculum. However, it is important to note the AP focus is on understanding the principles, not on memorizing details such as 2.5 is the assigned electronegativity of carbon. These details should only be studied as examples of how to explain/demonstrate principles, and not as a set of facts to be memorized. Although students are expected to understand Lewis, Valence Shell Electron Pair Repulsion, and Molecular Orbital theories of bonding, the Lewis theory is covered in this chapter and the other two theories are covered in Chapter 10. Understanding this chapter is crucial to several aspects of chemistry. One must understand not only Lewis structures, but also what those structures indicate in terms of molecule characteristic properties. The sections of the chapter to study include:

## Specific Learning Objectives Addressed in This Chapter:

**Learning objective 2.17** The student can predict the type of bonding present between two atoms in a binary compound based on position in the periodic table and the electronegativity of the elements. [*See* **SP 6.4**]

**Learning objective 2.18** The student is able to rank and justify the ranking of bond polarity on the basis of the locations of the bonded atoms in the periodic table. [*See* **SP 6.1**]

**Learning objective 2.19** The student can create visual representations of ionic substances that connect the microscopic structure to macroscopic properties, and/or use representations to connect the microscopic structure to macroscopic properties (e.g., boiling point, solubility, hardness, brittleness, low volatility, lack of malleability, ductility, or conductivity). [*See* **SP 1.1, 1.4, 7.1**]

**Learning objective 2.21** The student is able to use Lewis diagrams and VSEPR to predict the geometry of molecules, identify hybridization, and make predictions about polarity. [*See* **SP 1.4**]

**Learning objective 2.23** The student can create a representation of an ionic solid that shows essential characteristics of the structure and interactions present in the substance. [*See* **SP 1.1**]

**Learning objective 2.24** The student is able to explain a representation that connects properties of an ionic solid to its structural attributes and to the interactions present at the atomic level. [*See* **SP 1.1, 6.2, 7.1**]

**Learning objective 2.25** The student is able to compare the properties of metal alloys with their constituent elements to determine if an alloy has formed, identify the type of alloy formed, and explain the differences in properties using particulate level reasoning. [*See* **SP 1.4, 7.2**]

**Learning objective 2.26** Students can use the electron sea model of metallic bonding to predict or make claims about the macroscopic properties of metals or alloys. [*See* **SP 6.4, 7.1**]

**Learning objective 2.27** The student can create a representation of a metallic solid that shows essential characteristics of the structure and interactions present in the substance. [*See* **SP 1.1**]

**Learning objective 2.28** The student is able to explain a representation that connects properties of a metallic solid to its structural attributes and to the interactions present at the atomic level. [*See* **SP 1.1, 6.2, 7.1**]

**Learning objective 2.31** The student can create a representation of a molecular solid that shows essential characteristics of the structure and interactions present in the substance. [*See* **SP 1.1**]

**Learning objective 2.32** The student is able to explain a representation that connects properties of a molecular solid to its structural attributes and to the interactions present at the atomic level. [*See* **SP 1.1, 6.2, 7.1**]

**Learning objective 5.1** The student is able to create or use graphical representations in order to connect the dependence of potential energy to the distance between atoms and factors, such as bond order (for covalent interactions) and polarity (for intermolecular interactions), which influence the interaction strength. [*See* **SP 1.1, 1.4, 7.2**]

**Learning objective 5.8** The student is able to draw qualitative and quantitative connections between the reaction enthalpy and the energies involved in the breaking and formation of chemical bonds. [*See* **SP 2.3, 7.1, 7.2**]

**Specific Science Practices Addressed in This Chapter:**

**Science Practice 1:** The student can use representations and models to communicate scientific phenomena and solve scientific problems.

    1.1  The student can *create representations and models* of natural or man-made phenomena and systems in the domain.

    1.4  The student can *use representations and models* to analyze situations or solve problems qualitatively and quantitatively.

**Science Practice 2:** The student can use mathematics appropriately.

    2.3  The student can *estimate numerically* quantities that describe natural phenomena.

**Science Practice 6:** The student can work with scientific explanations and theories.

    6.1  The student can *justify claims with evidence*.

    6.2  The student can *construct explanations of phenomena based on evidence* produced through scientific practices.

    6.4  The student can *make claims and predictions about natural phenomena* based on scientific theories and models.

**Science Practice 7:** The student is able to connect and relate knowledge across various scales, concepts, and representations in and across domains.

    7.1  The student can *connect phenomena and models* across spatial and temporal scales.

    7.2  The student can *connect concepts* in and across domain(s) to generalize or extrapolate in and/or across enduring understandings and/or big ideas.

**Concepts and Vocabulary to Review:**

## Types of Chemical Bonds     Section 9.2

All chemical bonds involve the overlap of electron density between two (or more) positively charged nuclei, in one form or another. It is the coulomb force of attraction between species of opposite charge that provides the net energy gain. If the "sharing" arrangement is not energetically more stable than the isolated atoms, the chemical bonds will not form. When formed, ionic, covalent, and metallic bonds lower the potential energy between atoms within the resulting species. The transfer of electrons from a metal with low ionization energy to a nonmetal with high electron affinity creates oppositely charged ions, which are attracted to each other. A chemical bond involving a transfer of one or more electrons from one atom to another is called an ionic bond. In covalent compounds, electrons are shared. In metals, the atoms are packed closely together enabling the valence electron shells to overlap between atoms. These electrons are pooled among all the positively charged metal atoms and are called an *electron sea*. The electrons are delocalized, which means they do not belong to one particular atom. This overlap of shared electrons in metals is called a metallic bond. Students should be able to look at what makes up a species and determine if the bonding is ionic, covalent, or metallic, using available evidence about the individual components.

## Section 9.3    Representing Valence Electrons with Dots

In a Lewis symbol the valence electrons are represented as dots around the symbol of the element. This visual model along with the concept of the octet rule (filling ion until it holds eight electrons) has allowed for a simple way to represent atoms and molecules using simple drawings and symbols.

$$Li\cdot \quad \cdot Be\cdot \quad \cdot \overset{\cdot}{B}\cdot \quad \cdot \overset{\cdot}{\underset{\cdot}{C}}\cdot \quad \cdot \overset{\cdot}{\underset{\cdot}{N}}: \quad \cdot \overset{\cdot\cdot}{\underset{\cdot\cdot}{O}}: \quad :\overset{\cdot\cdot}{\underset{\cdot\cdot}{F}}: \quad :\overset{\cdot\cdot}{\underset{\cdot\cdot}{Ne}}:$$

## Section 9.4    Ionic Bonding: Lewis Symbols and Lattice Energies

The Lewis model can be used to write ionic equations, showing the transfer of electrons.

$$K\cdot \; + \; :\overset{\cdot\cdot}{\underset{\cdot\cdot}{Cl}}: \; \longrightarrow \; K^+ \left[ :\overset{\cdot\cdot}{\underset{\cdot\cdot}{Cl}}: \right]^-$$

The above example shows the transfer of one valence electron from potassium to chorine. In the example, the equation shows separate atoms as reactants and the Lewis structures for the ions as products. On the AP test, when students are asked to write an equation for an ionic compound, it is not required to use this format unless they are asked specifically to write the Lewis structures. They should recognize it is ionic and, as a solid, will form a stable lattice.

When comparing a group of compounds such as alkali metal chlorides, a trend in lattice energy emerges.

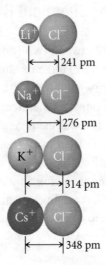

| Metal Chloride | Lattice Emergy (kJ/mol) |
|----------------|-------------------------|
| LiCl | −834 |
| NaCl | −788 |
| KCl | −701 |
| CsCl | −657 |

Remember Coulomb's law is $E = \dfrac{q_1 q_2}{r}$, where $q_1$ and $q_2$ are the charges of the involved electron(s) and proton(s). For one proton and one electron $q_1$ and $q_2$ are $+1$ and $-1$. In this example, the difference in attraction can be explained by the difference in the ionic radii. Going down the column in the bond length diagram above, it is apparent the radii are increasing, so the ions cannot get as close to each other. The metal cations increase in size due to increased more energy levels. This results in less energy being released when the lattice forms.

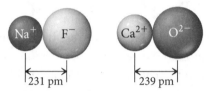

So why is the lattice energy of CaO so much greater than NaF when NaF has a shorter radius? Going back to the equation $E = \dfrac{q_1 q_2}{r}$, the reason is found in $q_1$ and $q_2$. Although both compounds have a 1:1 ratio of atoms, the CaO has $q_1$ and $q_2$ values of $+2$ and $-2$, whereas NaF has $+1$ and $-1$. The greater charge difference of $q_1 q_2$ is $2 \times (-2)$ versus $1 \times (-1)$, giving CaO approximately four times greater attraction, although the radius of CaO is slightly larger compared to NaF.

To summarize: lattice energies become more exothermic as the radius of the ions decreases and as the magnitude of ionic charge increases. The most important factor is the magnitude of ionic charge.

Why are ionic compounds nonconductors in the solid state, but conduct when liquid or when dissolved in water? In the solid form, the ions are localized and held tightly

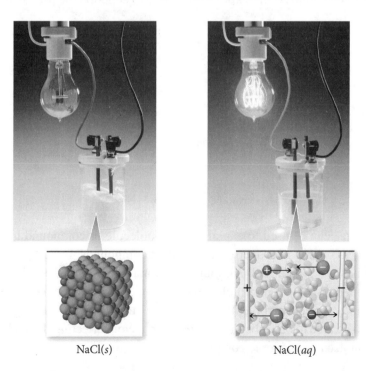

NaCl(*s*)                NaCl(*aq*)

in a lattice and no free electrons are available to conduct an electrical charge. When ionic compounds melt, the ions are free to move around and act as charge carriers. When they dissolve, they form ions in solution (usually surrounded by attracted water molecules); these can move freely to conduct an electrical charge.

Ionic compounds also have high melting points because the oppositely charged ions are attracted to each other in every direction in the lattice. Additionally, these forces are cumulatively strong and must be overcome in order for a solid to transform to a liquid during the melting process.

Can ionic compounds have covalent bonds? Yes. If the ionic compound contains a polyatomic ion, the polyatomic ion contains one or more covalent bonds. The compound is still ionic because the cation and anion are held together by electrostatic charge. An example of a polyatomic ion with a covalent bond is $NO_3^-$. The nitrate ion has three N—O covalent bonds.

## Section 9.5    Covalent Bonding: Lewis Structures

G. N. Lewis proposed a single bond is the result of two atoms sharing a pair of electrons. The two electrons are called a *bonding pair*. Any nonbonding pairs of electrons on an atom are called *lone pairs*. When four electrons are shared in a bond, a double bond forms. This is stronger than a single bond and will be shorter in length. If six electrons are shared, such as in the nitrogen molecule, $N_2$, a triple bond forms. It is stronger and shorter than a double bond. In general, the ranking of these bonds is single < double < triple in strength and a single > double > triple in length. On the AP Exam, data to support these concepts will need to be provided and the student will be expected to analyze and explain how the data supports the provided evidence.

$$:\ddot{C}l:\ddot{C}l: \quad or \quad :\ddot{C}l—\ddot{C}l:$$

$$\cdot\ddot{O}: + \cdot\ddot{O}:$$
$$\downarrow$$
$$:\ddot{O}::\ddot{O}: \quad or \quad :\ddot{O}=\ddot{O}: \qquad \text{Octet}\overbrace{:\ddot{O}\,:\,\ddot{O}:}\text{Octet}$$

$$:N:::N: \quad or \quad :N\equiv N:$$

Lewis structures can be used to explain why a molecule or compound has a certain formula. When looking at properties of covalent compounds, it is important to note covalent bonds are directional. Although there may be a strong bond within a covalently bonded molecule (intramolecular forces), the forces between two different molecules (intermolecular forces) are weaker, leading to a low melting point. Students need to be able to describe the difference in factors affecting the melting points of covalent molecules and ionic compounds.

**Molecular Compound**

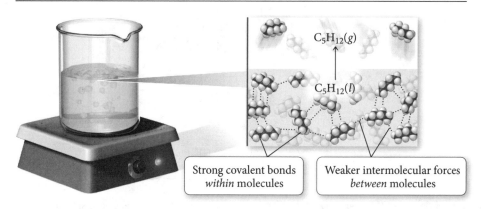

**Figure 9.1 Intermolecular and Intramolecular Forces**   The covalent bonds between atoms of a molecule are much stronger than the interactions between molecules. To boil a molecular substance, you simply have to overcome the relatively weak intermolecular forces, so molecular compounds generally have low boiling points.

## Electronegativity and Bond Polarity     Section 9.6

Covalent bonds share electrons, however, the sharing may not be equal. Similar to a tug-of-war, the nucleus in each atom's bond is pulling on the electrons. If the pull is equal, the bond is said to be *nonpolar* and electrons are being equally shared. When the pull is not equal, the sharing is not equal, and one atom will have a slight positive charge and the other a slight negative charge. The atom whose side the electrons have the stronger pull toward possess the slight partial negative charge, indicated by $\delta^-$, and the other atom is left with a slight partial positive charge, indicated by a $\delta^+$. This is also indicated by an arrow over the compound, showing the direction the electrons are being pulled. The two diagrams below show this representation. Technically, the "pull" will be unequal any time the atoms in the bond are not the same element (i.e., when it is not a homonuclear diatomic molecule), though sometimes the difference can be quite small for atoms of different elements.

$$\overset{\longmapsto}{\text{H}-\text{F}} \quad or \quad \overset{\delta^+ \;\; \delta^-}{\text{H}-\text{F}}$$

These bonds are given the special name *polar covalent*. In an electric field, you can tell the difference between polar covalent and nonpolar covalent molecules. The nonpolar does not align to the field, whereas polar covalent molecules align the partial charges toward the opposite pole, as seen in the figure on the next page.

As a result of their differing electronic structures, different atoms in a chemical bond will attract electrons differently. Chemists have simplified current thinking about this by using the property of *electronegativity* (EN). When two atoms form a bond, the more electronegative atom will pull the electrons in its direction and will have the higher electron density. We can determine this by looking at electronegativity values. Over time, several different schemes have been devised to compute electronegativity values. The most common scheme is used in this text.

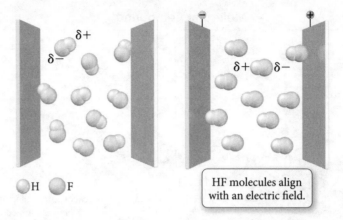

**Figure 9.2  Orientation of Gaseous Hydrogen Fluoride in an Electric Field**    Because one side of the HF molecule has a slight positive charge and the other side a slight negative charge, the molecules align themselves with an external electric field.

The most electronegative element is fluorine and the least is francium. This is an inverse relationship to atomic size. The smaller the atom is, the less the positive nucleus is shielded, and therefore, the greater the atom's ability to attract electrons in a bond. The differences in electronegativity can be generalized into a continuum to aid in predicting if a bond is nonpolar, polar, or ionic.

**Trends in Electronegativity**

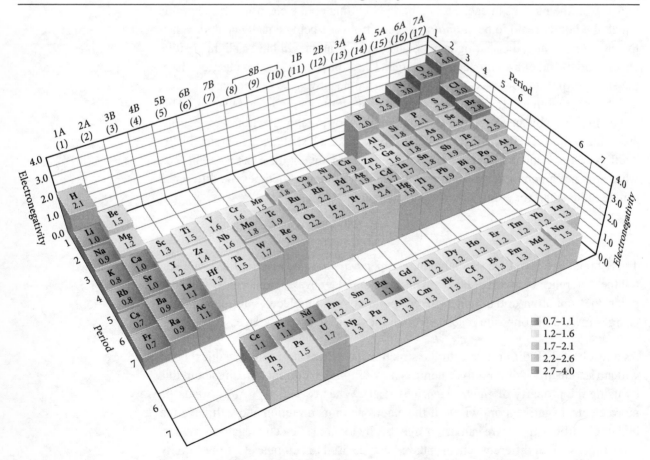

**Figure 9.3  Electronegativities of the Elements**    Electronegativity generally increases as we move across a row in the periodic table and decreases as we move down a column.

## The Continuum of Bond Types

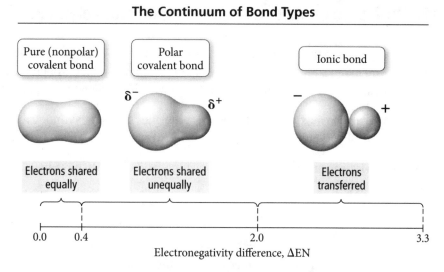

**Figure 9.4  Electronegativity Difference ($\Delta$EN) and Bond Type**

The magnitude of a bond's polarity is indicated by a dipole moment ($\mu$) and is expressed in the unit of *debye* (D). In the AP curriculum, students are not expected to calculate the dipole moment, but they should understand the concept of a dipole. The smaller the difference in EN, the smaller the dipole moment will be. The dipole moment can also be used to determine percent ionic character.

$$\text{Percent ionic character} = \frac{\text{measured dipole moment}}{\text{dipole moment if fully transferred}} \times 100\%$$

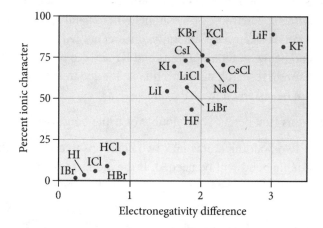

**Figure 9.5  Percent Ionic Character versus Electronegativity Difference for Some Compounds**

The percent ionic character indicates the degree to which an electron is actually transferred. If the electron was fully transferred in the ionic bond, this would be 100%. In reality, ionic bonds never achieve 100% transfer; a bond with greater than 50% ionic character is considered to be ionic.

The AP Curriculum does not include calculating percent ionic character, but does include explaining the concept.

Section 9.7    **Lewis Structures of Molecular Compounds and Polyatomic Ions**

Students are expected to draw simple Lewis structures. For more complex molecules, the structures are given and students are asked to explain and predict properties based on the structures. There are several general rules to writing a Lewis structure.

1. Draw a basic structure by positioning the atoms as symmetrically as possible around the central atom

   a. Hydrogen atoms are always terminal and can only have two electrons.

   b. The most electronegative atoms will be around the central atom.

2. Calculate the total number of electrons by adding up the total number of valence electrons of each atom in the molecule.

   a. If the species is an ion, the ion's charge must be considered. For anions, add electrons equal to the charge and for cations subtract electrons equal to the charge.

   b. Ion structures should be placed within square brackets and the charge of the ion placed on the outside upper right of the bracket.

3. Distribute the electrons around the atoms, filling octets around atoms except for hydrogen which is filled with two electrons.

   a. After placing two electrons in each bond, electrons should be distributed to terminal atoms first.

   b. See Section 9.9: Boron does not fill an octet of electrons, but fills with six electrons. Some atoms will expand and take more than an octet of electrons. Generally, this occurs with nonmetals P—S—Cl and below in their columns and Kr and Xe in the noble gases. Current research indicates this is not due to $d$ hybridization and will not be tested on the AP exam.

4. If atoms lack octets, form double or triple bonds with the central atoms.

   a. If two bonding atoms lack two electrons to complete the octets, a double bond will be needed. If the atoms lack four electrons, either two double bonds or a triple bond will be needed.

Section 9.8    **Resonance and Formal Charge**

The concept of resonance is used when two or more possible Lewis structures can be drawn for the same substance. The actual structure is an average of the possible structures. The different structures are drawn with a double-headed arrow between them to indicate this.

$$:\ddot{O}=\ddot{O}-\ddot{O}: \quad \longleftrightarrow \quad :\ddot{O}-\ddot{O}=\ddot{O}:$$

The resonance structures indicate the localization of electrons contributes to the stability of the molecule.

The formal charge of an atom in a Lewis structure is the charge it would have if all the bonding electrons were shared between the bonded atoms. Formal charge can be used to distinguish between different resonance structures and help determine which is the best model. The calculation of formal charge is done on each atom in a structure.

Formal charge = number of valence electrons − (number of nonbonding electrons + $\frac{1}{2}$ number of bonding electrons).

When assigned, comparing the formal charges in competing structures four rules generally apply:

1.  The sum of all formal charges in a neutral molecule is zero.

2.  The sum of all formal charges n an ion must equal the charge of the ion.

3.  Small (or zero) formal charges on individual atoms are better than large ones.

4.  If formal charges cannot be avoided, the most negative charge whould reside on the most electronegative atom.

$[OCN]^-$ has three resonance structures. The calculation of formal charge is shown below.

|  | A | | | B | | | C | | |
|---|---|---|---|---|---|---|---|---|---|
|  | $[:\ddot{O}-C\equiv N:]^-$ | | | $[:\ddot{O}=C=\ddot{N}:]^-$ | | | $[:O\equiv C-\ddot{N}:]^-$ | | |
| Number of valence $e^-$ | 6 | 4 | 5 | 6 | 4 | 5 | 6 | 4 | 5 |
| −number of nonbonding $e^-$ | −6 | −0 | −2 | −4 | −0 | −4 | −2 | −0 | −6 |
| $−\frac{1}{2}$(number of bond $e^-$) | −1 | −4 | −3 | −2 | −4 | −2 | −3 | −4 | −1 |
| **Formal charge** | **−1** | **0** | **0** | **0** | **0** | **−1** | **+1** | **0** | **−2** |

## Exceptions to the Octet Rule: Odd-Electron Species, Incomplete Octets, and Expanded Octets    Section 9.9

Some Lewis structures do not follow the octet rule. These include odd-electron species, incomplete octets, and expanded octets.

Odd-electron species are called free radicals and have an odd number of electrons. One electron will be always left unpaired in its orbital.

Some elements form incomplete octets with fewer than eight electrons around an atom. Examples include H, Be, and B. B for instance has three electrons and when all three are paired in bonding, it will have six electrons instead of eight.

Some elements can expand and have more than eight electrons. For instance, phosphorus has five valence electrons. It can bond with three additional electrons forming $PH_3$ to gain the octet of electrons but it can also form 5 bonds and have ten electrons around it as in $PF_5$. The possibility of expansion occurs in P, S, Cl, Ar and the elements below them in their column.

The shapes of these substances will be addressed in the next chapter.

## Section 9.10 Bond Energies and Bond Lengths

*Bond energy* is the amount of energy required to break one mole of the bonds in the gas phase molecules. Bond energies are always positive because they require the addition of energy to break a bond. The stronger the bond, the more energy that is required to break it. Generally, the stronger the bond the shorter the bond length will be.

It is possible to determine the enthalpy of a reaction from known bond energies of reactants and products. A balanced equation and the bond energy of every bond present are needed. Drawing a Lewis structure of each molecule is helpful to identify and

**Table 9.1** Average Bond Energies

| Bond | Bond Energy kJ/mol) | Bond | Bond Energy kJ/mol) | Bond | Bond Energy kJ/mol) |
|---|---|---|---|---|---|
| H—H | 436 | N—N | 163 | Br—F | 237 |
| H—C | 414 | N=N | 418 | Br—Cl | 218 |
| H—N | 389 | N≡N | 946 | Br—Br | 193 |
| H—O | 464 | N—O | 222 | I—Cl | 208 |
| H—S | 368 | N=O | 590 | I—Br | 175 |
| H—F | 565 | N—F | 272 | I—I | 151 |
| H—Cl | 431 | N—Cl | 200 | Si—H | 323 |
| H—Br | 364 | N—Br | 243 | Si—Si | 226 |
| H—I | 297 | N—I | 159 | Si—C | 301 |
| C—C | 347 | O—O | 142 | S—O | 265 |
| C=C | 611 | O=O | 498 | Si=O | 368 |
| C≡C | 837 | O—F | 190 | S=O | 523 |
| C—N | 305 | O—Cl | 203 | Si—Cl | 464 |
| C=N | 615 | O—I | 234 | S=S | 418 |
| C≡N | 891 | F—F | 159 | S—F | 327 |
| C—O | 360 | Cl—F | 253 | S—Cl | 253 |
| C=O | 736* | Cl—Cl | 243 | S—Br | 218 |
| C≡O | 1072 | | | S—S | 266 |
| C—Cl | 339 | | | | |

*799 in $CO_2$.

count all types of bonds in the reactants and products. The energy of bonds broken is always positive as energy is added to break bonds while the energy of bonds forming is always negative as energy is released.

$$\Delta H_{rxn} = \sum(\Delta H \text{ all bonds broken}) + \sum(\Delta H \text{ all bonds formed})$$

On the AP test, this equation is written with a minus sign between bonds broken and bonds formed so absolute values can be put in the equation.

$$\Delta H_{rxn} = \sum(\Delta H \text{ all bonds broken}) - \sum(\Delta H \text{ all bonds formed})$$

Energy is released when bonds form. Reactions are *exothermic* when weak bonds break and strong bonds form and are *endothermic* when strong bonds break and weak bonds form. A diagram showing this relationship is in the following figure.

**Estimating the Enthalpy Change of a Reaction from Bond Energies**

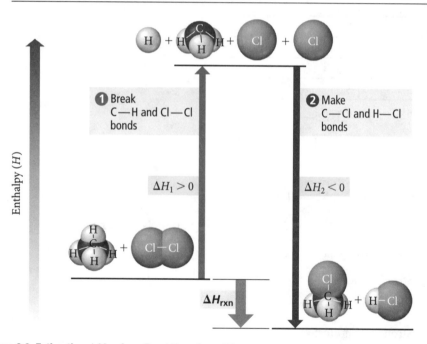

**Figure 9.6 Estimating $\Delta H_{rxn}$ from Bond Energies**   We can approximate the enthalpy change of a reaction by summing up the enthalpy changes involved in breaking old bonds and forming new ones.

## Bonding in Metals: The Electron Sea Model    Section 9.11

When atoms of the same metal pack close together, the valence electrons of the metal atoms form an electron sea. The electrons are not localized on a single atom, but are delocalized and can move among atoms, hence the term *sea*. In this model, metal exists as positively charged cations in the negative electron sea.

Because the electrons are free to move, metals tend to readily conduct electric charge and heat. Since the electrons can slide past one another, metals can generally be hammered into sheets (malleability) and drawn into wires (ductility).

## Additional Practice

*Self-Assessment Quiz Questions Q1, Q2, Q3, Q4, Q5, Q6, Q7, Q8, Q9, Q10, Q11, Q12, Q13, Q14, and Q15*

*Problems 3, 6, 11, 12, 13, 14, 15, 19, 20, 21, 22, 26, 27, 28, 31, 32, 33, 34, 37, 39, 43, 45, 48, 49, 50, 51, 52, 53, 54, 55, 56, 57, 59, 60, 63, 64, 65, 72, 75, 78, 82, 85, 86, 87, 91, 98, 99, 114, and 119*

## Practice AP® Test Questions

1.  Given a table of electronegativity values of elements, arrange the following X—Cl bonds in the following compounds in order of increasing ionic character: $BCl_3$, $PCl_3$, $ScCl_3$, and $LaCl_3$

    | Element | Electronegativity |
    |---------|-------------------|
    | B       | 2.0               |
    | La      | 1.1               |
    | P       | 2.1               |
    | Sc      | 1.3               |
    | Cl      | 3.0               |

    A)  B—Cl, P—Cl, Sc—Cl, La—Cl

    B)  Sc—Cl, La—Cl, B—Cl, P—Cl

    C)  La—Cl, P—Cl, Sc—Cl, B—Cl

    D)  P—Cl, B—Cl, Sc—Cl, La—Cl

2.  Of the bonds C—N, C=N, and C≡N, the C≡N bond is:

    A)  Weakest/longest

    B)  Strongest/longest

    C)  Weakest/shortest

    D)  Strongest/shortest

3.  A valid Lewis structure, obeying the Octet Rule, can be drawn for all of the following compounds except:

    A)  $CaCl_2$

    B)  $NCl_3$

    C)  $CCl_4$

    D)  $ICl_5$

4. How many contributing resonance structures can be drawn for the $SO_3$ molecule? Note that the Octet Rule for the sulfur atom applies.

   A) Two

   B) Three

   C) Four

   D) Five

5. Given the information in a table of bond dissociation energies, calculate the change in enthalpy, $\Delta H$, in units of kJ, for the following gas-phase reaction:

   $H_2C=CH_2 + H-Br \rightarrow CH_3CH_2Br$

   | Bond | D (kJ/mol) |
   |------|------------|
   | C—C  | 348        |
   | C=C  | 614        |
   | C—H  | 413        |
   | H—Br | 141        |
   | C—Br | 194        |

   A) +148

   B) −148

   C) +200

   D) −200

# CHAPTER 10

# CHEMICAL BONDING II: MOLECULAR SHAPES, VALENCE BOND THEORY, AND MOLECULAR ORBITAL THEORY

Additional theories in predicting shapes and properties of molecules are explored in this chapter. The first model is the Valence Shell Electron Pair Repulsion (VSEPR) model. This model is used in conjunction with Lewis structures from the last chapter. Additional theories are valence bond theory and molecular orbital theory. These models are more complex than the Lewis model but these models can explain properties and molecular shape. Most of this chapter is in the AP Curriculum. However, AP only expects an understanding of orbital theory basics, focusing on how molecular properties (e.g., strength of bonds and shapes of molecules) can be explained by models or theories, without in-depth details. Teachers should focus on student mastery of the basic ideas and should give little attention to exceptions. Mastery of the names of molecular geometries, as well as explanation (using VSEPR) of why molecules have a particular geometry is required.

10.2 **VSEPR Theory: The Five Basic Shapes**

10.3 **VSEPR Theory: The Effect of Lone Pairs**

10.4 **VSEPR Theory: Predicting Molecular Geometries**

10.5 **Molecular Shape and Polarity**

10.6 **Valence Bond Theory: Orbital Overlap as a Chemical Bond**

10.7 **Valence Bond Theory: Hybridization of Atomic Orbitals**

10.8 **Molecular Orbital Theory: Electron Delocalization**

## Specific Learning Objectives Addressed in This Chapter:

**Learning objective 2.21** The student is able to use Lewis diagrams and VSEPR to predict the geometry of molecules, identify hybridization, and make predictions about polarity. [*See* **SP 1.4**]

## Specific Science Practices Addressed in This Chapter:

**Science Practice1:** The student can use representations and models to communicate scientific phenomena and solve scientific problems.

> 1.4 The student can *use representations and models* to analyze situations or solve problems qualitatively and quantitatively.

## Concepts and Vocabulary to Review:

# VSEPR Theory: The Five Basic Shapes    Section 10.2

VSPER stands for Valence Shell Electron Pair Repulsion. This is a model with considerable success in predicting/explaining shapes of molecules made from atoms covalently bonded together. This model makes a simple assumption: The shape of a molecule is based on the number of electron groups on the central atom. Electron groups are usually pairs of electrons in single bonds, double bonds, triple bonds, or nonbonded pairs called lone pairs; in rare cases, they are single electrons. The electron groups will repel each other as much as possible in three-dimensional space. The number of electron groups surrounding a central atom result in the five basic shapes of molecules. When two electron groups are present such as in $CO_2$, they repulse to opposite sides of the central atom forming a linear shape. The angle formed between the electron groups surrounding the central atom is known as the *bond angle*, in this case, with 180° bond angles. In this section, basic shapes with only bonding pairs are discussed. In Section 10.3, the effect of lone pairs on molecular shape and bond angles will be explored.

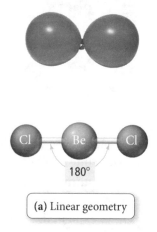

(a) Linear geometry

**Figure 10.1  Representing Electron Geometry with Balloons** **(a)** The bulkiness of balloons causes them to assume a linear arrangement when two of them are tied together. Similarly, the repulsion between two electron groups produces a linear geometry.

When three electron groups are present, the maximum angle is 120° from each other in a flat plane (two dimensional). This arrangement is called *trigonal planar*. *Trigonal* means *three* and *planar* indicates they will be *in the same plane*.

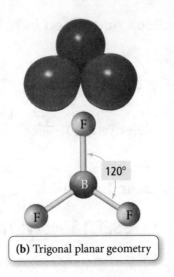

(b) Trigonal planar geometry

(b) Like three balloons tied together, three electron groups adopt a trigonal planar geometry.

Bond angles will only be exact and the resulting molecular shape will only be completely symmetrical when fully equivalent bonds are present. This means having only one type of bond and atom joined to a central atom. For instance, $CH_2O$ has three electron groups, but the angles are not 120° because the bonds are not equal. The double bond between the carbon and oxygen atoms involves two electron pairs. These additional electrons result in a greater electron density and increased repulsion resulting in bond angles that are actually 121.9° (H—C—O) and 116.2° (H—C—H). Similarly, $BF_3$ will be symmetrical, but $BF_2Cl$ will not.

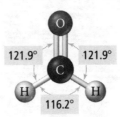

However, some molecules show symmetry even when the simple bonding model suggests otherwise. Chemists invoke something called *resonance structures* to explain such a phenomenon. For example, the nitrate ion $NO_3^-$ is symmetric, even though VSEPR predicts an asymmetric geometry because of the double bond. In this case, three resonance structures are used to explain this. The unfortunate use of the term *resonance* originally was used because chemists thought the structures "resonated" between one another. We now know that the different structures are never observed and the actual structure is a true "blend" of the three. However, the name persists.

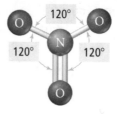

When four electron groups are present, the groups move into three-dimensional (3-D) space and form a tetrahedral shape. For symmetric tetrahedrons, the bonds will be 109.5°. A common error students make is thinking the angles are 90° because this is how a Lewis structure is drawn on flat paper. It is vital that students build 3-D models to assure they understand this difference, and practice properly representing these on flat paper (see Section 10.4 below).

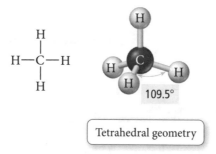

Tetrahedral geometry

When five electron groups are present, there has to be two different bond angles. Three of the electron groups form a trigonal planar shape with 120° angles, whereas the remaining two groups are arranged vertically with one atom above and one atom below the central atom. (However, note that the terms *above* and *below* mean nothing to the molecule.) This is only the way we represent it on a piece of paper. The vertical electron groups will be 90° from the electron groups in the plane. Be sure students convince themselves this must be the case by looking at a physical model. Although not reported as a bond angle, the two electron groups above and below the axis are 180° away from each other. Only adjacent atoms form angles referred to as *bond angles*.

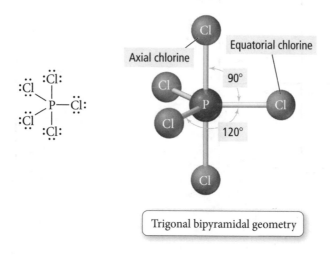

Trigonal bipyramidal geometry

Six electron groups form an octahedral geometry. All angles are 90°. Four of the groups are in a plane and take the shape of a square around the central atom. The other two pairs are above and below the plane at maximum distance from each other.

Octahedral geometry

**Summary Table of the Five Basic Shapes**

| Number of Electron Groups | Example(s) | Name of Shape | Bond Angles | Drawing |
|---|---|---|---|---|
| 2 | $BeCl_2$ $CO_2$ | Linear | 180° | $:\ddot{O}=C=\ddot{O}:$ |
| 3 | $BF_3$ $CH_2O$ | Trigonal planar | 120° if bonds are equal | |
| 4 | $CH_4$ | Tetrahedral | 109.5° if bonds are equal | |
| 5 | $PCl_5$ | Trigonal bipyramidal | 90° and 120° | |
| 6 | $SF_6$ | Octahedral | 90° | |

# VSEPR Theory: The Effect of Lone Pairs    Section 10.3

A *lone pair* refers to a pair of valence electrons on the central atom that are not used to covalently bond the central atom to another atom. When lone pairs of electrons are present in the electron groups, there are usually unequal repulsions.

When four electron groups are present and at least one group is a lone pair, there are two possibilities: Three bonding pairs and one lone pair or two bonding groups and two lone pairs. In the case of ammonia, there are three bonding pairs and one lone pair. The lone pair exerts a greater repulsive force on the neighboring electrons and pushes on the N—H bond electrons slightly compressing the bond angle together. The geometry of the resulting molecule is trigonal pyramidal. In the case of water, there are two bonding groups and two lone pairs. Two lone pairs have a greater repulsive force than one lone pair, compressing the H—O—H bond angles even more than in ammonia. The resulting molecular geometry is *bent*. Another way to form the bent shape is when there are three electron groups, two bonding groups, and one lone pair, such as in $SO_2$. Be sure in learning names and shapes students realize there is logical reason for the names. Three atom molecules cannot form anything other than linear or bent shapes. Lone pairs are not considered when determining the name of the molecular shape.

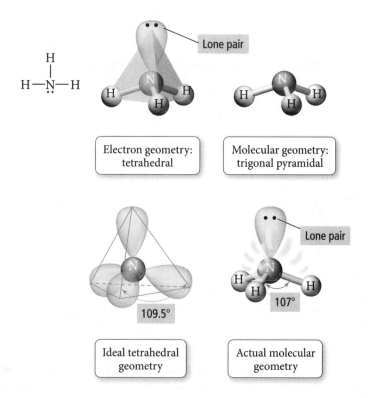

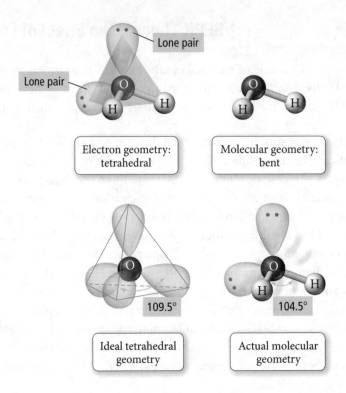

In general, the more lone pairs on the central atom, the smaller the bond angles.

## Effect of Lone Pairs on Molecular Geometry

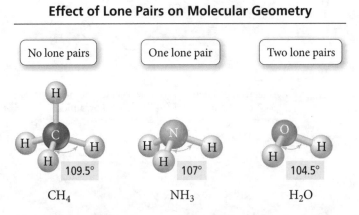

**Figure 10.2  The Effect of Lone Pairs on Molecular Geometry**    The bond angles get progressively smaller as the number of lone pairs on the central atom increases from zero in $CH_4$ to one in $NH_3$ to two in $H_2O$.

When there are five electron groups present, there are possibilities of one, two, or three lone pairs. When there is one lone pair, the resulting molecular geometry is *seesaw*. If there are two lone pairs, the molecular geometry is *t-shaped*, whereas three lone pairs results in a linear molecular shape.

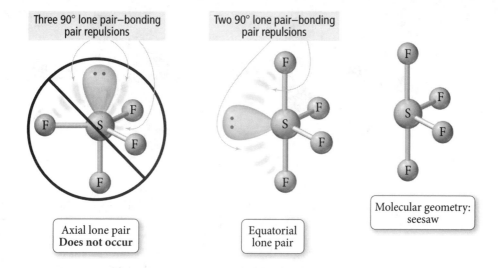

Three 90° lone pair–bonding pair repulsions

Two 90° lone pair–bonding pair repulsions

Axial lone pair
**Does not occur**

Equatorial lone pair

Molecular geometry: seesaw

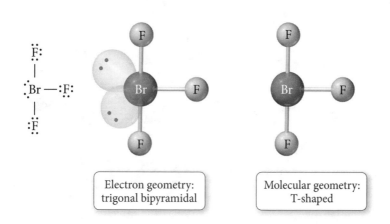

Electron geometry: trigonal bipyramidal

Molecular geometry: T-shaped

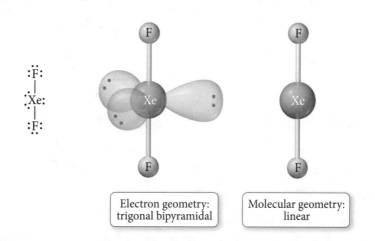

Electron geometry: trigonal bipyramidal

Molecular geometry: linear

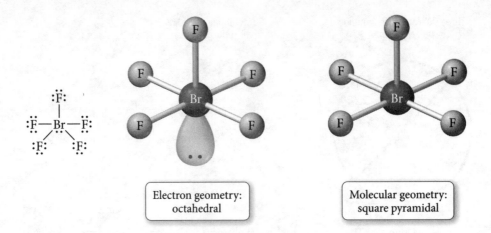

When there are six electron groups there are possibilities of one or two lone pairs. If there is one lone pair, the molecular geometry is *square pyramidal* while two lone pairs results in a *square planar* molecular geometry.

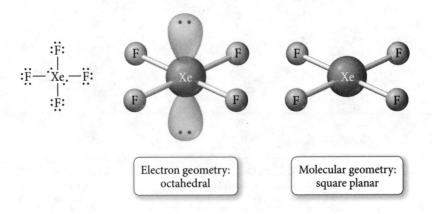

| Number of Electron Groups | Number of Lone Pairs | Name of Molecular Shape |
|---|---|---|
| 4 | 1 | Trigonal pyramidal |
| 4 | 2 | Bent |
| 5 | 1 | Seesaw |
| 5 | 2 | T-shape |
| 5 | 3 | Linear |
| 6 | 1 | Square pyramidal |
| 6 | 2 | Square planar |

This is summarized in the following table. Note students do not need to memorize this table, but they must understand why each shape forms and as well as the properties and intermolecular forces associated with each of these shapes.

**TABLE 10.1**   Electron and Molecular Geometries

| Electron Groups* | Bonding Groups | Lone Pairs | Electron Geometry | Molecular Geometry | Approximate Bond Angles | Example |
|---|---|---|---|---|---|---|
| 2 | 2 | 0 | Linear | Linear | 180° | $\ddot{\mathrm{O}} = \mathrm{C} = \ddot{\mathrm{O}}$ |
| 3 | 3 | 0 | Trigonal planar | Trigonal planar | 120° | $\ddot{\mathrm{F}} - \mathrm{B} - \ddot{\mathrm{F}}$ with $\ddot{\mathrm{F}}$ |
| 3 | 2 | 1 | Trigonal planar | Bent | <120° | $\ddot{\mathrm{O}} = \ddot{\mathrm{S}} - \ddot{\mathrm{O}}$ |
| 4 | 4 | 0 | Tetrahedral | Tetrahedral | 109.5° | $\mathrm{H} - \mathrm{C} - \mathrm{H}$ with H above and below |
| 4 | 3 | 1 | Tetrahedral | Trigonal pyramidal | <109.5° | $\mathrm{H} - \ddot{\mathrm{N}} - \mathrm{H}$ with H below |
| 4 | 2 | 2 | Tetrahedral | Bent | <109.5° | $\mathrm{H} - \ddot{\mathrm{O}} - \mathrm{H}$ |
| 5 | 5 | 0 | Trigonal bipyramidal | Trigonal bipyramidal | 120° (equatorial) 90° (axial) | $PCl_5$ |
| 5 | 4 | 1 | Trigonal bipyramidal | Seesaw | < 120° (equatorial) <90° (axial) | $SF_4$ |
| 5 | 3 | 2 | Trigonal bipyramidal | T-shaped | <90° | $BrF_3$ |
| 5 | 2 | 3 | Trigonal bipyramidal | Linear | 180° | $XeF_2$ |
| 6 | 6 | 0 | Octahedral | Octahedral | 90° | $SF_6$ |
| 6 | 5 | 1 | Octahedral | Square pyramidal | <90° | $BrF_5$ |
| 6 | 4 | 2 | Octahedral | Square planar | 90° | $XeF_4$ |

"Count only electron groups around the central atom. Each of the following is considered one electron group: a lone pair, a single bond, a double bond, a triple bond, or a single electron

Section 10.4    # VSEPR Theory: Predicting Molecular Geometries

When drawing structures on paper, there are ways to indicate the shape in 3-D depending on whether the bond is going into the page (a hatched wedge) or coming out of the page (solid wedge). The following diagrams show how to draw several 3-D shapes.

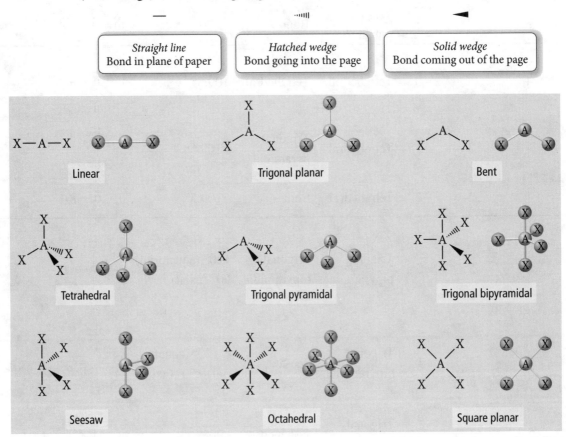

In larger molecules, with more than one central atom, there will be combinations of shapes, such as in methanol, in which a tetrahedral shape is around the carbon atom, whereas a bent shape is around the oxygen atom.

Section 10.5    # Molecular Shape and Polarity

Molecular polarity depends on *both* molecular shape *and* bond polarity. Do not confuse this with bond polarity. It is possible to have polar bonds and be a nonpolar molecule. This depends on the shape of the molecule and whether or not there is a resulting net dipole. The molecule will be polar if the shape and bond polarity results in a *net* dipole greater than zero. For instance, in carbon dioxide, the C—O bonds are polar, but because the two bonds are equal and on opposite sides of the molecule, with a bond angle of EXACTLY 180°, the two opposite dipole moments cancel each other, resulting in a net dipole of zero. Thus, $CO_2$ is nonpolar as a molecule. If there is even a slight deviation from exact angular cancellation, the net dipole will not be zero and the molecule will be slightly polar.

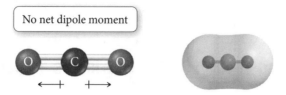

No net dipole moment

In contrast, water also has polar bonds, but the orientation of the two H—O bonds and the two lone electron pairs results in a net dipole, therefore water is a polar molecule.

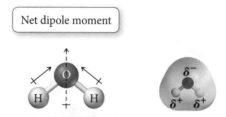

Net dipole moment

Students are not expected to add vectors, but if they have an understanding of vectors from mathematics, it helps them understand resulting dipoles. There is a review of vector addition on page 440. By looking at each general molecular shape, the general presence of a dipole can be predicted. We use *generally* here because it depends on the atoms in the bonds as well as the angles. If a central atom has all the same atoms attached to it, a tetrahedral shape is *generally* nonpolar. An example would be $CCl_4$. Different bond polarities among the bonded atoms of a symmetric shape can also result in a polar molecule. An example would be $CH_3Cl$. Students should be able to look at shapes and determine polarity; they should be capable of explaining why it is present or why it is not present. Molecular polarity is important because several molecular properties depend on the degree of polarity present. For instance, molecules with similar polar properties can dissolve in each other and form solutions. Water is polar and hence other polar molecules will dissolve in it, but nonpolar molecules such as oil will not. When water and oil are mixed together, the water layer stays separate from the oil layer. The layer on top will be the less dense layer. When cleaning oil-based paintbrushes, one must use a nonpolar solvent such as turpentine or mineral oil instead of water.

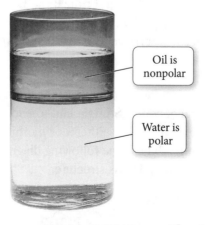

Oil is nonpolar

Water is polar

An interesting question arises when you consider washing oil from your hands using soap and water. How does soap work if water and oil do not mix? Soap is a unique type of molecule having a polar end attracted to water and a nonpolar end attracted to oil. The soap acts as a link between the two, so you can clean oil off your clothes, skin, or dishes.

Section 10.6

## Valence Bond Theory: Orbital Overlap as a Chemical Bond

Another model used to explain how atoms form bonds is called valence bond theory. In this theory, a lone electron in an atomic orbital overlaps another lone electron in its atomic orbital. The result is a blend of two or more atomic orbitals and the geometry of the overlap will determine the shape of the molecule. This is shown using $H_2S$ in the following diagram.

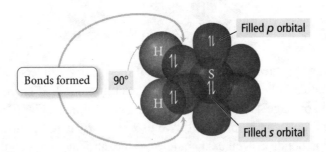

Section 10.7

## Valence Bond Theory: Hybridization of Atomic Orbitals

Simple overlaps cannot adequately explain all bonding and resulting molecular shapes. Hybridization theory is used to explain these examples. In this theory, when atomic orbitals combine, the new orbitals can be hybrids of the original orbitals. Hybrid orbitals minimize the energy of the molecule by maximizing the orbital overlap in a bond. The number of atomic orbitals shown in the hybrid notation always equals the number of hybrid orbitals formed. The shape of the molecule depends on the number of these hybrid orbitals formed. For example, the tetrahedral shape results from $sp^3$ hybridization. One $s$ and three $p$ atomic orbitals hybridize to form four equivalent $sp^3$ hybrid orbitals. All four $sp^3$ hybrid orbitals are exactly equal. In $sp^2$ hybridization, three equal $sp^2$ orbitals form resulting in a trigonal planar geometry.

Another concept in molecular bonding that uses atomic orbital overlap theory is the formation of sigma and pi bonds. Straight end-to-end overlap bonds are called *sigma bonds*. These overlaps can involve either *s* or *p* orbitals. *Pi bonds* are formed from side-to-side overlap of *p* orbitals. The following diagram illustrates both sigma and pi bonds as well as the resulting Lewis structure.

## Formation of *sp³* Hybrid Orbitals

One *s* orbital and three *p* orbitals combine to form four *sp³* orbitals.

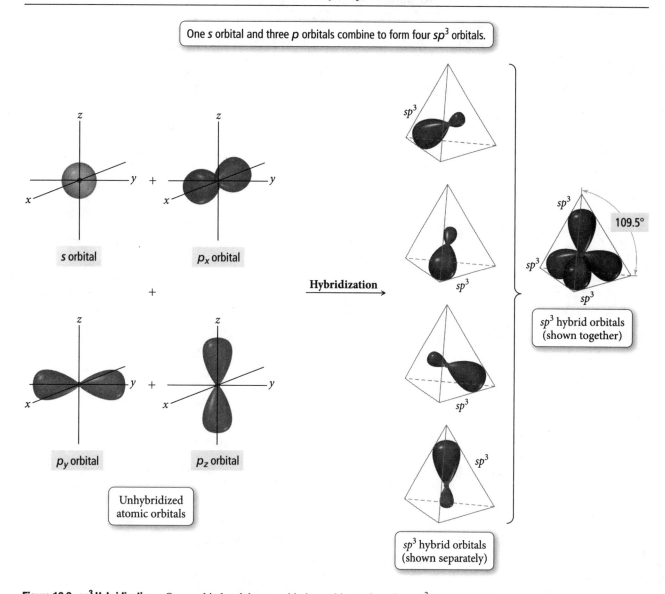

**Figure 10.3** *sp³* **Hybridization**   One *s* orbital and three *p* orbitals combine to form four *sp³* hybrid orbitals.

When a sigma and pi bond form between two atoms, a double bond is produced. A triple bond forms from a sigma and two pi bonds. Generally, pi bonds are weaker than sigma bonds. However the combination of sigma and pi bonds in a double bond is stronger than a single sigma bond. A triple bond is even stronger, explaining why $N_2$

## Formation of $sp^2$ Hybrid Orbitals

One $s$ orbital and two $p$ orbitals combine to form three $sp^2$ orbitals.

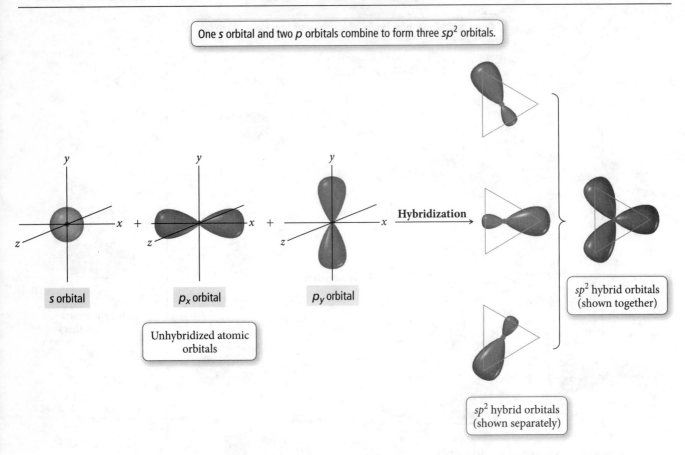

Unhybridized atomic orbitals

$sp^2$ hybrid orbitals (shown together)

$sp^2$ hybrid orbitals (shown separately)

**Figure 10.4  $sp^2$ Hybridization**   One $s$ orbital and two $p$ orbitals combine to form three $sp^2$ hybrid orbitals. One $p$ orbital (not shown) remains unhybridized.

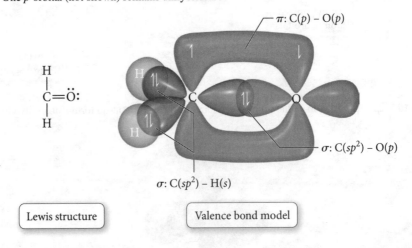

Lewis structure

Valence bond model

which has a triple bond is one of the strongest bonds known. This model also explains why the rotation in a double bond is limited due to the side-to-side overlap of the pi bonds. The sigma bonding in single bonds does not limit bond rotation. This is very important in organic chemistry. When a double bond forms, there are two possible arrangement of atoms; *cis* and *trans*. In a *cis* formation, the atoms on each side of the bond stay on the same side. In a *trans* formation, the two atoms on each side will be on opposite sides of the bond. This can be thought of as one atom *up* and the other atom *down*. Molecules that have the same formula, but different shapes are called isomers. Two isomers could have the same formula while one is *cis* and the other *trans*.

Another type of hybridization is *sp*. An example is acetylene (ethyne) in which a triple bond forms between the carbon atoms. The *sp* hybrid on each C atom is only involved in the sigma bond formation, leaving two *p* orbitals on each C to form the two pi bonds.

## Formation of *sp* Hybrid Orbitals

One *s* orbital and one *p* orbital combine to form two *sp* orbitals.

Hybridization

*s* orbital

$p_x$ orbital

*sp* hybrid orbitals (shown separately)

*sp* hybrid orbitals (shown together)

Unhybridized atomic orbitals

**Figure 10.5  *sp* Hybridization**   One *s* orbital and one *p* orbital combine to form two *sp* hybrid orbitals. Two *p* orbitals (not shown) remain unhybridized.

In the AP curriculum, only *sp*, $sp^2$, and $sp^3$ hybridizations are covered.

## Molecular Orbital Theory: Electron Delocalization     Section 10.8

Another theory of bonding is molecular orbital theory. In this theory, orbitals are delocalized, whereas in the valence bond theory, they are attributed to a particular atom. Students do not need to know how to solve mathematically the wave functions of these orbitals, nor do they need to know the order of filling. However, students should understand that Hund's rule is still followed. Bonding orbitals are lower in energy than the atomic orbitals from which they were formed.

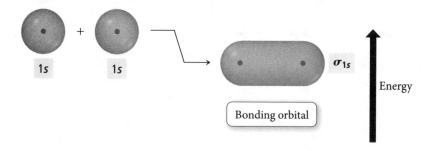

1s     1s     $\sigma_{1s}$

Energy

Bonding orbital

Some electrons fill antibonding orbitals, which have higher energies than the atomic orbitals from which they were formed.

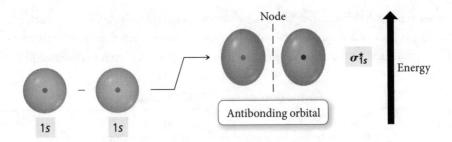

The bonding orbitals have a greater electron density compared to the antibonding orbitals.

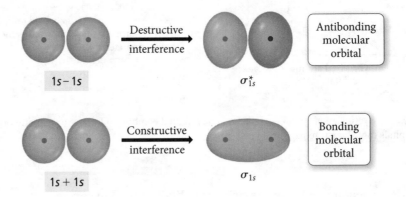

Molecular orbital theory can predict the bond order and whether certain bonds will form. For instance, it predicts $H_2$ will have a single bond and $He_2$ will not form since it has a bond order of zero. The equation used is:

$$\text{Bond order} = \frac{(\text{number of electrons in bonding MOs}) - (\text{number of electrons in antibonding MOs})}{2}.$$

Stable bonds require a positive bond order, which can even be $\frac{1}{2}$. Although the order of filling bonding and antibonding orbitals will not be tested on the AP Exam, students should practice filling the orbitals and determining the bond order. The stability and strength of the bond is determined by the relationship of the number of electrons in lower energy bonding orbitals to the number of electrons in higher energy antibonding orbitals. Lewis structures predict $O_2$ is diamagnetic, but molecular orbital theory explains why $O_2$ is actually paramagnetic.

Looking at the MO diagram for NO we can see an unpaired electron making it paramagnetic.

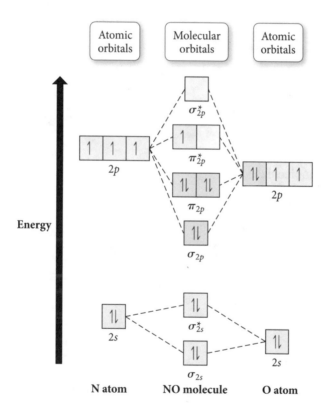

These bonding theories can help us predict the properties of molecules. They can be used to determine bond order, paramagnetic or diamagnetic properties, polarity, bond angles, hybridization, and molecular shapes.

### Additional Practice

*Self-Assessment Quiz Questions Q1, Q2, Q3, Q4, Q5, Q6, Q7, Q8, Q9, Q10, Q11, Q12, Q13, Q14, and Q15*

*Problems 3, 4, 5, 7, 9, 15, 17, 27, 30, 33, 34, 35, 43, 44, 47, 48, 51, 67, 77, 80, 87, 89, 90, 92, 109, and 111*

### Practice AP® Test Questions

1.  Given the following table of electronegativity values, the $PCl_3$ molecule overall can be classified as:

    | Element | Electronegativity |
    |---------|-------------------|
    | B       | 2.0               |
    | La      | 1.1               |
    | P       | 2.1               |
    | Sc      | 1.3               |
    | Cl      | 3.0               |

    A)  a nonpolar molecule

    B)  a polar molecule

    C)  an ionic compound

    D)  a coordinate covalent compound

2.  The Cl—C—Cl bond angle in $CCl_4$ is closest to:

    A)  60°

    B)  90°

    C)  109°

    D)  120°

3.  What is the molecular geometry of the $AsCl_3$ molecule?

    A)  Trignonal pyramidal

    B)  Trignonal planar

    C)  Tetrahedral

    D)  Trigonal bipyramidal

4. What is the molecular geometry of the $ICl_4^-$ ion?

   A) Trignonal pyramidal

   B) Octahedral

   C) Tetrahedral

   D) Square planar

5. The orbital hybridization on the carbon atom in $CH_2O$ is:

   A) $sp$

   B) $sp^2$

   C) $sp^3$

   D) $sp^4$

# LIQUIDS, SOLIDS, AND INTERMOLECULAR FORCES

The state of matter of a substance reflects the structure of the particles composing the substance. This chapter has many concepts students answer incorrectly on the AP exam due to common misconceptions. In this chapter, the main AP curriculum is as follows:

## Specific Learning Objectives Addressed in This Chapter:

**Learning objective 2.1** Students can predict properties of substances based on their chemical formulas, and provide explanations of their properties based on particle views. [*See* **SP 6.4, 7.1**]

**Learning objective 2.3** The student is able to use aspects of particulate models (i.e., particle spacing, motion, and forces of attraction) to reason about observed differences between solid and liquid phases and among solid and liquid materials. [*See* **SP 6.4, 7.1**]

**Learning objective 2.9** The student is able to create or interpret representations that link the concept of molarity with particle views of solutions. [*See* **SP 1.1, 1.4**]

**Learning objective 2.11** The student is able to explain the trends in properties and/or predict properties of samples consisting of particles with no permanent dipole on the basis of London dispersion forces. [*See* **SP 6.2, 6.4**]

**Learning objective 2.12** The student can qualitatively analyze data regarding real gases to identify deviations from ideal behavior and relate these to molecular interactions. [*See* **SP 5.1**, **6.5**]

**Learning objective 2.13** The student is able to describe the relationships between the structural features of polar molecules and the forces of attraction between the particles. [*See* **SP 1.4**]

**Learning objective 2.14** The student is able to apply Coulomb's Law qualitatively (including using representations) to describe the interactions of ions, and the attractions between ions and solvents to explain the factors that contribute to the solubility of ionic compounds. [*See* **SP 1.4**, **6.4**]

**Learning objective 2.15** The student is able to explain observations regarding the solubility of ionic solids and molecules in water and other solvents on the basis of particle views that include intermolecular interactions and entropic effects. [See **SP 1.4**, **6.2**]

**Learning objective 2.16** The student is able to explain the properties (phase, vapor pressure, viscosity, etc.,) of small and large molecular compounds in terms of the strengths and types of intermolecular forces. [*See* **SP 6.2**]

**Learning objective 2.18** The student is able to rank and justify the ranking of bond polarity on the basis of the locations of the bonded atoms in the periodic table. [*See* **SP 6.1**]

**Learning objective 2.19** The student can create visual representations of ionic substances that connect the microscopic structure to macroscopic properties, and/or use representations to connect the microscopic structure to macroscopic properties (e.g., boiling point, solubility, hardness, brittleness, low volatility, lack of malleability, ductility, or conductivity). [*See* SP **1.1**, **1.4**, **7.1**]

**Learning objective 2.20** The student is able to explain how a bonding model involving delocalized electrons is consistent with macroscopic properties of metals (e.g., conductivity, malleability, ductility, and low volatility) and the shell model of the atom. [*See* **SP 6.2**, **7.1**]

**Learning objective 2.23** The student can create a representation of an ionic solid that shows essential characteristics of the structure and interactions present in the substance. [*See* **SP 1.1**]

**Learning objective 2.24** The student is able to explain a representation that connects properties of an ionic solid to its structural attributes and to the interactions present at the atomic level. [*See* **SP 1.1**, **6.2**, **7.1**]

**Learning objective 2.25** The student is able to compare the properties of metal alloys with their constituent elements to determine if an alloy has formed, identify the type of alloy formed, and explain the differences in properties using particulate level reasoning. [*See* **SP 1.4**, **7.2**]

**Learning objective 2.26** Students can use the electron sea model of metallic bonding to predict or make claims about the macroscopic properties of metals or alloys. [*See* **SP 6.4**, **7.1**]

**Learning objective 2.27** The student can create a representation of a metallic solid that shows essential characteristics of the structure and interactions present in the substance. [*See* **SP 1.1**]

**Learning objective 2.28** The student is able to explain a representation that connects properties of a metallic solid to its structural attributes and to the interactions present at the atomic level. [*See* **SP 1.1, 6.2, 7.1**]

**Learning objective 2.29** The student can create a representation of a covalent solid that shows essential characteristics of the structure and interactions present in the substance. [*See* **SP 1.1**]

**Learning objective 2.30** The student is able to explain a representation that connects properties of a covalent solid to its structural attributes and to the interactions present at the atomic level. [*See* **SP 1.1, 6.2, 7.1**]

**Learning objective 2.31** The student can create a representation of a molecular solid that shows essential characteristics of the structure and interactions present in the substance. [*See* **SP 1.1**]

**Learning objective 2.32** The student is able to explain a representation that connects properties of a molecular solid to its structural attributes and to the interactions present at the atomic level. [*See* **SP 1.1, 6.2, 7.1**]

**Learning objective 5.9** The student is able to make claims and/or predictions regarding relative magnitudes of the forces acting within collections of interacting molecules based on the distribution of electrons within the molecules and the types of intermolecular forces through which the molecules interact. [*See* **SP 6.4**]

**Learning objective 5.10** The student can support the claim about whether a process is a chemical or physical change (or may be classified as both) based on whether the process involves changes in intramolecular versus intermolecular interactions. [*See* **SP 5.1**]

**Learning objective 5.11** The student is able to identify the noncovalent interactions within and between large molecules, and/or connect the shape and function of the large molecule to the presence and magnitude of these interactions. [*See* **SP 7.2**]

## Specific Science Practices Addressed in This Chapter:

**Science Practice1:** The student can use representations and models to communicate scientific phenomena and solve scientific problems.

   1.1   The student can *create representations and models* of natural or man-made phenomena and systems in the domain.

   1.4   The student can *use representations and models* to analyze situations or solve problems qualitatively and quantitatively.

**Science Practice 5:** The student can perform data analysis and evaluation of evidence.

   5.1   The student can *analyze data* to identify patterns or relationships.

**Science Practice 6:** The student can work with scientific explanations and theories.

   6.1   The student can *justify claims with evidence*.

6.2  The student can *construct explanations of phenomena based on evidence* produced through scientific practices.

6.4  The student can *make claims and predictions about natural phenomena* based on scientific theories and models.

6.5  The student can *evaluate alternative scientific explanations.*

**Science Practice 7:** The student is able to connect and relate knowledge across various scales, concepts, and representations in and across domains.

7.1  The student can *connect phenomena and models* across spatial and temporal scales.

7.2  The student can *connect concepts* in and across domain(s) to generalize or extrapolate in and/or across enduring understandings and/or big ideas.

## Concepts and Vocabulary to Review:

## Solids, Liquids, and Gases: A Molecular Comparison     Section 11.2

This section should be review for most students, but it is fundamental to understanding Section 11.3, which is an important section of the AP Curriculum.

**Table 11.1**   The Three States of Water

| Phase | Temperature (°C) | Density (g/cm³, at 1 atm) | Molar Volume | Molecular View |
|---|---|---|---|---|
| Gas (steam) | 100 | $5.90 \times 10^{-4}$ | 30.5 L | |
| Liquid (water) | 20 | 0.998 | 18.0 mL | |
| Solid (ice) | 0 | 0.917 | 19.6 mL | |

Most substances increase in density when they solidify because the molecules move closer together when they go from the liquid to solid state. Water is an unusual, but very important, exception because liquid water is denser than ice. This is due to the structure water adopts when freezing into its crystal—the molecules are organized so that they actually get further apart.

In gases, molecules are far apart and move randomly throughout the entire volume. The relatively large distance between individual molecules allows gases to be easily compressed thus demonstrating one of their unique properties.

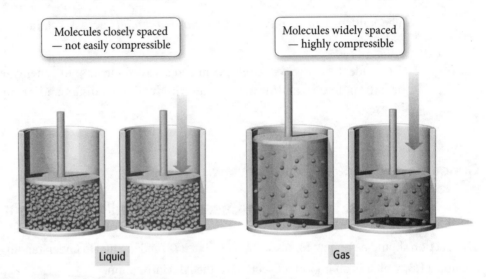

**Figure 11.1  Gases Are Compressible**    Molecules in a liquid are closely spaced and are not easily compressed. Molecules in a gas have a great deal of space between them, making gases compressible.

In liquids, molecules are in close contact but move relatively freely. The degree of this freedom of motion depends on the amount of attraction between the molecules. This freedom of motion explains why we can pour liquids. Liquids assume the shape of the container they are in, but interact somewhat with their container, such as when forming a meniscus at the surface, or climbing in a capillary tube.

In solids, the atoms are essentially locked into a position and do not move freely around each other. They do move, however, by vibrating in position. Some solids may be crystalline where a very ordered structure exists or they may be amorphous where no long-range order exists.

A summary of the properties of each state is in the following table.

**Table 11.2    Properties of the States of Matter**

| State | Density | Shape | Volume | Strength of Intermolecular Forces (Relative to Thermal Energy) |
|-------|---------|-------|--------|---------------------------------------------------------------|
| Gas | Low | Indefinite | Indefinite | Weak |
| Liquid | High | Indefinite | Definite | Moderate |
| Solid | High | Definite | Definite | Strong |

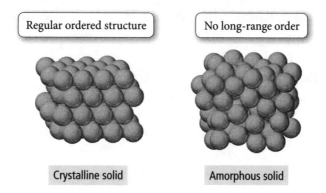

Crystalline solid          Amorphous solid

**Figure 11.2 Crystalline and Amorphous Solids**     In a crystalline solid, the arrangement of the particles displays long-range order. In an amorphous solid, the arrangement of the particles has no long-range order.

To change from one state to another requires a change in energy content. This can occur through a change in temperature, pressure, or both. When the state changes, this is known as a *phase change*.

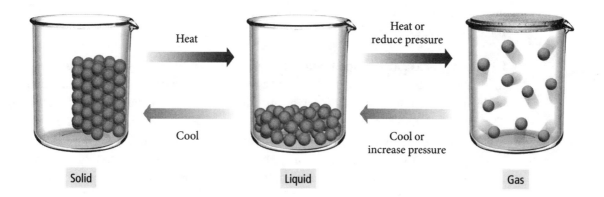

Gases can be changed noticeably by small variations in either temperature and/or pressure. Liquids will be changed only slightly and solids even less so in response to temperature and pressure changes. Common terms used in describing these phase (state) transitions are:

|  |  |
|---|---|
| Solid → Liquid | *Melting* |
| Liquid → Gas | *Evaporating* |
| Gas → Liquid | *Condensing* |
| Liquid → Solid | *Freezing* |
| Solid → Gas | *Subliming* |
| Gas → Solid | *Depositing* |

Section 11.3

# Intermolecular Forces: The Forces That Hold Condensed States Together

The structure of matter is influenced by interactions or forces holding the substances together. These interactions are called *intermolecular forces*. Strong forces of attraction tend to result in the substance being a solid or liquid, except at high temperatures. Weak forces of attractions tend to result in substances being in the gas phase at room temperature.

Teachers should make sure their students understand the forces between substances are not bonds within the substance. Interfering with intermolecular forces between molecules does not change the intramolecular bonding within the substance and does not result in new substances. Adding energy to boiling water does not break the O—H bonds within H—O—H to form hydrogen and oxygen gas, but rather the forces between neighboring $H_2O$ molecules are overcome and water molecules are able to pull away from each other and enter the vapor phase. Students should draw what is happening in phase changes and explain this in words while teachers watch for misconceptions.

The strength of the intermolecular forces is reflected in boiling points. The types of these forces **between molecules** are dispersion forces, dipole–dipole forces, and hydrogen bonding. Although the forces are separately classified according to their origins, they can all be present at the same time. An additional type, ion–dipole force, is present in some mixtures.

Dispersion forces, also called London forces—after the scientist who first explained them, are due to the lack of homogeneity of the electron distribution within each molecule. Nonpolar molecules have only dispersion forces between molecules. The greater the number of electrons, the greater the dispersion force because the electrons are less strongly attracted to the positively charged nucleus, and their electron orbital-distribution is easier to distort or become asymmetrical. Remembering that a dipole is created by uneven positive and negative charge, when electrons become

## Dispersion Force

An instantaneous dipole on any one helium atom induces instantaneous dipoles on neighboring atoms, which then attract one another.

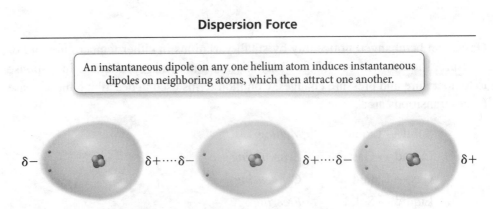

**Figure 11.3 Dispersion Interactions**   The temporary dipole in one helium atom induces a temporary dipole in its neighbor. The resulting attraction between the positive and negative charges creates the dispersion force.

less evenly distributed around the positive nucleus, this creates uneven distributions of charge called *instantaneous dipoles*. (These are also called *temporary dipoles*.) These temporary dipoles result in forces of attraction between molecules called *dispersion forces*. The stronger the dispersion force, the higher the boiling point. (Remember boiling is adding enough thermal energy to the molecules to overcome the attractions holding liquid molecules together.

The shape of the molecule will affect the boiling point since shape affects the number of possible interactions. Molecules whose shape allows for them to "fit together" will have a greater area of interaction and higher boiling points. This concept explains why different isomers, especially nonpolar organic isomers, have different boiling points.

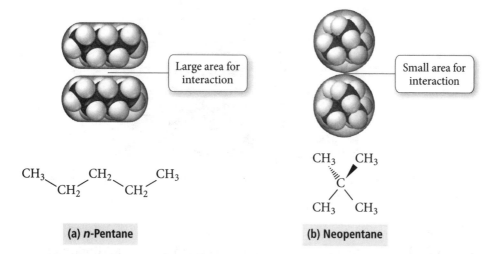

**(a) *n*-Pentane**     **(b) Neopentane**

**Figure 11.4  Dispersion Force and Molecular Shape    (a)** The straight shape of *n*-pentane molecules allows them to interact with one another along the entire length of the molecules. **(b)** The nearly spherical shape of neopentane molecules allows for only a small area of interaction. Thus, dispersion forces are weaker in neopentane than in *n*-pentane, resulting in a lower boiling point.

Polar molecules have dipole–dipole forces as well as dispersion forces acting between them. These permanent dipoles contain areas of electrostatic charge in the polar molecules and are attracted to the oppositely charged area in another molecule.

**Dipole–Dipole Interaction**

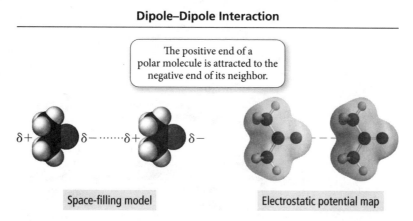

Space-filling model     Electrostatic potential map

**Figure 11.5  Dipole–Dipole Interaction**   Molecules with permanent dipoles, such as acetone, are attracted to one another via dipole–dipole interactions.

Be sure students realize dispersion forces are not "switched off" in these molecules, but contain additional forces of the added dipole interactions.

The polarity of two different molecules affects their *miscibility*—the ability to mix two liquids without the liquids separating out as two liquids, like oil and water. Water and ethanol are miscible while oil and water are not. In oil and water, the intermolecular forces between the polar water molecules are too strong for its molecules to disperse among the nonpolar oil molecules.

$C_5H_{12}(l)$

$H_2O(l)$

**Figure 11.6  Polar and Nonpolar Compounds**   Water and pentane do not mix because water molecules are polar and pentane molecules are nonpolar.

An extreme version of a dipole–dipole interaction is hydrogen bonding. This occurs when molecules with hydrogen atoms are bonded to very small highly electronegative atoms, like fluorine, oxygen, or nitrogen, and interact with other similar molecules. The hydrogen bond is not inside the molecule, but is a strong attraction between molecules and is a type of intermolecular force.

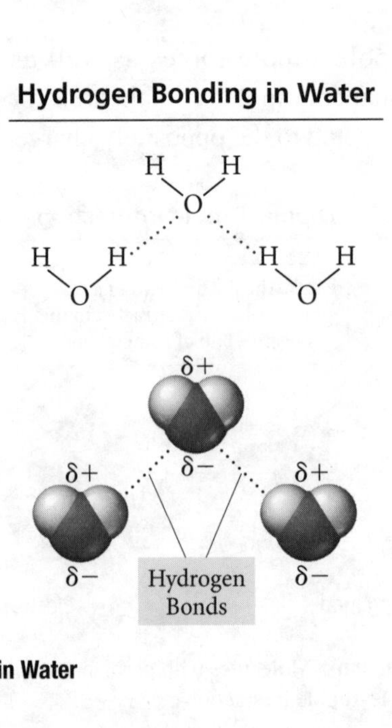

**Hydrogen Bonding in Water**

**Figure 11.7  Hydrogen Bonding in Water**

Examples of hydrogen bonding include the interactions between HF molecules, $NH_3$ molecules, and/or $H_2O$ molecules. When comparing families of molecules, molecules with hydrogen bonding have higher boiling points. In the following diagram, water has a much higher boiling point than the rest of the molecules in its family. This is explained given the increased intermolecular forces resulting from hydrogen bonding.

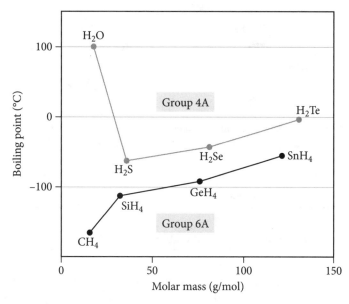

**Figure 11.8  Boiling Points of Group 4A and 6A Compounds**    Because of hydrogen bonding, the boiling point of water is anomalous compared to the boiling points of other hydrogen-containing compounds.

Keep in mind, a compound can have hydrogen atoms and small highly electronegative atoms in it and not exhibit hydrogen bonding. An example is fluoromethane. It contains both H and F atoms, however, they are not bonded to each other, but are both bonded to the central carbon atom.

Ion–dipole forces result when ionic compounds are mixed with a polar compound. An example is NaCl in water. The positive poles of the water molecules are attracted to the negatively charged chloride ion, whereas the negative poles of the water molecules are attracted to the positively charged sodium ion (see Figure 11.9 on next page).

The types of intermolecular forces are summed up in Table 11.3 on the next page. Remember they are not exclusive and all are often present simultaneously.

An interesting cross-domain occurrence vital to biology is that the bases in DNA are held together by hydrogen bonding. Additionally, the helix structures of both proteins and nucleic acids (e.g., DNA and RNA) are due to hydrogen bonding between one part of these (very long) molecules and another part of the *same* molecule (see Figure 11.10 on p. 149).

## Ion–Dipole Forces

The positively charged end of a polar molecule such as $H_2O$ is attracted to negative ions and the negatively charged end of the molecule is attracted to positive ions.

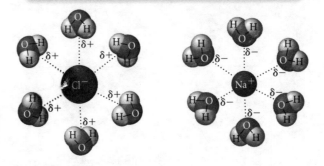

**Figure 11.9 Ion–Dipole Forces**    Ion–dipole forces exist between $Na^+$ and the negative ends of $H_2O$ molecules and between $Cl^-$ and the positive ends of $H_2O$ molecules.

**Table 11.3**   Types of Intermolecular Forces

| Type | Present in | Molecular Perspective | General strength |
|---|---|---|---|
| Dispersion | All molecules and atoms | | |
| Dipole–dipole | Polar molecules | | |
| Hydrogen bonding | Molecules containing H bonded to F, O, or N | | |
| Ion–dipole | Mixtures of ionic compounds and polar compounds | | |

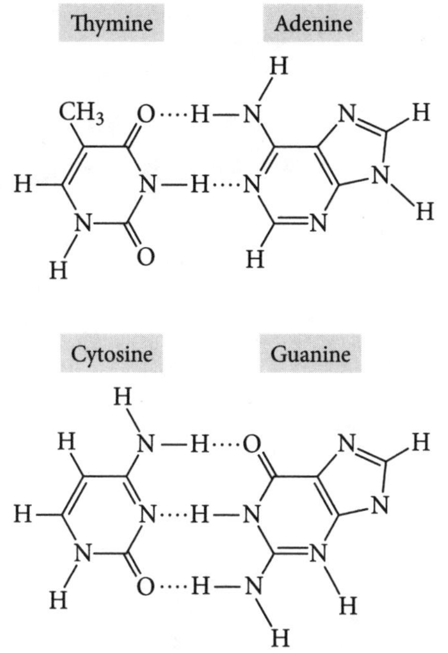

**Figure 11.10 Complementary Base Pairing via Hydrogen Bonds**   The individual bases in DNA interact with one another via specific hydrogen bonds that form between A and T and between C and G.

# Intermolecular Forces in Action: Surface Tension, Viscosity, and Capillary Action

Section 11.4

Three observable consequences of intermolecular forces in liquids are surface tension, viscosity, and capillary action. *Surface tension* results from the molecules on the surface interacting only with the molecules to either side of them and below them, whereas a molecule in the center of the liquid interacts with molecules in all directions. Thus, there is a net force in toward the body of the liquid forming a "skin" of tightly bonded surface molecules.

The stronger the intermolecular forces, the stronger the surface tension. The surface tension creates a film on the surface of the liquid resisting penetration. Water has hydrogen bonds, dipole interactions, and dispersion forces between water molecules resulting in a high surface tension. Hence, water skippers appear to walk on water and paper clips can float on the surface of water. In contrast, benzene has only dispersion forces resulting in a much lower surface tension (see Figure 11.12 on page 150).

*Viscosity* is a measure of a liquid's resistance to flow. Temperature affects viscosity as most liquids flow more freely at a higher temperature. More viscous liquids have stronger intermolecular forces. Molasses is more viscous than water. Motor oil developers take this into consideration when trying to produce formulas for oil that will flow well and lubricate effectively at high and low temperatures.

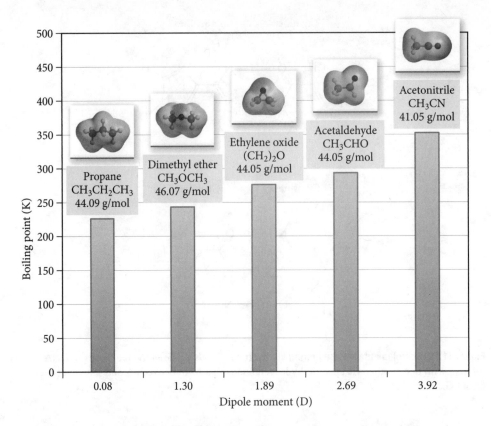

**Figure 11.11  Dipole Moment and Boiling Point**    The molecules shown here all have similar molar masses but different dipole moments. The boiling points increase with increasing dipole moment.

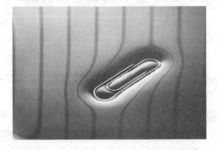

**Figure 11.12  Surface Tension in Action**    A paper clip floats on water because of surface tension.

*Capillary action* is the phenomenon of a liquid rising or depressing in a narrow tube against gravity. Two forces are actually involved—adhesion and cohesion. *Adhesion* is the attraction of molecules to different materials such as the surface of the tube and *cohesion* is the attraction of the molecules to themselves. If the adhesive forces between glass and a liquid are stronger than the cohesive forces within the liquid, the level of liquid will rise in a tube of glass until the force of gravity on the column is balanced. The balance between the adhesive and cohesive forces can also be observed in the shape of the meniscus in the tube or a graduated cylinder. Water has a concave meniscus because the adhesive forces are stronger than the cohesive forces. The meniscus of liquid mercury is convex because the cohesive forces are greater than the adhesive forces.

**Figure 11.13 Meniscuses of Water and Mercury**    The meniscus of water is concave because water molecules are more strongly attracted to the glass wall than to one another. The meniscus of mercury is convex because mercury atoms are more strongly attracted to one another than to the glass walls.

## Vaporization and Vapor Pressure    Section 11.5

In order for a liquid to change to a vapor, it must overcome the forces of attraction holding its molecules together in the liquid. As some liquid molecules escape as vapor, the vapor is now a gas creating pressure over the liquid. When a liquid is placed in a closed container, some of the liquid might change to a gas. If a dynamic equilibrium is reached, then there are liquid molecules escaping as vapor at the same rate vapor molecules are condensing back into liquid. The partial pressure that develops in the closed container when the liquid is in equilibrium with its own vapor is called *vapor pressure*. We can use the term *pressure exerted by the vapor* to describe the behavior of the vapor in the container. We can also refer to the vapor pressure of a liquid as the liquid's ability to vaporize at a given temperature. If not in a closed system, this pressure is not constant, but in a closed system, it reaches an equilibrium vapor pressure, depending only on the chemical nature of the liquid and the temperature. This is the principle used in raising the boiling point of water by using a pressure cooker. Increasing the pressure in the closed system of the pressure cooker results in the boiling point of the liquid increasing.

Kinetic molecular theory provides an explanation for why the vapor pressure of a liquid depends on the temperature. When the temperature of a liquid is raised, the *average* kinetic energy of the molecules increases. Remember in a liquid there is a range of kinetic energies. The molecules with the higher kinetic energy may have enough energy to overcome the attractive intermolecular forces and vaporize.

In the Figure 11.12 on the next page, you can see there are more molecules at the higher temperature with the energy to overcome the intermolecular forces and vaporize. If the surface area of the liquid is increased, a greater number of molecules have the ability to escape the surface. However, the relative number at equilibrium will

**Distribution of Thermal Energy**

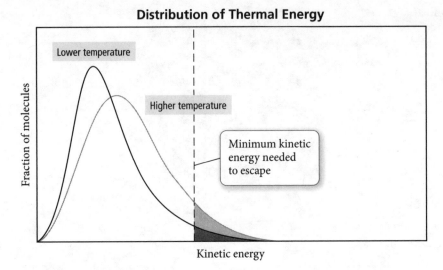

**Figure 11.14 Distribution of Thermal Energy**    The thermal energies of the molecules in a liquid are distributed over a range. The peak energy increases with increasing temperature.

be independent of the surface area. A substance whose molecules vaporize easily is called *volatile* and those that tend not to vaporize are called *nonvolatile*.

A phase change from liquid to gas requires the addition of energy. This is an endothermic process.

$$\text{Liquid} \rightarrow \text{gas} \quad Evaporating \quad +\Delta H_{vap} \quad \text{Endothermic}$$

Going to a more condensed phase requires the removal of the same amount of energy needed to change the phase in the opposite direction. Condensation is an exothermic process, the sign is opposite, but has the same numerical value of $\Delta H_{vap}$.

$$\text{Gas} \rightarrow \text{liquid} \quad Condensing \quad -\Delta H_{vap} \quad \text{Exothermic}$$

We use a combination of these processes to keep our bodies cool. When we get hot from exercising, we sweat. When sweat evaporates from our skin (endothermic), heat is absorbed by the liquid water in sweat. We, in turn, are cooled down due to this loss of heat. The amount is 40.7 kJ per mole of water in sweat at 100 °C. This is also affected by the surrounding conditions. If there is high humidity or lots of moisture in the air,

When we sweat, water evaporates from the skin. Since evaporation is endothermic, the result is a cooling effect.

vaporization will occur more slowly; and if the air is dry, vaporization will occur more quickly. The total cooling will be the same, but the rate of cooling will be different.

In a sealed container, when a liquid and its vapor reach a point where the rate of molecules going into the vapor phase is equal to the rate of molecules coming back to the liquid phase, the system is said to be in a *dynamic equilibrium.*

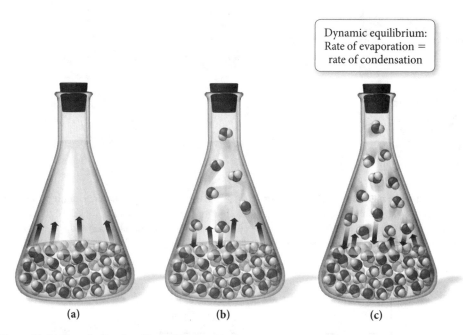

Dynamic equilibrium:
Rate of evaporation =
rate of condensation

(a)                    (b)                    (c)

**Figure 11.15 Vaporization in a Sealed Flask    (a)** When water is in a sealed container, water molecules begin to vaporize. **(b)** As water molecules build up in the gas state, they begin to recondense into the liquid. **(c)** When the rate of evaporation equals the rate of condensation, dynamic equilibrium is reached.

It is important to understand, the amount of vapor pressure is a reflection of the magnitude of the intermolecular forces. If a lot of vapor is present, the attraction between molecules in the liquid is weak. If something disturbs the dynamic equilibrium, the system will react to restore the equilibrium (See Figure 11.16 on next page).

A substance boils at the temperature at which the liquid's vapor pressure equals the external pressure. The normal boiling point of water is considered as 100 °C. What is a *normal boiling point*? It is the boiling temperature at 1 atmosphere of pressure. These are the temperatures published in manuals as standard (See Figure 11.17 on next page).

What if the pressure is not at 1 atmosphere? At any temperature when the vapor pressure equals the external pressure, the liquid will boil. This explains why, when water is boiled at a different altitude and the pressure is not 1 atmosphere, the boiling point will vary. The external pressure changes and therefore the vapor pressure required to equal it changes. For example, the boiling points at higher elevations (lower atmospheric pressure) will be lower than at sea level (See Table 11.4 on page 155).

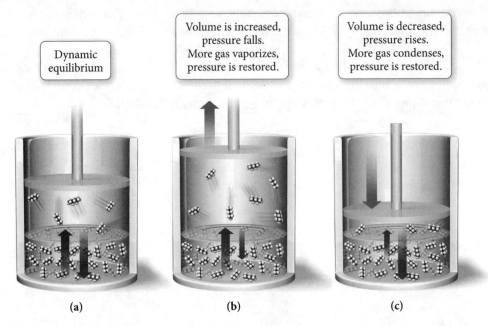

**Figure 11.16  Dynamic Equilibrium in *n*-Pentane**    **(a)** Liquid *n*-pentane is in dynamic equilibrium with its vapor. **(b)** When the volume is increased, the pressure drops and some liquid is converted to gas to bring the pressure back up. **(c)** When the volume is decreased, the pressure increases and some gas is converted to liquid to bring the pressure back down.

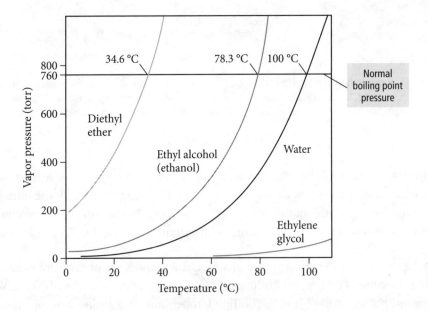

**Figure 11.17  Vapor Pressure of Several Liquids at Different Temperatures**    At higher temperatures, more molecules have enough thermal energy to escape into the gas state, so vapor pressure increases with increasing temperature.

As long as liquid is present, the temperature will not rise above the boiling point. Knowing this, one can look at a graph and determine the boiling point by seeing where the temperature remains constant between the liquid and gas phases (Figure 11.18 on next page).

**Table 11.4**   Boiling Points of Water at Several Locations of Varied Altitudes

| Location | Elevation (ft) | Approximate Pressure (atm)* | Approximate Boiling Point of Water (°C) |
|---|---|---|---|
| Mt. Everest, Tibet (highest mountain peak on Earth) | 29,035 | 0.32 | 78 |
| Mt. McKinley (Denali), Alaska (highest mountain peak in North America) | 20,320 | 0.46 | 83 |
| Mt. Whitney, California (highest mountain peak in 48 contiguous U.S. states) | 14,495 | 0.60 | 87 |
| Denver, Colorado (mile high city) | 5,280 | 0.83 | 94 |
| Boston, Massachusetts (sea level) | 20 | 1.0 | 100 |

*The atmospheric pressure in each of these locations is subject to weather conditions and can vary significantly from these values.

**Figure 11.18  Spherical Water Droplets**   On the space shuttle in orbit, under weightless conditions, collections of water molecules coalesce into nearly perfect spheres held together by intermolecular forces between molecules.

## Sublimation and Fusion     Section 11.6

*Sublimation* is the process of transformation of a solid directly to a gas. Solid carbon dioxide, also called dry ice, does this at normal conditions of temperature and pressure. At the surface of the solid substance, the molecules are vibrating faster, are not bound as tightly by the intermolecular forces as they are within the body of the material, and when they have enough thermal energy to overcome the intermolecular forces, they can escape as a gas.

Dry ice (solid $CO_2$ ) sublimes but does not melt at atmospheric pressure.

Ice also does this at temperatures below freezing. This explains why frozen foods kept in a freezer develop ice crystals and the food dries out. The ice (water) within the food sublimes and is then deposited on the outside as fresh ice.

Solid → gas    *Subliming*    $+\Delta H_{sub}$    Endothermic

Gas → solid    *Depositing*    $-\Delta H_{sub}$    Exothermic

When the rate of the gas being formed is equal to the rate of the gas being deposited, the phase change is at dynamic equilibrium. The pressure at dynamic equilibrium is the vapor pressure of the solid.

Most substances change from a solid into a liquid when heat is added and then back into a solid when cooled.

Solid → liquid    *Melting*    $+\Delta H_{fus}$    Endothermic

Liquid → solid    *Freezing*    $-\Delta H_{fus}$    Exothermic

When the temperature during heating and cooling is graphed, the temperature remains constant at the point where the transition between states occurs (see Figure 11.19). Students need to read these graphs and identify melting points and freezing points. As with boiling and condensing, the amount of energy absorbed during melting, which is an endothermic process, is the same amount of energy removed for freezing, which is an exothermic process. Thus, one graph represents the transitions in either direction. If the graph is transitioning downward, heat is being removed (lost by the system) indicating a cooling curve and in a transition moving upward heat is being added to the system which indicates a heating curve.

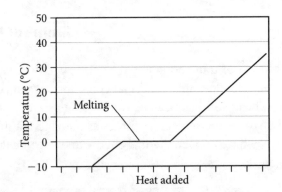

**Figure 11.19 Temperature during Melting**    The temperature of water during melting remains at 0.0°C as long as both solid and liquid water remain.

**Section 11.7**    ## Heating Curve for Water

When the graphs for melting and boiling are added together, both the transitions between solid and liquid and liquid to gas can be identified.

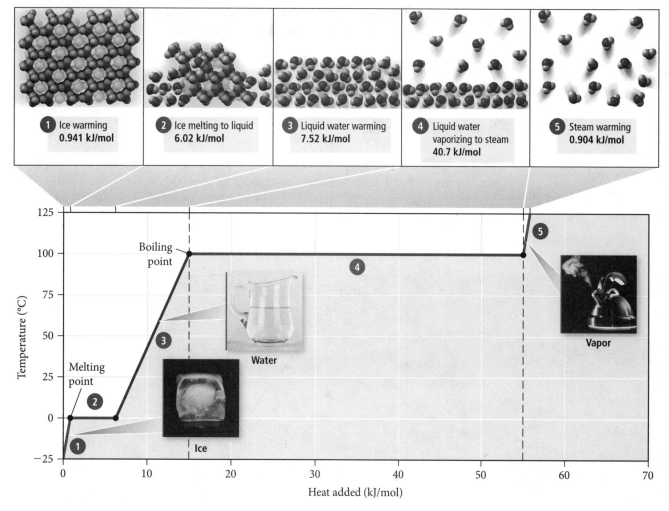

**Figure 11.20  Heating Curve for Water**

There are two different kinds of overall change represented in such a curve, the change within a state such as heating liquid water and the change of state called a phase change such as changing solid ice to liquid water. The calculation of the amount of energy involved in each type of change has to be done separately. In the stages where the substance is heating and not changing state, such as heating the solid, heating the liquid, or heating the gas, a specific heat equation is used. Each state has its own value for specific heat ($c$); $q = mc\Delta T$ (remember the equation used for specific heat on the AP test is slightly different than the equation in the text). The specific heat of ice is $2.09 \text{ J/g} \cdot {}^\circ\text{C}$, the specific heat of water (liquid) is $4.18 \text{ J/g} \cdot {}^\circ\text{C}$, and the specific heat of water vapor is $2.01 \text{ J/g} \cdot {}^\circ\text{C}$.

During each state transition or phase change, the equations used are similar, but each uses different constants; $q = n\Delta H_{\text{fus}}$ and $q = n\Delta H_{\text{vap}}$. Notice in Figure 11.20, evidence of the temperature of a phase change is not observing a temperature change. The $\Delta H_{\text{fus}}$ is $6.02 \text{ kJ/mol}$ and $\Delta H_{\text{vap}}$ is $40.7 \text{ kJ/mol}$. A common mistake in these calculations where a mass of substance is given is forgetting to convert mass to moles of substance.

The total enthalpy change, $\Delta H$, through any series of steps is simply the sum of the $\Delta H$ values for each step, provided that the amount of substance remains constant.

## Section 11.9   Water: An Extraordinary Substance

Why is water extraordinary?

It is a liquid at room temperature due to the dipole interactions, dispersion forces, and hydrogen bond attractions between the molecules. Other compounds with a similar molar mass such as methane are gases at room temperature. For its molar mass, water has a high boiling point.

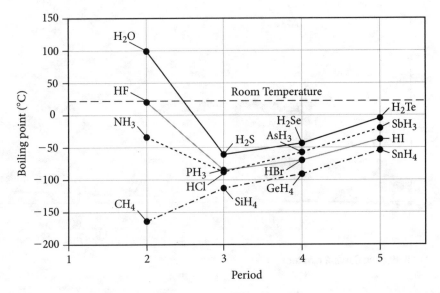

**Figure 11.21  Boiling Points of Main Group Hydrides**   Water is the only common main group hydride that is a liquid at room temperature.

Due to water's polarity, it can dissolve polar and ionic substances. This can be a problem when contaminates get into the water supply, but is a great advantage to living cells where many substances are needed in solution.

When water freezes, it forms a less dense state, so its solid floats on its liquid. This is an important feature for life on earth. Ice forms on the tops of lakes, and fish and other life forms can continue to live in the water below. A disadvantage of this property is that when water freezes, the expansion of the solid causes water delivery pipes to break or living cells to burst (e.g., frostbite). What is flash freezing? Flash freezing is done so quickly the water molecules do not have time to arrange themselves in a regular pattern, which prevents the cells in food from bursting.

The high specific heat of water relative to land keeps coastal areas and islands at fairly constant temperatures.

# Crystalline Solids: The Fundamental Types        Section 11.12

Crystalline solids can be classified into three groups based on the individual units in the solid. They are molecular solids, ionic solids, and atomic solids. Students need to be able to distinguish and explain each type of solid and relate its properties to its structure.

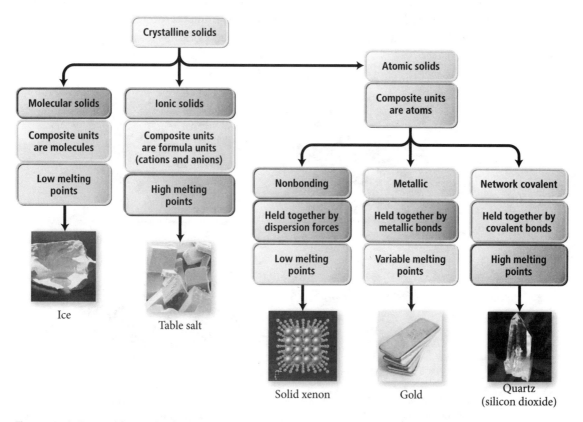

**Figure 11.22  Types of Crystalline Solids**

Molecular solids have molecules held together by intermolecular forces. Those forces can include dispersion forces, dipole–dipole forces, and hydrogen bonding. In general, molecular solids have low melting points.

Ionic solids are composed of ions held together by coulombic attractions between the cations and anions in the lattice. Coulombic attractions are generally much stronger than intermolecular forces, which explains why ionic solids having higher melting points than molecular solids.

Atomic solids are broken into three categories: nonbonding atomic solids, metallic atomic solids, and network covalent solids.

*Nonbonding atomic solids* include the noble gases, such as neon and helium. They only have dispersion forces and have very low melting points.

*Metallic atomic solids* have metallic bonds involving metal cations with a delocalized sea of electrons. The strength of metallic bonds varies, so there is a wide range of melting points. The stronger the metallic bond, the higher the melting point is. The only elemental metal that is a liquid at room temperature is mercury.

*Network covalent solids* have very strong covalent bonds. Examples include diamond, graphite, and silicon dioxide. A diamond is a giant molecule made of carbon atoms covalently bonding to four other carbon atoms with covalent bonds. The electrons are held in position and are not free to flow; therefore, they do no not conduct electricity. This strong covalently bonded network has a melting point of about 3800 °C.

(a) Diamond    (b) Graphite

**Figure 11.23  Network Covalent Atomic Solids**    **(a)** In diamond, each carbon atom forms four covalent bonds to four other carbon atoms in a tetrahedral geometry. **(b)** In graphite, carbon atoms are arranged in sheets. Within each sheet, the atoms are covalently bonded to one another by a network of sigma and pi bonds. Neighboring sheets are held together by dispersion forces.

Graphite is another solid form of pure carbon where atoms are covalently bonded to each other. In graphite, however, four bonds are not formed, but only two and only in the horizontal plane. Between each plane, or "sheet," are delocalized sigma and pi bonds allowing some electrons to move throughout the material. Thus, graphite can conduct an electrical charge. The weak dispersion forces between the layers of graphite allow the sheets to move past one another explaining why graphite is a good lubricant.

Silicon dioxide and the silicates are also network covalent solids. The networked structure is held together by covalent bonds. Various forms are also observed, such as the diamond-like network in quartz, and the graphite-like network in mica.

## Additional Practice

*Self-Assessment Quiz Questions Q1, Q2, Q3, Q4, Q5, Q6, Q7, Q8, Q9, Q10, Q11, Q12, Q13, Q14, and Q15*

*Problems 10, 15, 16, 17, 19, 22, 23, 29, 31, 32, 49, 54, 60, 62, 67, 72, 79, 80, 84, 94, 105, 119, 120, 125, and 150*

## Practice AP® Test Questions

1. Solid KBr dissolves in water to form a solution of potassium bromide, KBr(*aq*). The predominate intermolecular force between the bromide ions and water molecules is:

   A) Ion–ion

   B) Ion–dipole

   C) Hydrogen bond

   D) Dipole–dipole

2. Given the following information:

   |                      | $CH_4$ | $SiH_4$ | $GeH_4$ | $SnH_4$ |
   |----------------------|--------|---------|---------|---------|
   | MW (g/mol)           | 16     | 32      | 76      | 122     |
   | Boiling Point (°C)   | −162   | −112    | −88     | −52     |

   Which statement *best* explains the increase in boiling point of the four compounds from $CH_4$ to $SnH_4$.

   A) The strength of London dispersion forces increases due to an increased number of electrons making the electron cloud more polarizable. The increase in the strength of the London dispersion forces between molecules requires an increase in energy to separate the molecules.

   B) When the molecular weight increases an increase in energy is needed to get the heavier molecules moving faster.

   C) The strength of London dispersion forces and dipole–dipole interactions increases thus requiring more energy to separate the molecules.

   D) The strength of London dispersion forces increases and the molecular weight increases. Both factors are required to explain the increase in the boiling point.

3. Diethyl ether has a boiling point of 34.5 °C and 1-butanol has a boiling point of 117 °C. Both compounds have the same molecular weight and same molecular formula ($C_4H_{10}O$). Which statement best explains the difference in boiling points?

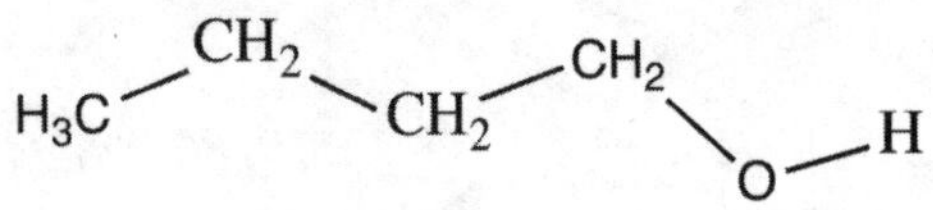

1-butanol 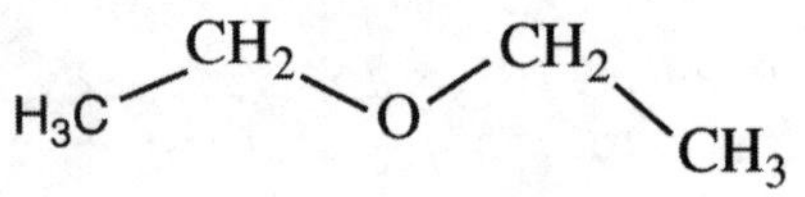                                    Diethyl ether

A) The strength of London dispersion forces is greater in 1-butanol.

B) Oxygen is toward the end of the structure in 1-butanol and in the middle of the structure in diethyl ether.

C) The 1-butanol molecules can form strong hydrogen bonds with other 1-butanol molecules. Diethyl ether forms dipole–dipole intermolecular forces, which are not as strong as hydrogen bonds.

D) The diethyl ether molecules have more hydrogen atoms in place to form strong hydrogen bonds with other diethyl ether molecules. 1-butanol also forms hydrogen bonds, but not as many as diethyl ether.

4. Which drawing best indicates where hydrogen bonding occurs in methylamine, $CH_3NH_2$?

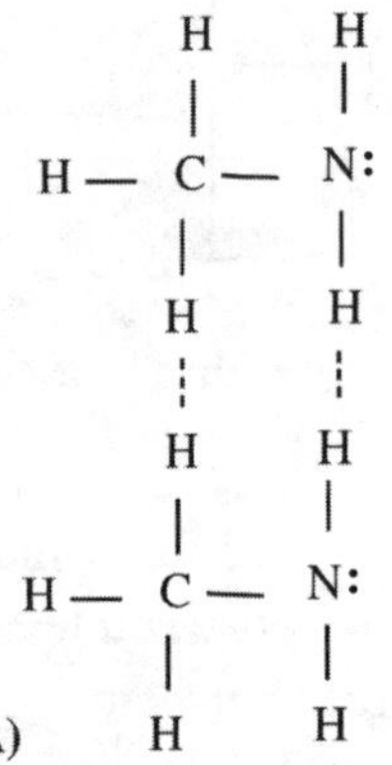

A)

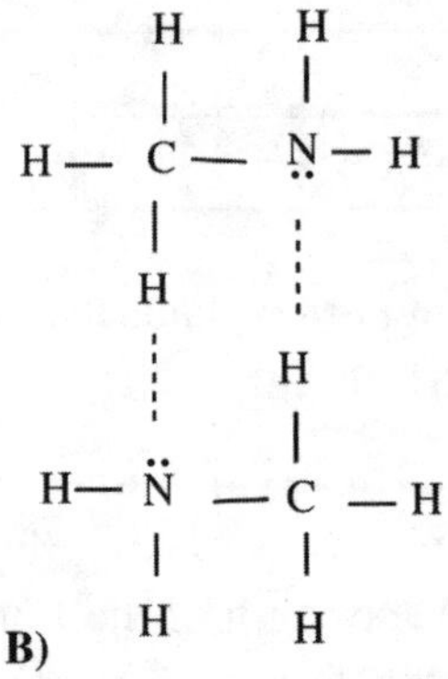

B)

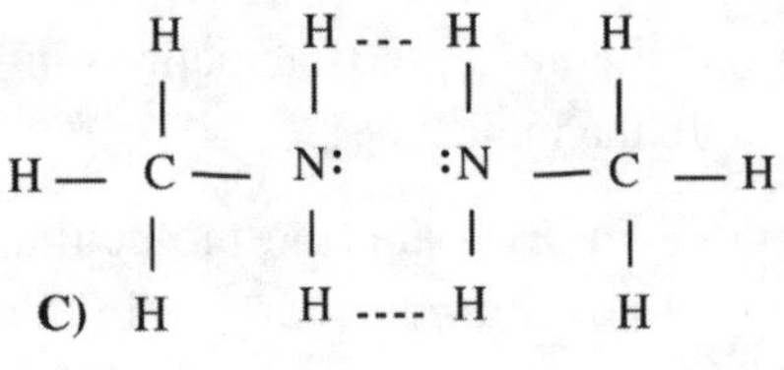

C)

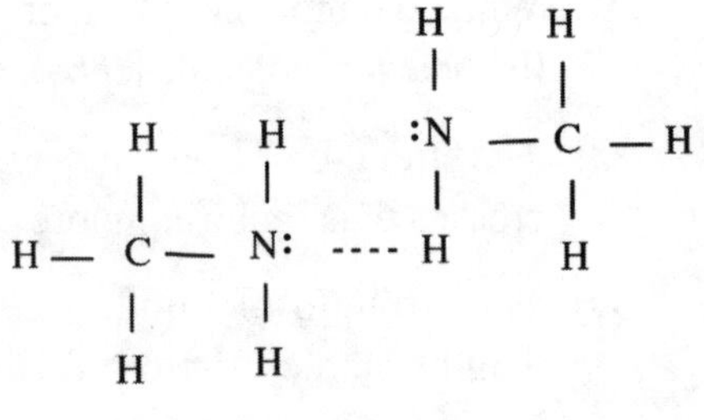

D)

5. The graph below plots the vapor pressure of methanol as a function of temperature. Estimate the normal boiling point of methanol.

A) 20 °C

B) 50 °C

C) 62 °C

D) 72 °C

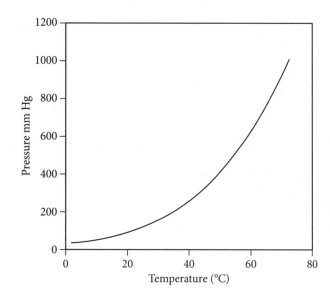

# CHAPTER 12

# SOLUTIONS

Solutions are all around us. Normally, we only think of solutions as aqueous, but the air we breathe is a solution of mostly oxygen in nitrogen. In this chapter properties of solutions will be addressed. A majority of this chapter is not in the AP curriculum, but some of what is discussed here may have been addressed in an earlier course, including molality and colligative properties. The primary sections pertaining to AP material are:

12.1  **Thirsty Solutions: Why You Shouldn't Drink Seawater**

12.2  **Types of Solutions and Solubility**

12.3  **Energetics of Solution Formation**

12.4  **Solution Equilibrium and Factors Affecting Solubility**

12.5  **Expressing Solution Concentration**

12.8  **Colloids**

## Specific Learning Objectives Addressed in This Chapter:

**Learning objective 2.8** The student can draw and/or interpret representations of solutions that show the interactions between the solute and solvent. [*See* **SP 1.1, 1.2, 6.4**]

**Learning objective 2.12** The student can qualitatively analyze data regarding real gases to identify deviations from ideal behavior and relate these to molecular interactions. [*See* **SP 5.1, 6.5**]

**Learning objective 6.24** The student can analyze the enthalpic and entropic changes associated with the dissolution of a salt, using particulate level interactions and representations. [*See* **SP 1.4, 7.1**]

## Specific Science Practices Addressed in This Chapter:

**Science Practice 1:** The student can use representations and models to communicate scientific phenomena and solve scientific problems.

> 1.1  The student can *create representations and models* of natural or man-made phenomena and systems in the domain.

1.2 The student can *describe representations and models* of natural or man-made phenomena and systems in the domain.

1.4 The student can *use representations and models* to analyze situations or solve problems qualitatively and quantitatively.

**Science Practice 5:** The student can perform data analysis and evaluation of evidence.

5.1 The student can *analyze data* to identify patterns or relationships.

**Science Practice 6:** The student can work with scientific explanations and theories.

6.4 The student can *make claims and predictions about natural phenomena* based on scientific theories and models.

6.5 The student can *evaluate alternative scientific explanations.*

**Science Practice 7:** The student is able to connect and relate knowledge across various scales, concepts, and representations in and across domains.

7.1 The student can *connect phenomena and models* across spatial and temporal scales.

## Concepts and Vocabulary to Review:

# Thirsty Solutions: Why You Shouldn't Drink Seawater     Section 12.1

Some basic vocabulary of solutions includes the terms *solute* and *solvent*. These terms apply to any type of solution, although most think of solutions as aqueous. *Solute* is the substance in the minority and is being dissolved (often but not necessarily a solid) and the *solvent* is the majority component and is doing the dissolving. For instance, in salt water, water is the solvent and salt is the solute. If two substances are soluble in each other, they will naturally start to mix when they are put together until they are uniformly distributed in each other. An example of a liquid in liquid solution is alcohol in water.

# Types of Solutions and Solubility     Section 12.2

For an aqueous solution the solvent is water, but the solute can be a solid, liquid, or gas. In the air we breathe, nitrogen is the solvent and oxygen and carbon dioxide are the solutes. The gases in the air mix due to the molecule's random motions and *entropy*, which is a measure of the energy randomization in a system. Each of the components and kinetic energy will disperse or spread out over the largest possible volume. This tendency explains why kinetic energy will disperse from a hot object to a cold object.

**Table 12.1**  Common Types of Solutions

| Solution Phase | Solute Phase | Solvent Phase | Example |
|---|---|---|---|
| Gaseous solution | Gas | Gas | Air (mainly oxygen and nitrogen) |
| Liquid solution | Gas<br>Liquid<br>Solid | Liquid<br>Liquid<br>Liquid | Club soda ($CO_2$ and water)<br>Vodka (ethanol and water)<br>Seawater (salt and water) |
| Solid solution | Solid | Solid | Brass (copper and zinc) and other alloys |

When a substance does dissolve, it is said to be *soluble*; if a substance does not dissolve, it is said to be *insoluble*. This is not a strict definition, as a tiny amount will dissolve even for "insoluble" substances. The amount of the solute dissolving depends mostly on the interaction of intermolecular forces between the substances. There are several types of intermolecular forces whose interactions are reviewed in the diagram below.

**Intermolecular Forces**

These forces may contribute to or oppose the formation of a solution.

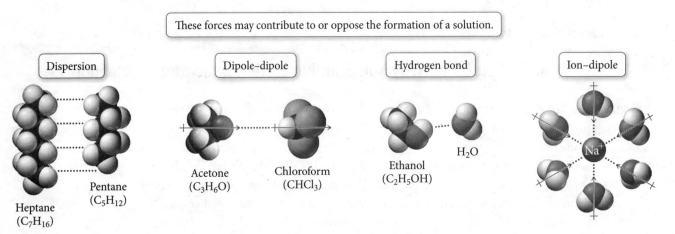

Dispersion — Heptane ($C_7H_{16}$), Pentane ($C_5H_{12}$)

Dipole–dipole — Acetone ($C_3H_6O$), Chloroform ($CHCl_3$)

Hydrogen bond — Ethanol ($C_2H_5OH$), $H_2O$

Ion–dipole — $Na^+$

**Figure 12.1  Intermolecular Forces Involved in Solutions**

The interactions between the solute and solvent molecules determine if a solution forms. If the interactions between the solute and solvent are greater than or equal to the interaction of the solvent with itself or the solute with itself, a solution will form. For instance, water is a polar molecule and has hydrogen-bonding interactions with other water molecules. Ammonia is a polar molecule and has hydrogen-bonding interactions with other ammonia molecules as well. When combined, ammonia and water will also form hydrogen bonding with each other and therefore will dissolve in each other forming an ammonia–water solution.

When all three interactions are the same (e.g., water-water; ammonia-ammonia; ammonia-water), the substances are called *miscible*.

In the case of water and hexane, water forms hydrogen bonds with other water molecules, and hexane molecules are attracted to other hexane molecules by dispersion forces. The water does not form hydrogen bonds with the hexane and the amount of energy needed to pull the water molecules away from each other to form a solution is too great. A solution does not form. In contrast, hexane with dispersion forces will dissolve in heptane, which also has dispersion forces. Be careful of using the phrase "like dissolves like," because it is never accepted on the AP test as it is not a complete enough explanation for why two substances dissolve in each other. The interactions must be fully described as in the examples above. Although students will say water is the universal solvent, and it is very diverse, it does not dissolve everything.

## Energetics of Solution Formation    Section 12.3

When solutions form, the process can be exothermic or endothermic. It depends on the relationship of the energy required to pull the solute particles apart, the energy required to pull the solvent particles apart, and the energy released when the solute and solvent interact to make the solution. Pulling the solute ($\Delta H_{solute}$) and solvent ($\Delta H_{solvent}$) particles apart always requires energy, whereas the bonding of the solute and solvent always releases energy. In an endothermic enthalpy of solution ($\Delta H_{soln}$), the energy released is less than the magnitude of solute ($\Delta H_{solute}$) and solvent ($\Delta H_{solvent}$). In an exothermic enthalpy of solution, the energy released is greater than the magnitude of solute ($\Delta H_{solute}$) and solvent ($\Delta H_{solvent}$). If the energy released is equal to the magnitude of solute ($\Delta H_{solute}$) and solvent ($\Delta H_{solvent}$), entropy will drive the mixing of the solution.

*Heat of hydration* is the energy change when one mole of gaseous solute ions is dissolved in water. Using heat of hydration, the solution process can be written as $\Delta H_{soln} = \Delta H_{solute} + \Delta H_{hydration}$. The $\Delta H_{solute}$ is always endothermic (positive) and the $\Delta H_{hydration}$ is always exothermic (negative).

$|\Delta H_{solute}| < |\Delta H_{hydration}|$ results in an exothermic enthalpy of solution and the temperature of the solution will increase.

$|\Delta H_{solute}| > |\Delta H_{hydration}|$ results in an endothermic enthalpy of solution and the temperature of the solution will decrease.

$|\Delta H_{solute}| \approx |\Delta H_{hydration}|$ results in an isothermic enthalpy of solution and the temperature of the solution does not change.

**Energetics of Solution Formation**

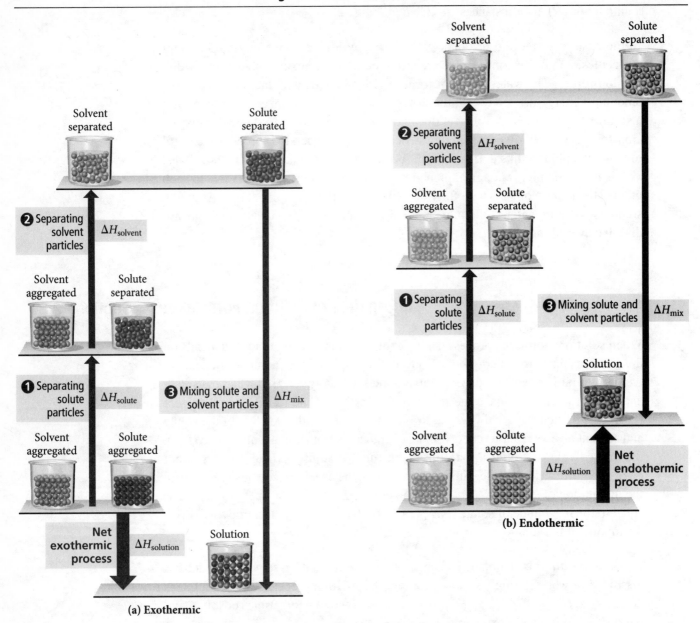

**Figure 12.2 Energetics of the Solution Process**    (a) When $\Delta H_{mix}$ is greater in magnitude than the sum of $\Delta H_{solute}$ and $\Delta H_{solvent}$, the heat of solution is negative (exothermic). (b) When $\Delta H_{mix}$ is smaller in magnitude than the sum of $\Delta H_{solute}$ and $\Delta H_{solvent}$, the heat of solution is positive (endothermic).

## Section 12.4    Solution Equilibrium and Factors Affecting Solubility

The solvation process can eventually reach equilibrium. To reach this state, there needs to be both undissolved solute and dissolved solute. When the rate of dissolving of the solute equals the rate of recrystallization of the solute, the system has reached dynamic equilibrium. In an equation, a double arrow is used to indicate the equilibrium state.

## Solution Equilibrium

| NaCl(s) | $NaCl(s) \longrightarrow Na^+(aq) + Cl^-(aq)$ | $NaCl(s) \rightleftharpoons Na^+(aq) + Cl^-(aq)$ |
|---|---|---|
| When sodium chloride is first added to water, sodium and chloride ions begin to dissolve into the water. | As the solution becomes more concentrated, some of the sodium and chloride ions can begin to recrystallize as solid sodium chloride. | When the rate of dissolution equals the rate of recrystallization, dynamic equilibrium has been reached. |

Rate of dissolution > Rate of recrystallization

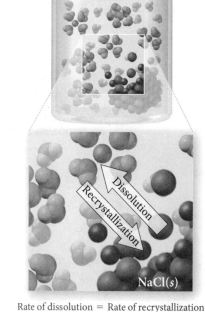

Rate of dissolution = Rate of recrystallization

**(a) Initial**          **(b) Dissolving**          **(c) Dynamic equilibrium**

**Figure 12.3 Dissolution of NaCl**    (a) When sodium chloride is first added to water, sodium and chloride ions dissolve into the water. (b) As the solution becomes more concentrated, some of the sodium and chloride ions recrystallize as solid sodium chloride. (c) When the rate of dissolution equals the rate of recrystallization, dynamic equilibrium is reached.

Solutions with the maximum amount of dissolved particles are called *saturated*. If additional solute is added to a saturated solution, no *net* dissolving will occur since the system is in dynamic equilibrium. Unsaturated solutions do not have the maximum amount of solute dissolved and if additional solute is added, the additional solute will dissolve.

Supersaturated solutions contain more than the maximum amount of dissolved solute. These are normally formed by slowly cooling a saturated solution. These solutions are not in a state of dynamic equilibrium (no excess solute can be present), are thus unstable and if disturbed, some solute will crystallize out, or in the case of a liquid solute, form a separate layer.

**Figure 12.4  Precipitation from a Supersaturated Solution**    When a small piece of solid sodium acetate is added to a supersaturated sodium acetate solution, the excess solid precipitates out of the solution.

The amount of solute dissolved in a saturated solution is affected by temperature. For most solids, the amount that can dissolve will increase with increasing temperature. For gases, the opposite is true; less gas dissolves as the temperature increases. This is easily seen in soda pop. As a soda warms, the soda releases more of the dissolved carbon dioxide and eventually goes flat.

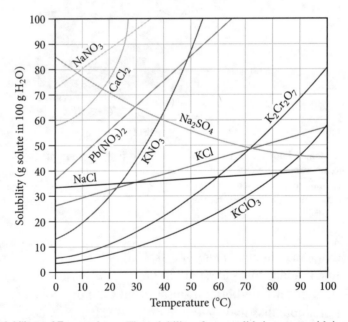

**Figure 12.5  Solubility and Temperature**    The solubility of most solids increases with increasing temperature.

Pressure also changes the solubility of gases in solution. The greater the pressure of the gas above the solution, the greater the amount of gas dissolved. When a soda-pop can is opened, the pressure of the $CO_2$ on the liquid in the can of soda immediately decreases and in response, some of the $CO_2$ comes out of the solution. This relationship is known as Henry's Law.

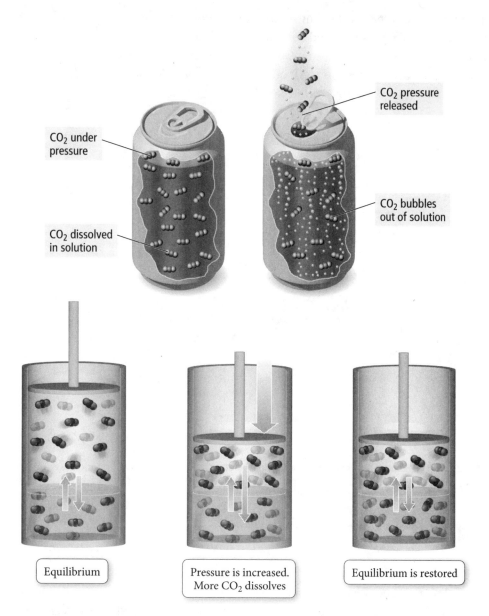

**Figure 12.6  Soda Fizz**   The bubbling that occurs when a can of soda is opened results from the reduced pressure of carbon dioxide over the liquid. At lower pressure, the carbon dioxide is less soluble and bubbles out of solution.

One important process used to purify a solid is recrystallization. A saturated solution is formed at a higher temperature and as the solution cools, the excess crystal comes out as a more pure sample of crystal.

## Expressing Solution Concentration    Section 12.5

The AP curriculum only emphasizes molarity as a concentration unit. *Molarity (M)* is the number of moles of solute per liter of solution. $M = \dfrac{\text{moles solute}}{\text{liters of solution}}$. Students must explain in writing how to make a solution of any amount and any concentration.

Two important terms used about solutions are *dilute* and *concentrated*. *Dilute solutions* have very little solute and *concentrated solutions* have large amounts of solute relative to the amount of solution. Obviously, these are relative terms and do not have exact definitions in chemistry. AP questions usually give actual concentration values, for example, 0.1M for a dilute solution and greater than 1M for a concentrated solution.

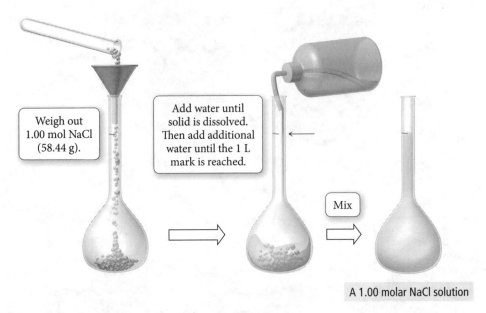

**Figure 12.7  Preparing a Solution of Known Concentration**    To make a 1 M NaCl solution, we add 1 mol of the solid to a flask and dilute with water to make 1 L of solution.

## Section 12.8    Colloids

Some mixtures are not true solutions. Colloidal dispersions are an example. Finely divided particles between 1 nm and 1000 nm, which are dispersed in the medium, are *colloids*. Examples include soapy water, fog, smoke in the air, whipped cream, milk, blood, and opal. AP has rarely addressed colloids.

*Brownian motion* is the random motion of particles suspended in a medium. This motion is caused by collisions between the particles and molecules of the medium.

Colloids can be identified by the Tyndall effect. If a light beam passes through a colloidal suspension, light is scattered. When light comes through a window and you see dust in the air, this is the Tyndall effect.

**Table 12.2**   Types of Colloidal Dispersions

| Classification | Dispersing Substance (Solute-like) | Dispersing Medium (Solvent-like) | | Example |
|---|---|---|---|---|
| Aerosol | Liquid | Gas | | Fog (water droplets in air) |
| Solid aerosol | Solid | Gas | | Smoke (ash in air) |
| Foam | Gas | Liquid | | Whipped cream (air bubbles in butterfat) |
| Emulsion | Liquid | Liquid | | Milk (milk fat globules in water) |
| Solid emulsion | Liquid | Solid | | Opal (water in silica glass) |

### Additional Practice

*Self-Assessment Quiz Questions Q1, Q2, Q3, Q4, Q8, Q10, Q12, and Q15*
*Problems 5, 7, 10, 11, 12, 13, 14, 26, 29, 33, 35, 43, 46, 48, 61a, 134, and 135*

### Practice AP® Test Questions

1.  A laboratory procedure requires 0.270 mole of methanol, $CH_3OH$ to be added as a solvent. What volume of 1.50 M $CH_3OH$ is needed to attain this number of moles?

    A)  5.55 mL

    B)  45.0 mL

    C)  405 mL

    D)  180 mL

2.  Which substance is least soluble in water?

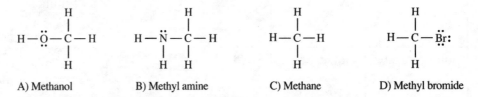

    A) Methanol         B) Methyl amine         C) Methane         D) Methyl bromide

3.  The reason for your choice in Test Question #2 is:

    A)  Methanol forms the strongest hydrogen bonding with the water molecules.

    B)  Methyl amine forms the strongest hydrogen bonding with the water molecules.

    C)  Methane exhibits London dispersion forces with water molecules.

    D)  Methyl bromide has the highest molar mass.

Questions 4 and 5 refer to the following statement. When solid ammonium chloride dissolves in water, the solution becomes cool.

4.  For such a process, which statement best describes the reason why dissolving occurs spontaneously?

    A)  Enthalpy decreases.

    B)  Enthalpy increases.

    C)  Vapor pressure decreases.

    D)  Entropy increases.

5.  Which double-sided arrow in the following diagram represents the change in enthalpy of solution, $\Delta H_{solution}$? The length of the double-sided arrows are proportional to enthalpy changes involved when a solid dissolves to form a solution.

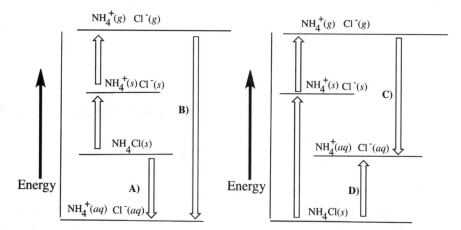

A) A

B) B

C) C

D) D

# 13

# CHEMICAL KINETICS

This chapter has many places for students to interpret data and analyze graphs which are addressed in the science practices and learning objectives associated with this chapter. This whole chapter addresses Big Idea 4 on rates of reactions. Pay particular attention to analyzing graphs and data to support a claim such as a rate law. To go along with this chapter, students should do a lab experiment determining rate laws. Laboratory experiments involving Beer's law and laboratory experiments using colorimetry are useful for developing a better understanding of kinetics. The sections of the most importance in the textbook are below:

13.2 **The Rate of a Chemical Reaction**

13.3 **The Rate Law: The Effect of Concentration on a Reaction Rate**

13.4 **The Integrated Rate Law: The Dependence of Concentration on Time**

13.5 **The Effect of Temperature on Reaction Rate**

13.6 **Reaction Mechanisms**

13.7 **Catalysis**

## Specific Learning Objectives Addressed in This Chapter:

**Learning objective 3.1** Students can translate among macroscopic observations of change, chemical equations, and particle views. [*See* **SP 1.5, 7.1**]

**Learning objective 4.1** The student is able to design and/or interpret the results of an experiment regarding the factors (i.e., temperature, concentration, surface area) that may influence the rate of a reaction. [*See* **SP 4.2, 5.1**]

**Learning objective 4.2** The student is able to analyze concentration vs. time data to determine the rate law for a zeroth-, first-, or second-order reaction. [*See* **SP 5.1**]

**Learning objective 4.3** The student is able to connect the half-life of a reaction to the rate constant of a first-order reaction and justify the use of this relation in terms of the reaction being a first-order reaction. [*See* **SP 2.1, 2.2**]

**Learning objective 4.4** The student is able to connect the rate law for an elementary reaction to the frequency and success of molecular collisions, including connecting the frequency and success to the order and rate constant, respectively. [*See* **SP 7.1**]

**Learning objective 4.5** The student is able to explain the difference between collisions that convert reactants to products and those that do not in terms of energy distributions and molecular orientation. [*See* **SP 6.2**]

**Learning objective 4.6** The student is able to use representations of the energy profile for an elementary reaction (from the reactants, through the transition state, to the products) to make qualitative predictions regarding the relative temperature dependence of the reaction rate. [*See* **SP 1.4**, **6.4**]

**Learning objective 4.7** The student is able to evaluate alternative explanations, as expressed by reaction mechanisms, to determine which are consistent with data regarding the overall rate of a reaction, and data that can be used to infer the presence of a reaction intermediate. [*See* **SP 6.5**]

**Learning objective 4.8** The student can translate among reaction energy profile representations, particulate representations, and symbolic representations (chemical equations) of a chemical reaction occurring in the presence and absence of a catalyst. [*See* **SP 1.5**]

**Learning objective 4.9** The student is able to explain changes in reaction rates arising from the use of acid-base catalysts, surface catalysts, or enzyme catalysts, including selecting appropriate mechanisms with or without the catalyst present. [*See* **SP 6.2, 7.2**]

## Specific Science Practices Addressed in This Chapter:

**Science Practice 1:** The student can use representations and models to communicate scientific phenomena and solve scientific problems.

1.4  The student can *use representations and models* to analyze situations or solve problems qualitatively and quantitatively.

1.5  The student can *re-express key elements* of natural phenomena across multiple representations in the domain.

**Science Practice 2:** The student can use mathematics appropriately.

2.1  The student can *justify the selection of a mathematical routine* to solve problems.

2.2  The student can *apply mathematical routines* to quantities that describe natural phenomena.

**Science Practice 4:** The student can plan and implement data collection strategies in relation to a particular scientific question.

4.2  The student can *design a plan* for collecting data to answer a particular scientific question.

**Science Practice 5:** The student can perform data analysis and evaluation of evidence.

5.1  The student can *analyze data* to identify patterns or relationships.

**Science Practice 6:** The student can work with scientific explanations and theories.

> 6.2 The student can *construct explanations of phenomena based on evidence* produced through scientific practices.
>
> 6.4 The student can *make claims and predictions about natural phenomena* based on scientific theories and models.
>
> 6.5 The student can *evaluate alternative scientific explanations*.

**Science Practice 7:** The student is able to connect and relate knowledge across various scales, concepts, and representations in and across domains.

> 7.1 The student can *connect phenomena and models* across spatial and temporal scales.
>
> 7.2 The student can *connect concepts* in and across domain(s) to generalize or extrapolate in and/or across enduring understandings and/or big ideas.

**Concepts and Vocabulary to Review:**

Section 13.2

## The Rate of a Chemical Reaction

As a reaction proceeds, reactants decrease as products increase, although this depends on the direction the equation is written relative to the initial concentrations of reactants and products. When recording rates for reactants a negative sign is in front of the ratio of the change in concentration with change in time and for products the sign is positive. Rates are measured using changes in concentration such as molarity over the change in time.

In a reaction if the rate of change of one species is known, using stoichiometry, the rate of change of all other species can be determined. Rates of change should be able to be determined from a graph by taking the tangent of the curve of concentration with time.

In Figure 13.1 on the following page, the upward graphical curve represents a product species starting at zero, although products do not always start at zero in every reaction, and increase with time whereas the reactants start with higher concentration and decrease with time, forming a downward curve on a typical concentration against time graph. On the graph the exact rate which is called an instantaneous rate can be determined at any point by drawing a tangent line through the point and then determining the slope of the tangent line. By contrast, an average rate is determined by the rate of change over a time interval. It is similar to saying you average 50 km/hr or saying at this moment we are going 65 km/hr.

Generally we can relate the measure rates for different species using:

$$aA + bB \rightarrow cC + dD$$

$$\text{Rate} = -\frac{1}{a}\frac{\Delta[A]}{\Delta t} = -\frac{1}{b}\frac{\Delta[B]}{\Delta t} = +\frac{1}{c}\frac{\Delta[C]}{\Delta t} = +\frac{1}{d}\frac{\Delta[D]}{\Delta t}$$

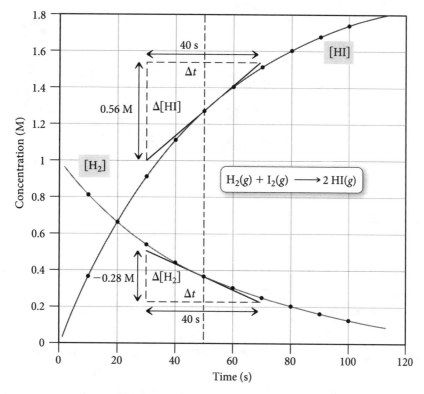

**Figure 13.1  Reactant and Product Concentrations as a Function of Time**   The graph shows the concentration of one of the reactants ($H_2$) and the product (HI) as a function of time. The other reactant ($I_2$) is omitted for clarity.

Measuring reaction rates when either a reactant or product is a colored solution is often done with spectroscopy. The reaction can be monitored by measuring the change in intensity of the light absorbed. A variety of methods can be used to determine the concentration by taking samples at intervals. Gas chromatography, mass

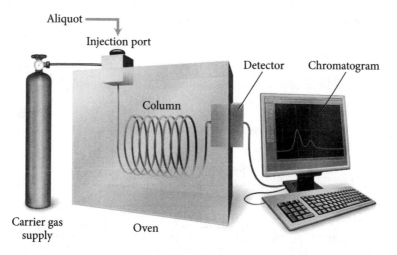

**Figure 13.2  The Gas Chromatograph**   In a gas chromatograph (GC), a sample of the reaction mixture, or aliquot, is injected into a specially constructed column. Because of their characteristic physical and chemical properties, different components of the mixture pass through the column at different rates and thus exit at different times. As each component leaves the column, it is identified electronically and a chromatogram is recorded. The area under each peak in the chromatogram is proportional to the amount of one particular component in the sample mixture.

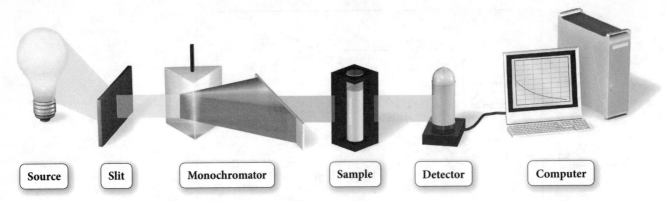

**Figure 13.3  The Spectrometer**   In a spectrometer, light of a specific wavelength is passed through the sample and the intensity of the transmitted light—which depends on how much light is absorbed by the sample—is measured and recorded.

| Source | Slit | Monochromator | Sample | Detector | Computer |

spectroscopy, or titrations are some techniques which can be used so long as the measurement does not take a significant time relative to the reaction time. Figures 13.2 and 13.3 show the use of the gas chromatograph and the spectrometer.

## Section 13.3    The Rate Law: The Effect of Concentration on a Reaction Rate

An equation representing the rate of the reaction as it relates to the concentration of reactants(s) is called the rate law. The rate law is determined experimentally and is different for different reactions although it has the basic formula, rate $= k[A]^n$, where $k$ is called the rate constant, A is a reactant species, and $n$ is the order.

Before $k$ can be calculated, the value(s) of $n$ must be determined. Experimental evidence where a reactant concentration is changed while other reactant concentrations remain unchanged allows for the determination of the effect of each reactant on the rate, through the order, $n$. If there are several reactants, a whole series of reaction rate determinations must be carried out. The evidence of the change of rate allows for the determination of the order ($n$).

- If $n$ is zero, it indicates changing the concentration of this particular reactant has no effect on the rate of reaction. For one reactant the rate law would be rate $= k[A]^0$ or rate $= k$.

  - If the following was the experimental evidence, $n = 0$.

    Zero Order ($n = 0$)

    | $[A]$(M) | Initial Rate (M/s) |
    |---|---|
    | 0.10 | 0.015 |
    | 0.20 | 0.015 |
    | 0.40 | 0.015 |

- If $n$ is one, it indicates a change in concentration of this reactant will result in a proportional change on the rate. For instance if the concentration is doubled, the rate will double, or if the concentration is halved, the reaction rate halves. For a one-reactant system, the rate law would be rate $= k[A]^1$ or rate $= k[A]$.

- If the following was the experimental evidence, $n = 1$.

| [A] (M) | Initial Rate (M/s) |
|---------|--------------------|
| 0.10    | 0.015              |
| 0.20    | 0.030              |
| 0.40    | 0.060              |

- If $n$ is two, it indicates a change in concentration of this reactant will result in the rate changing with a square function. If the concentration is doubled, the rate will increase by $2^2$ or a factor of 4. If the concentration is tripled, the rate will increase by $3^2$ or a factor of 9. For a one-reactant system, the rate law would be rate $= k[A]^2$.

  - If the following was the experimental evidence, $n = 2$.

Second Order ($n = 2$)

| [A] (M) | Initial Rate (M/s) |
|---------|--------------------|
| 0.10    | 0.015              |
| 0.20    | 0.060              |
| 0.40    | 0.240              |

These orders can also be determined graphically. In a zero order reaction, the concentration changes as the rate changes therefore, a plot of concentration versus time results in a linear relationship as shown in Figure 13.4 below. The slope of the line is equal to $-k$, where $k$ is the rate constant. In a first-order reaction, the plot to get a straight line is ln[A] versus time. In this case, the slope of the line is again equal to $-k$ (this is the way usually shown on the AP test for first-order reactions). When graphing a second order reaction, the plot to get the linear relationship is $1/[A]$ versus time. The line will have positive slope, therefore the slope $= k$.

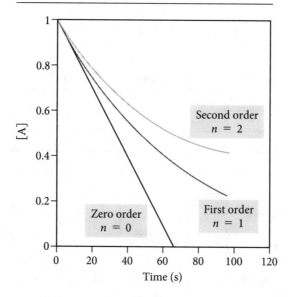

**Reactant Concentration versus Time**

**Figure 13.4  Reactant Concentration as a Function of Time for Different Reaction Orders**

When there is more than one reactant, each reactant must have its order determined from experimental evidence. For the reaction $aA + bB \rightarrow cC + dD$ the rate law would be Rate $= k[A]^m[B]^n$.

The total reaction order is the sum of all the reactant orders. If there are two reactants A and B, and each has an order of 1, the total order would be 2.

Section 13.4

# The Integrated Rate Law: The Dependence of Concentration on Time

As a reaction proceeds, we can determine a concentration at a certain time if the rate law is known. The integrated rate law on the AP Exam, which is also called the differential rate law in the Tro text, is dependent on the order of the reaction.

In a first-order reaction, remember the rate is proportional to the concentration as shown in $-\dfrac{\Delta[A]}{\Delta t} = k[A]$. To find a concentration at time $t$, the equation can be rearranged to $\dfrac{\ln([A]_t)}{[A]_0} = -kt$ or $\ln[A]_t = -kt + \ln[A]_0$. The subscript 0 is for original or beginning time. Taking data and making a graph to determine $k$ also allows you to determine concentrations at other times.

### Example 13.1

### The First-Order Integrated Rate Law: Using Graphical Analysis of Reaction Data

*Consider the equation for the decomposition of $SO_2Cl_2$:*

$$SO_2Cl_2(g) \rightarrow SO_2(g) + Cl_2(g)$$

*The concentration of $SO_2Cl_2$ was monitored at a fixed temperature as a function of time during the decomposition reaction, and the following data were tabulated:*

| Time (s) | $[SO_2Cl_2]$ (M) | Time (s) | $[SO_2Cl_2]$ (M) |
|---|---|---|---|
| 0 | 0.100 | 800 | 0.0793 |
| 100 | 0.0971 | 900 | 0.0770 |
| 200 | 0.0944 | 1000 | 0.0748 |
| 300 | 0.0917 | 1100 | 0.0727 |
| 400 | 0.0890 | 1200 | 0.0706 |
| 500 | 0.0865 | 1300 | 0.0686 |
| 600 | 0.0840 | 1400 | 0.0666 |
| 700 | 0.0816 | 1500 | 0.0647 |

*Show that the reaction is first order, and determine the rate constant for the reaction.*

## Solution

*In order to show that the reaction is first order, prepare a graph of $\ln[SO_2Cl_2]$ versus time as shown.*

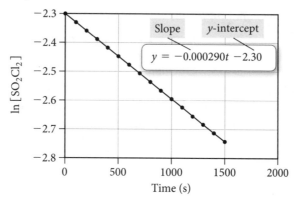

*The plot is linear, confirming that the reaction is indeed first order. To obtain the rate constant, fit the data to a line. The slope of the line will be equal to $-k$. Since the slope of the best fitting line (which is most easily determined on a graphing calculator or with spreadsheet software such as Microsoft Excel) is $-2.90 \times 10^{-4} s^{-1}$, the rate constant is therefore $+2.90 \times 10^{-4} s^{-1}$.*

This results in the general format observed in the graph shown below.

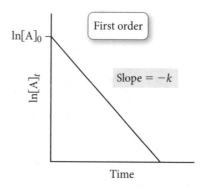

**Figure 13.5 First-Order Integrated Rate Law** For a first-order reaction, a plot of the natural log of the reactant concentration as a function of time yields a straight line. The slope of the line is equal to $-k$ and the y-intercept is $\ln[A]_0$.

At any point of time on the graph, the natural log of the concentration can be used to calculate the concentration. Plotting data on other types of graphs using linear or exponential scales may provide useful information.

For a second order reaction, the concentration time equation is different: $\dfrac{1}{[A]_t} = kt + \dfrac{1}{[A]_0}$. Again, using data to make a graph is an important skill and is shown in Example 13.2.

## Example 13.2

### The Second-Order Integrated Rate Law: Using Graphical Analysis of Reaction Data

*Consider the equation for the decomposition of $NO_2$:*

$$NO_2(g) \rightarrow NO(g) + O(g)$$

*The concentration of $NO_2$ is monitored at a fixed temperature as a function of time during the decomposition reaction and the data tabulated in the margin at right. Show by graphical analysis that the reaction is not first order and that it is second order. Determine the rate constant for the reaction.*

### Solution

*In order to show that the reaction is not first order, prepare a graph of $[NO_2]$ versus time as shown.*

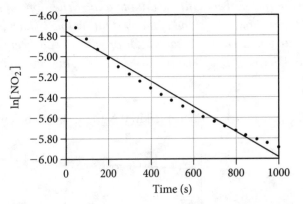

*The plot is not linear (the straight line does not fit the data points), confirming that the reaction is not first order. In order to show that the reaction is second order, prepare a graph of $1/[NO_2]$ versus time as shown.*

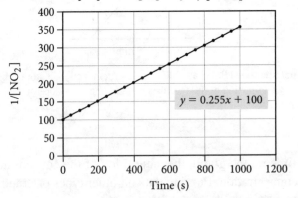

*This graph is linear (the data points fit well to a straight line), confirming that the reaction is indeed second order. To obtain the rate constant, determine the slope of the best fitting line. The slope is $0.255\ M^{-1} \cdot s^{-1}$; therefore, the rate constant is $0.255\ M^{-1} \cdot s^{-1}$.*

The second-order reaction then can be summarized to look like the graph below.

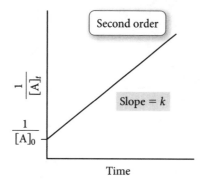

**Figure 13.6  Second-Order Integrated Rate Law**   For a second-order reaction, a plot of the inverse of the reactant concentration as a function of time yields a straight line. The slope of the line is equal to $k$ and the $y$-intercept is $1/[A]_0$.

For a zero-order reaction where the rate law is rate $= k$, the integrated rate law is $[A]_t = [A]_0 - kt$. From data a graph would have the appearance of the figure below.

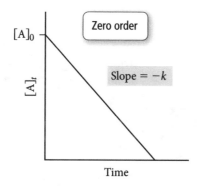

**Figure 13.7  Zero-Order Integrated Rate Law**   For a zero-order reaction, a plot of the reactant concentration as a function of time yields a straight line. The slope of the line is equal to $-k$ and the $y$-intercept is $[A]_0$.

The negative slope of the line indicates the *slope* $= -k$. In a problem, you may have to take data and try several graphs to determine which gives a linear relationship to determine the order, write an appropriate rate law, and determine the value of $k$ (with correct units!).

The half-life of a reaction occurs when half of the initial amount of reactant reacts. The concentration time equation can be used but if it is known to be at the half-life $(t_{1/2})$, then the half-life equation can be used. The most common equation used is for first-order reaction since all nuclear reactions are first order. Graphically, it is observed that the length of each half-life for a first-order reaction is constant and independent of the concentration.

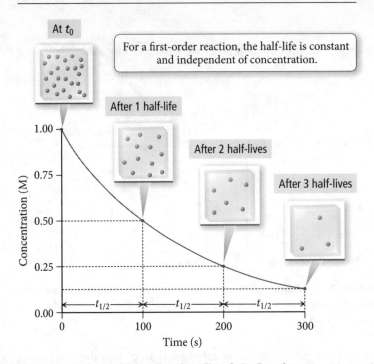

For a first-order reaction, the half-life is constant and independent of concentration.

At $t_0$

After 1 half-life

After 2 half-lives

After 3 half-lives

**Figure 13.8  Half-Life: Concentration versus Time for a First-Order Reaction**   For this reaction, the concentration decreases by one-half every 100 seconds ($t_{1/2} = 100$ s). The blue spheres represent reactant molecules (the products are omitted for clarity).

The following table summarizes the equations and relationships:

| Order of reaction and rate law | Units of $k$ (time unit is in seconds) | Concentration time equation | Relationship slope and $k$ | Half-life equation | Graph |
|---|---|---|---|---|---|
| 0 rate $= k$ | M/s or Ms$^{-1}$ | $[A]_t = -kt + [A]_0$ | slope $= -k$ | $t_{1/2} = \dfrac{[A]_0}{2k}$ | y-intercept $= [A]_0$ <br> Slope $= -k$ |
| 1 rate $= k[A]$ | s$^{-1}$ | $\dfrac{\ln([A]t)}{[A]_0} = -kt$ or <br> $\ln[A]_t = -kt + \ln[A]_0$ | slope $= -k$ | $t_{1/2} = \dfrac{0.693}{k}$ | y-intercept $= \ln[A]_0$ <br> Slope $= -k$ |
| 2 rate $= [A]^2$ | M$^{-1}$s$^{-1}$ | $\dfrac{1}{[A]_t} = kt + \dfrac{1}{[A]_0}$ | slope $= k$ | $t_{1/2} = \dfrac{1}{k[A]_0}$ | Slope $= k$ <br> y-intercept $= 1/[A]_0$ |

# The Effect of Temperature on Reaction Rate    Section 13.5

Students are not expected to solve the Arrhenius equation but are expected to understand how it indicates the temperature dependence for a reaction and the activation energy needed to reach the transition state for the reaction to proceed.

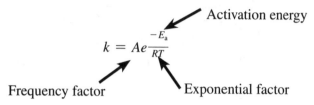

Activation energy

$$k = Ae^{\frac{-E_a}{RT}}$$

Frequency factor    Exponential factor

In the equation $E_a$ is the activation energy and $T$ is temperature.

## Activation Energy

$$2\,H_2(g) + O_2(g) \rightleftharpoons 2\,H_2O(g)$$

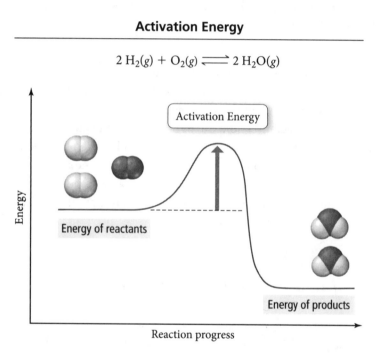

Activation Energy

Energy

Energy of reactants

Energy of products

Reaction progress

**Figure 13.9  The Activation Energy Barrier**    Even though the reaction is energetically favorable (the energy of the products is lower than that of the reactants), an input of energy is needed for the reaction to take place.

In the figure above, the number of molecules that can reach the activation energy and proceed to product formation depends on their energy, which is temperature dependent. When the reactants reach the top of the activation energy barrier, they are in a transition state which has a higher energy than either the reactants or products. The higher the activation energy, the slower the reaction is.

As the temperature increases, the number of reactant species with the energy needed to reach the activation energy increases. Supporting evidence is found in figure 13.11.

See figure 13.11. Notice this is not a temperature graph but the fraction of molecules with the energy needed. $T_2$ is the higher temperature as there is a greater fraction of reactant species with the activation energy. This data supports the claim that a reaction rate will proceed faster at a higher temperature.

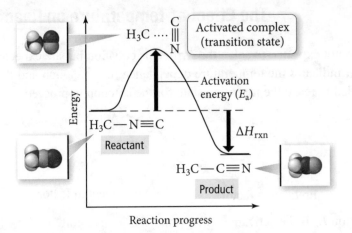

**Figure 13.10  The Activated Complex**   The reaction pathway includes a transitional state—the activated complex—that has a higher energy than either the reactant or the product.

Not only do reactants need to reach the activation energy, they also need to collide with each other and in the correct orientation. If the reactants are individual atoms, the orientation does not matter but when molecules are reacting orientation does matter. The parts of each reactant where the bond will form need to collide. How often the reactants actually collide with the right orientation is called the orientation factor. If this factor which is a fraction less than 1, is very small, the reaction will proceed slowly. A way to visualize this is to think of all the ways a puzzle piece can fit in, only one way of fitting it in will work. If 1 in 5 collisions are effective, the fraction is 0.20, if it is 1 in 4 then the fraction is 0.25.

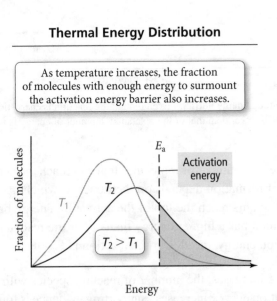

**Figure 13.11  Thermal Energy Distribution**   At any given temperature, the atoms or molecules in a gas sample have a range of energies. The higher the temperature, the wider the energy distribution and the greater the average energy. The fraction of molecules with enough energy to surmount the activation energy barrier and react (shaded regions) increases sharply as the temperature rises.

# Reaction Mechanisms     Section 13.6

Not only do the reactant molecules need to collide with each other, many reactions actually occur in a series of steps, with the collisions with the right intermediates in the steps of the reaction. Intermediates are products formed but are then used in another step. These steps are called the mechanism of a reaction. Each step is called an elementary step. By analyzing the steps in a reaction mechanism, the rate law and balanced equation can be determined. To determine the balanced equation, all the elementary steps are added together. Intermediates will cancel out of the balanced equation as they will be found as both reactant and product. For example,

Step 1    $A_2 + BC \rightarrow AB + AC$
Step 2    $AB + BC \rightarrow AC + B_2$
Total     $A_2 + 2BC \rightarrow 2AC + B_2$

Notice AB is a product in the first reaction and a reactant in the second reaction. AB is an intermediate which will cancel in the overall reaction. In each of the two elementary steps in this example species need to collide. These steps are then called bimolecular. If there is a reaction such as $A_2 \rightarrow 2A$, this reaction is unimolecular since there is only one reactant molecule, but two product molecules. Each step of the mechanism has a rate law.

Within a mechanism, one of the steps will be much slower than the other(s). This step is called the rate determining step and determines the overall rate law of the reaction. When looking at an energy diagram comparing each step in a two-step mechanism,

### Energy Diagram for a Two-Step Mechanism

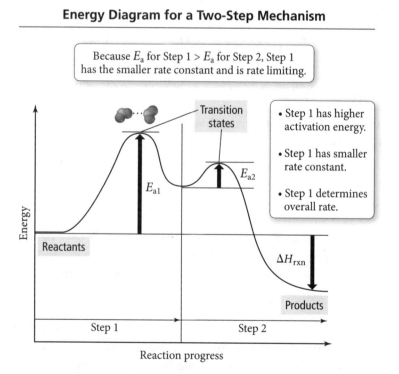

Because $E_a$ for Step 1 > $E_a$ for Step 2, Step 1 has the smaller rate constant and is rate limiting.

Transition states

- Step 1 has higher activation energy.
- Step 1 has smaller rate constant.
- Step 1 determines overall rate.

**Figure 13.12  Energy Diagram for a Two-Step Mechanism**

**Table 13.1**   Rate Laws for Elementary Steps

| Elementary Step | Molecularity | Rate Law |
|---|---|---|
| A $\rightarrow$ products | 1 | Rate $= k[A]$ |
| A + A $\rightarrow$ products | 2 | Rate $= k[A]^2$ |
| A + B $\rightarrow$ products | 2 | Rate $= k[A][B]$ |
| A + A + A $\rightarrow$ products | 3 (rare) | Rate $= k[A]^3$ |
| A + A + B $\rightarrow$ products | 3 (rare) | Rate $= k[A]^2[B]$ |
| A + B + C $\rightarrow$ products | 3 (rare) | Rate $= k[A][B][C]$ |

the slow step will have a higher activation energy. Another possible contributing factor to a slow step in a reaction mechanism is the orientation or the alignment of the molecules for a favorable collision.

The rate law of the slow step will be the rate law of the whole reaction.

Students will not be expected to write a mechanism but will be asked to evaluate the rate law for a mechanism from provided data.

If there is a fast step before the rate determining step, often that step will go to an equilibrium where the reaction starts going backward to reactants. The overall rate law will be added from the first fast equilibrium and the following slow step to form the overall rate law, keeping in mind intermediates do not appear in the rate law. For example

$$2\,NO(g) \underset{k_{-1}}{\overset{k_1}{\rightleftharpoons}} N_2O_2(g) \qquad\qquad \text{Fast}$$
$$H_2(g) + N_2O_2(g) \overset{k_2}{\rightarrow} H_2O(g) + N_2O(g) \qquad \text{Slow (rate limiting)}$$
$$N_2O(g) + H_2(g) \overset{k_3}{\rightarrow} N_2(g) + H_2O(g) \qquad \text{Fast}$$
$$\overline{2\,H_2(g) + 2\,NO(g) \rightarrow 2\,H_2O(g) + N_2(g)} \qquad \text{Overall}$$

The first step has 2NO and the second step has $H_2$. This will give a rate law of rate $= k[H_2][NO]^2$.

## Section 13.7    Catalysis

Reaction rates and mechanisms can be altered by catalysts. A catalyst is a chemical species which is added and is not consumed in the reaction but which speeds up a reaction by providing an alternate mechanism or pathway. The alternate mechanism has a lower activation energy than the original pathway of the reaction.

Homogeneous catalysts are in the same phase as the reactants whereas heterogeneous catalysts are in a different phase. Catalysts can be destructive to the environment such as the destruction of the ozone layer in the stratosphere by chlorine catalysts from chlorofluorocarbons or they can be advantageous such as in a catalytic converter in a car which contains solid catalysts like platinum and converts pollutants in the automobile exhaust into less harmful substances. An important group of catalysts are biological enzymes. These enzymes are large complex proteins which are very specific and which often only affect one reaction. For instance, there are several digestive enzymes and each breaks down a particular food into its constituent parts.

**Energy Diagram for Catalyzed and Uncatalyzed Pathways**

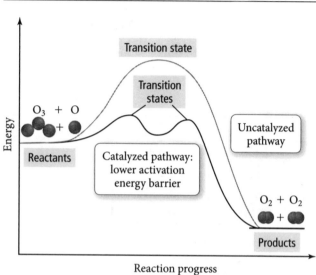

**Figure 13.13  Catalyzed and Uncatalyzed Decomposition of Ozone**   In the catalytic destruction of ozone, the activation barrier for the rate-limiting step is much lower than in the uncatalyzed process.

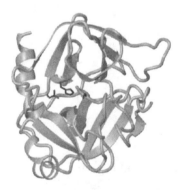

**Figure 13.14  Chymotrypsin, a Digestive Enzyme**   This model of chymotrypsin shows a section of a protein substrate in the active site.

## Additional Practice

*Self-Assessment Quiz Questions Q1, Q2, Q3, Q4, Q5, Q6, Q7, Q8, Q9, Q10, Q11, Q12, Q13, Q14, and Q15*

*Problems: 6, 9, 20, 25, 27, 31, 32, 33, 34, 35, 36, 38, 39, 41, 42, 43, 44, 47, 48, 49, 50, 51, 57, 58, 73, 74, 75, 76, 83, 93, 94, 118, 119, and 120*

## Practice AP® Test Questions

Use the following information to help answer Questions 1 and 2.

For the following, data were collected during a method of initial rates experiment for the gas phase reaction

$$BF_3(g) + NH_3(g) \rightarrow F_3BNH_3 \ (g)$$

| Experiment | $[BF_3]$ | $[NH_3]$ | Initial rate M/sec |
|---|---|---|---|
| 1 | 0.350 | 0.350 | 0.418 |
| 2 | 0.150 | 0.350 | 0.179 |
| 3 | 0.350 | 0.233 | 0.278 |
| 4 | 0.700 | 0.700 | |

1.  The rate equation for the reaction is

    A)  rate $= k[BF_3]^2 [NH_3]^2$

    B)  rate $= k[BF_3]^{2.33} [NH_3]^{1.50}$

    C)  rate $= k[BF_3] [NH_3]$

    D)  rate $= k[BF_3]^2 [NH_3]$

2.  The initial rate of the reaction, in units of M/s, for Experiment 4 is

    A)  0.818

    B)  0.836

    C)  0.868

    D)  1.67

Use the following information to help answer Questions 3 and 4.

3.  The following particulate diagrams represent mixtures of $H_2(g)$ and $NO(g)$ at the molecular level at the beginning of a reaction. Two open circles joined together represent a $H_2$ molecule, while a filled-in circle and a triangle joined together represent a NO molecule. The diagrams show a small portion of the reaction mixture using the same volume. The two substances react as follows:

    $$2H_2(g) + 2NO(g) \rightarrow N_2(g) + 2H_2O(g)$$

    Experimentally, the rate is first order with respect to $H_2$ and second order with respect to NO. Based on this fact, which of the following mixtures will have the fastest initial rate?

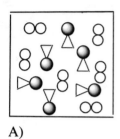
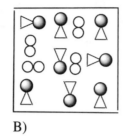
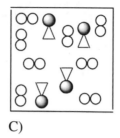
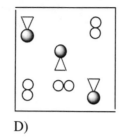

A)                    B)                    C)                    D)

4. If the rate of consumption for NO is 0.44 M/s, what is the rate of formation of nitrogen, in units of M/s?

   A) 0.11

   B) 0.22

   C) 0.88

   D) 1.76

5. The reaction $2Mn(CO)_5 \rightarrow Mn_2(CO)_{10}$ is second order. At 25 °C the rate constant for this reaction is $3.0 \times 10^9 \, M^{-1}s^{-1}$. A series of experiments to track the rate of consumption of the reactants were conducted. The initial concentration of the reactant in Experiment #1 was $1.0 \times 10^{-5}$ M. The initial concentration of the reactant in Experiment #2 was $2.0 \times 10^{-5}$ M. How long will it take for 90% of the reactants to be consumed in Experiment #1 and Experiment #2?

   A) $3.0 \times 10^{-4} \, s : 6.0 \times 10^{-4} \, s$

   B) $3.0 \times 10^{-4} \, s : 1.5 \times 10^{-4} \, s$

   C) $6.0 \times 10^{-4} \, s : 3.0 \times 10^{-4} \, s$

   D) $1.5 \times 10^{-4} \, s : 3.0 \times 10^{-4} \, s$

# CHEMICAL EQUILIBRIUM

This chapter is the main focus of Big Idea 6. All sections of this chapter except Section 14.1 need to be mastered. This chapter is foundational to understanding the chapters on acid-base and solubility product equilibria. Although it is important to know how to do the calculations in the chapter, understanding what the calculations mean is much more essential. The sections of importance are

## Specific Learning Objectives Addressed in This Chapter:

**Learning objective 5.17** The student can make quantitative predictions for systems involving coupled reactions that share a common intermediate, based on the equilibrium constant for the combined reaction. [*See* **SP 6.4**]

**Learning objective 6.1** The student is able to, given a set of experimental observations regarding physical, chemical, biological, or environmental processes that are reversible, construct an explanation that connects the observations to the reversibility of the underlying chemical reactions or processes. [*See* **SP 6.2**]

**Learning objective 6.2** The student can, given a manipulation of a chemical reaction or set of reactions (e.g., reversal of reaction or addition of two reactions), determine the effects of that manipulation on $Q$ or $K$. [*See* **SP 2.2**]

**Learning objective 6.4** The student can, given a set of initial conditions (concentrations or partial pressures) and the equilibrium constant, $K$, use the tendency of $Q$ to approach $K$ to predict and justify the prediction as to whether the reaction will proceed toward products or reactants as equilibrium is approached. [*See* **SP 2.2**, **6.4**]

**Learning objective 6.5** The student can, given data (tabular, graphical, etc.) from which the state of a system at equilibrium can be obtained, calculate the equilibrium constant, $K$. [*See* **SP 2.2**]

**Learning objective 6.6** The student can, given a set of initial conditions (concentrations or partial pressures) and the equilibrium constant, $K$, use stoichiometric relationships and the law of mass action ($Q$ equals $K$ at equilibrium) to determine qualitatively and/or quantitatively the conditions at equilibrium for a system involving a single reversible reaction. [*See* **SP 2.2**, **6.4**]

**Learning objective 6.7** The student is able, for a reversible reaction that has a large or small $K$, to determine which chemical species will have very large versus very small concentrations at equilibrium. [*See* **SP 2.2**, **2.3**]

**Learning objective 6.8** The student is able to use Le Châtelier's principle to predict the direction of the shift resulting from various possible stresses on a system at chemical equilibrium. [*See* **SP 1.4**, **6.4**]

**Learning objective 6.9** The student is able to use Le Châtelier's principle to design a set of conditions that will optimize a desired outcome, such as product yield. [*See* **SP 4.2**]

**Learning objective 6.10** The student is able to connect Le Châtelier's principle to the comparison of $Q$ to $K$ by explaining the effects of the stress on $Q$ and $K$. [*See* **SP 1.4**, **7.2**]

## Specific Science Practices Addressed in This Chapter:

**Science Practice 1:** The student can use representations and models to communicate scientific phenomena and solve scientific problems.

    1.4  The student can *use representations and models* to analyze situations or solve problems qualitatively and quantitatively.

**Science Practice 2:** The student can use mathematics appropriately.

    2.2  The student can *apply mathematical routines* to quantities that describe natural phenomena.

    2.3  The student can *estimate numerically* quantities that describe natural phenomena.

**Science Practice 4:** The student can plan and implement data collection strategies in relation to a particular scientific question.

4.2   The student can *design a plan* for collecting data to answer a particular scientific question.

**Science Practice 6:** The student can work with scientific explanations and theories.

6.2   The student can *construct explanations of phenomena based on evidence* produced through scientific practices.

6.4   The student can *make claims and predictions about natural phenomena* based on scientific theories and models.

**Science Practice 7:** The student is able to connect and relate knowledge across various scales, concepts, and representations in and across domains.

7.2   The student can *connect concepts* in and across domain(s) to generalize or extrapolate in and/or across enduring understandings and/or big ideas.

**Concepts and Vocabulary to Review:**

Section 14.2

## The Concept of Dynamic Equilibrium

When reactions begin, the reactant concentrations are high and the product concentrations are low. As the reaction proceeds, the reactant concentrations decrease and the product concentrations increase. As the products start to form, the reaction begins to reverse and product will begin to make reactant. Eventually the rate of reactants making product will equal the rate of the product making reactant. When the two rates are equal, the reaction has reached dynamic equilibrium. The reaction is still going on, but there will be no apparent change in concentrations. The reaction moving from reactant to product is called the forward reaction and the reaction moving from product to reactant is called the reverse reaction.

When observing particulate figures, comparing the amount of reactant to product, you can see in (a) only reactant is present so the reaction is just beginning. In (b) product is forming. In (c) and (d), the reactant and product concentrations are remaining the same, indicating the reaction has reached equilibrium. In a graph of concentration versus time for a simple equilibrium system,

$$A \rightleftharpoons B$$

when the concentrations of both A and B flatten out this indicates the concentrations of A and B are remaining constant. This is the data needed to indicate the reaction has reached equilibrium. Keep in mind, this does NOT necessarily mean the concentrations are the same.

## Dynamic Equilibrium

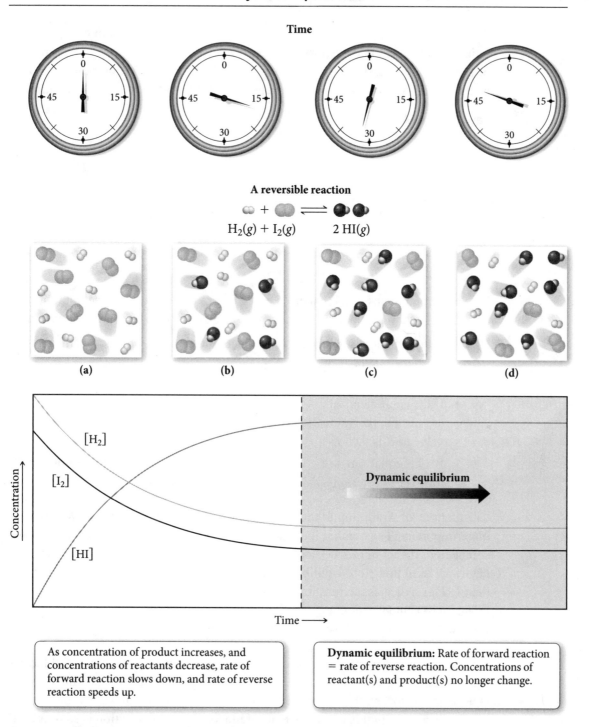

**Time**

**A reversible reaction**

$H_2(g) + I_2(g) \rightleftharpoons 2 HI(g)$

(a)        (b)        (c)        (d)

Concentration

[H₂]

[I₂]

[HI]

**Dynamic equilibrium**

Time ⟶

As concentration of product increases, and concentrations of reactants decrease, rate of forward reaction slows down, and rate of reverse reaction speeds up.

**Dynamic equilibrium:** Rate of forward reaction = rate of reverse reaction. Concentrations of reactant(s) and product(s) no longer change.

**Figure 14.1 Dynamic Equilibrium** Equilibrium is reached in a chemical reaction when the concentrations of the reactants and products no longer change. The molecular images depict the progress of the reaction $H_2(g) + I_2(g) \rightleftharpoons 2 HI(g)$. The graph shows the concentrations of $H_2$, $I_2$, and HI as a function of time. When equilibrium is reached, both the forward and reverse reactions continue, but at equal rates, so the concentrations of the reactants and products remain constant.

Section 14.3

# The Equilibrium Constant (*K*)

At equilibrium, the concentrations of reactant and products remain constant. The ratio of product raised to the power of their coefficients divided by the concentrations of the reactants raised to their coefficients is called the mass action ratio. The ratio is the equilibrium constant. For the reaction $a\text{A} + b\text{B} \rightleftharpoons c\text{C} + d\text{D}$, the ratio is

**Law of Mass Action**

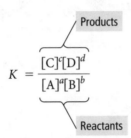

$$K = \frac{[\text{C}]^c[\text{D}]^d}{[\text{A}]^a[\text{B}]^b}$$

Products

Reactants

Since the coefficients of the balanced equation are part of the mass action ratio, the balanced equation is important. If the equation changes, then the ratio also changes.

- If the equation is reversed, the products and reactants change positions in the ratio, causing the value of $K$ to be the inverse, $\frac{1}{K}$.

- If the coefficients are doubled, the value of $K$ is squared. If the coefficients are tripled, the value of $K$ is cubed. When the coefficients change ($n$), the value of $K$ is then $K^n$.

- If two equations are added together, the value of the $K$s are multiplied together to determine the overall $K$. $K_{overall} = K_1 K_2$

Calculations of $K$ are important, but understanding what the value of $K$ means is more important. The number indicates how far the forward reaction moves toward completion. If a lot of product forms (numerator) and most of the reactants (denominator) are used up before equilibrium is reached, the ratio will be a number greater than 1. This indicates the reaction is favoring product formation. Since products are on the right in an equation, the reaction favoring products is said to have its equilibrium to the right and the forward reaction is favored.

If very little product is formed before equilibrium is reached, the ratio will have a small amount of product on top in the ratio (numerator) and a large amount of reactant (denominator) on the bottom. The result will be a small number less than 1, but greater than zero. In this case, reactants are favored and the reaction is said to have its equilibrium to the left, indicating the reverse reaction is favored.

If $K$ is close to 1, the concentration of products and reactants is about the same. This reaction will have progressed approximately half way.

It is important to recognize that the value of $K$ does NOT indicate anything about the rate of reaction.

## Expressing the Equilibrium Constant in Terms of Pressure    Section 14.4

There are different forms of $K$. When using concentration values, the molarity is indicated by the use of brackets. For example, the concentration of A would be [A]. In this case, the constant is called $K_c$. When calculating with pressures, the brackets are not used. Parentheses may be used, but are not required, and $P$ is used to indicate pressure. For the reaction $2SO_3(g) \rightleftharpoons 2SO_2(g) + O_2(g)$, the $K_c$ would be written as $K_c = \dfrac{[SO_2][O_2]}{[SO_3]^2}$ and the $K_p$ would be $K_P = \dfrac{P(SO_2)^2 PO_2}{P(SO_3)^2}$. Gases must be present to calculate a $K_p$. If only a reactant is a gas, the numerator is 1 and if only a product is a gas, the denominator is 1. It is possible to convert from $K_p$ and $K_c$ using $K_p = K_c(RT)^{\Delta n}$. Since gases are creating pressure, $R$ is the gas constant 0.0821 L·atm/K·mol, $T$ is temperature in Kelvin and $\Delta n$ is the moles of gaseous product minus the number of moles of gaseous reactant. $\Delta n$ can be determined by using the coefficients in the balanced equation. If the moles of gas reactant and moles of gas product are equal, $\Delta n = 0$, then $K_p$ will equal $K_c$.

Even though $K_c$ uses molarity units in its calculation and $K_p$ uses units of atmospheres, the ratio values of $K_c$ and $K_p$ are considered unitless.

## Heterogeneous Equilibria: Reactions Involving Solids and Liquids    Section 14.5

Not all reactions have all reactant and products in the same state of matter or phase, these are called heterogeneous. There are a few special circumstances to remember

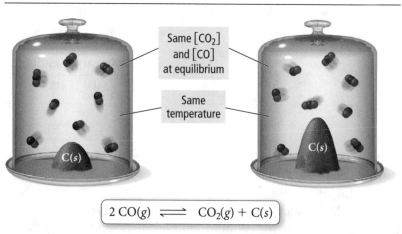

**A Heterogeneous Equilibrium**

Same $[CO_2]$ and $[CO]$ at equilibrium

Same temperature

$C(s)$    $C(s)$

$2\,CO(g) \rightleftharpoons CO_2(g) + C(s)$

**Figure 14.2 Heterogeneous Equilibrium**    The concentration of solid carbon (the number of atoms per unit volume) is constant as long as some solid carbon is present. The same is true for pure liquids. For this reason, the concentrations of solids and pure liquids are not included in equilibrium constant expressions.

about equilibrium expressions. Solids do not change concentration as their concentration is their density and the same is true of pure liquids. For this reason, solids and pure liquids are not included in equilibrium expressions. The states of matter must be taken into account to write the different $K$ expressions. $K_c$ only has concentrations in molarity and solids and pure liquids are not included. $K_p$ only has pressures so only gases from the balanced equation are used.

**Section 14.6**

# Calculating the Equilibrium Constant from Measured Equilibrium Concentrations

The value of $K$ for a given reaction is always the same at a given temperature regardless of the starting concentrations. This is shown in the following example.

**Table 14.1**    Initial and Equilibrium Concentrations for the Reaction
$H_2(g) + I_2(g) \rightleftharpoons 2\,HI(g)$ at 445 °C

| Initial Concentrations | | | Equilibrium Concentrations | | | Equilibrium Constant |
|---|---|---|---|---|---|---|
| $[H_2]$ | $[I_2]$ | $[HI]$ | $[H_2]$ | $[I_2]$ | $[HI]$ | $K_c = \dfrac{[HI^2]}{[H_2][I_2]}$ |
| 0.50 | 0.50 | 0.0 | 0.11 | 0.11 | 0.78 | $\dfrac{(0.78)^2}{(0.11)(0.11)} = 50$ |
| 0.0 | 0.0 | 0.50 | 0.055 | 0.055 | 0.39 | $\dfrac{(0.39)^2}{(0.055)(0.055)} = 50$ |
| 0.50 | 0.50 | 0.50 | 0.165 | 0.165 | 1.17 | $\dfrac{(1.17)^2}{(0.165)(0.165)} = 50$ |
| 1.0 | 0.50 | 0.0 | 0.53 | 0.033 | 0.934 | $\dfrac{(0.934)^2}{(0.53)(0.033)} = 50$ |
| 0.50 | 1.0 | 0.0 | 0.033 | 0.53 | 0.934 | $\dfrac{(0.934)^2}{(0.033)(0.53)} = 50$ |

It is easy to substitute into the $K$ expression if the equilibrium concentrations or pressures are known, but what if only the starting concentrations are given? An ICE table is used to help find the values to substitute for the equilibrium concentrations into the $K$ expression. Making an ICE table is a crucial skill to master. I stands for initial, C for change, and E stands for equilibrium. For the reaction $A(g) \rightleftharpoons 2B(g)$, at the beginning of the reaction no product is present. If the starting concentration of A is 1.00 M for whatever amount A loses, B gains twice that amount since the coefficients are 1:2. If the amount lost is $x$, then the amount gained is $2x$.

| ICE TABLE | [A] | [B] |
|-----------|-----|-----|
| I | 1.00 | 0 |
| C | $-x$ | $+2x$ |
| E | $1.00 - x$ | $2x$ |

If the amount of change is known, the values can be determined and $K$ solved for. If the amount of change is 0.30, then using the table [A] is 0.70 and [B] is 0.60.

The $K$ expression is $K = \dfrac{[B]^2}{[A]}$. When substituted into the expression, this would be

$K = \dfrac{[0.60]^2}{[0.70]}$, which equals 0.51.

## The Reaction Quotient: Predicting the Direction of Change    Section 14.7

If a reaction is not at equilibrium, the ratio of reactant and products is called the reaction quotient, $Q_c$ for concentrations and $Q_p$ for pressures. The calculation is the same, but the end result is used to indicate what direction the reaction will proceed to reach equilibrium unless the value of $Q$ is the same as $K$, indicating the reaction is at equilibrium.

- If $Q = K$, the reaction is at equilibrium.
- If $Q > K$, the numerator (product) is too large and to reach $K$, the reactant value will need to increase, indicating the reaction will proceed to the left.
- If $Q < K$, the denominator (reactant) is too large and to reach $K$, the product value will need to increase, indicating the reaction will proceed to the right.

The figure on next page shows a graphical example of predicting the direction of change.

## Finding Equilibrium Concentrations    Section 14.8

If $K$ is known, then the values in the ICE tables can be substituted and the values of $x$ solved for. Using the reaction $A(g) \rightleftharpoons 2B(g)$ and the example earlier:

| ICE TABLE | [A] | [B] |
|-----------|-----|-----|
| I | 1.00 | 0 |
| C | $-x$ | $+2x$ |
| E | $1.00 - x$ | $2x$ |

## Q, K, and the Direction of a Reaction

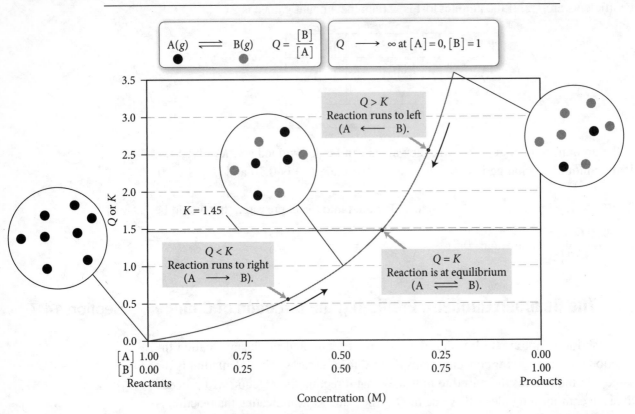

**Figure 14.3 Q, K, and the Direction of a Reaction**    The graph shows a plot of $Q$ as a function of the concentrations of the reactants and products in a simple reaction $A \rightleftharpoons B$, in which $K = 1.45$ and the sum of the reactant and product concentrations is 1 M. The far left of the graph represents pure reactant and the far right represents pure product. The midpoint of the graph represents an equal mixture of A and B. When $Q$ is less than $K$, the reaction moves in the forward direction (A → B). When $Q$ is greater than $K$, the reaction moves in the reverse direction (A ← B). When $Q$ is equal to $K$, the reaction is at equilibrium.

and $K = \dfrac{[B]^2}{[A]}$, then $K = \dfrac{[2x]^2}{[1.00 - x]}$. This requires solving the quadratic equation, but many times the value of $-x$ is so small that when subtracted from the original value it does not make a difference. If this is the case, the equation can be simplified and the quadratic does not need to be solved. For instance if $x = 0.0021$ M then $1.00 - 0.0021 = 0.9979$. When rounded to two places past the decimal point, the answer is 1.00 M and $K = \dfrac{[2x]^2}{[1.00]}$. Assuming $K$ is $3.40 \times 10^{-5}$; was it reasonable to ignore the $-x$? $1.00 - 0.00292 = 1.00$, so yes it was. From the ICE table, the value of $3.40 \times 10^{-5} = \dfrac{[2x]^2}{1.00}$ and $x = 0.00292$. B is $2x$ which is 0.0584. To use this approximation method, the difference between the original concentration and $x$ should be less than 5% of the original value. In this case, $\dfrac{0.00292}{1.00} \times 100 = 0.292\%$ indicating the approximation method was okay to use.

# Le Châtelier's Principle: How a System at Equilibrium Responds to Disturbances

Changing concentrations, pressures, or temperatures causes the reaction to adjust to reobtain equilibrium. Le Châtelier's Principle states when a chemical system at equilibrium is disturbed, the system shifts in a direction to minimize the disturbance. To reestablish equilibrium, the system either shifts to the right forming additional product or shifts to the left forming additional reactant. Analysis of the $K$ value and how the disturbance affects the value is important to predict the direction to get back to the equilibrium value.

## Concentration Changes:

If adding to a concentration value, the reaction system will move away from the side of the reaction where added species is.

- If the species added is a reactant causing $Q < K$, the reaction will shift to the right and make additional product.

- If the species is a product causing $Q > K$, the reaction will shift to the left and make additional reactant.

If a species is removed, the system will move to replace the removed species.

- If the species is a reactant causing $Q > K$, the reaction will shift to the left to make more reactant.

- If the species is a product causing $Q < K$, the reaction will move to the right to produce more product.

### Le Châtelier's Principle: Changing Concentration

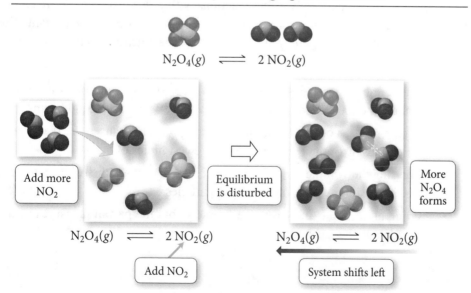

**Figure 14.4  Le Châtelier's Principle: The Effect of a Concentration Change**   Adding $NO_2$ causes the reaction to shift left, consuming some of the added $NO_2$ and forming more $N_2O_4$.

Graphically this would look like the following:

**Le Châtelier's Principle: Graphical Representation**

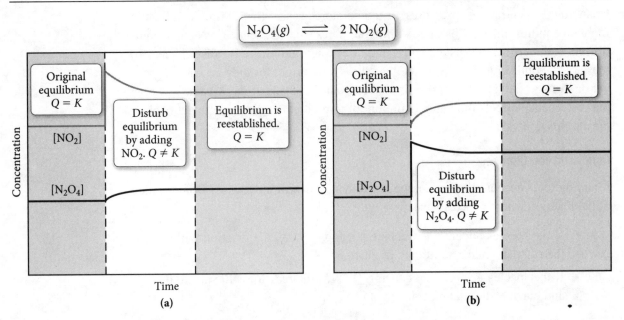

**Figure 14.5  Le Châtelier's Principle: Changing Concentration**   The graph shows the concentrations of $NO_2$ and $N_2O_4$ for the reaction $N_2O_4(g) \rightarrow 2NO_2(g)$ as a function of time in three distinct stages of the reaction: initially at equilibrium (left), upon disturbance of the equilibrium by addition of more $NO_2$ **(a)** or $N_2O_4$ **(b)** to the reaction mixture (center), and upon reestablishment of equilibrium (right).

## Volume or Pressure Changes:

Volume or pressure changes only affect reactions with gases involved. For reactions involving gases, the balanced equation and states of matter are very important. The reaction must be analyzed to determine which side of the reaction has the most moles of gas.

- If the number of moles of gas on both sides of the equation is the same, changing the pressure or volume will have no effect on the equilibrium.

- Decreasing the volume (or increasing the pressure) causes the reaction to shift to the side of the reaction with the fewest moles of gas.

- Increasing the volume (or reducing the pressure) causes the reaction to shift to the side with the most moles of gas particles.

- Adding an inert gas increases the pressure, but the partial pressures of the gases do not change, and so it has no effect on the equilibrium.

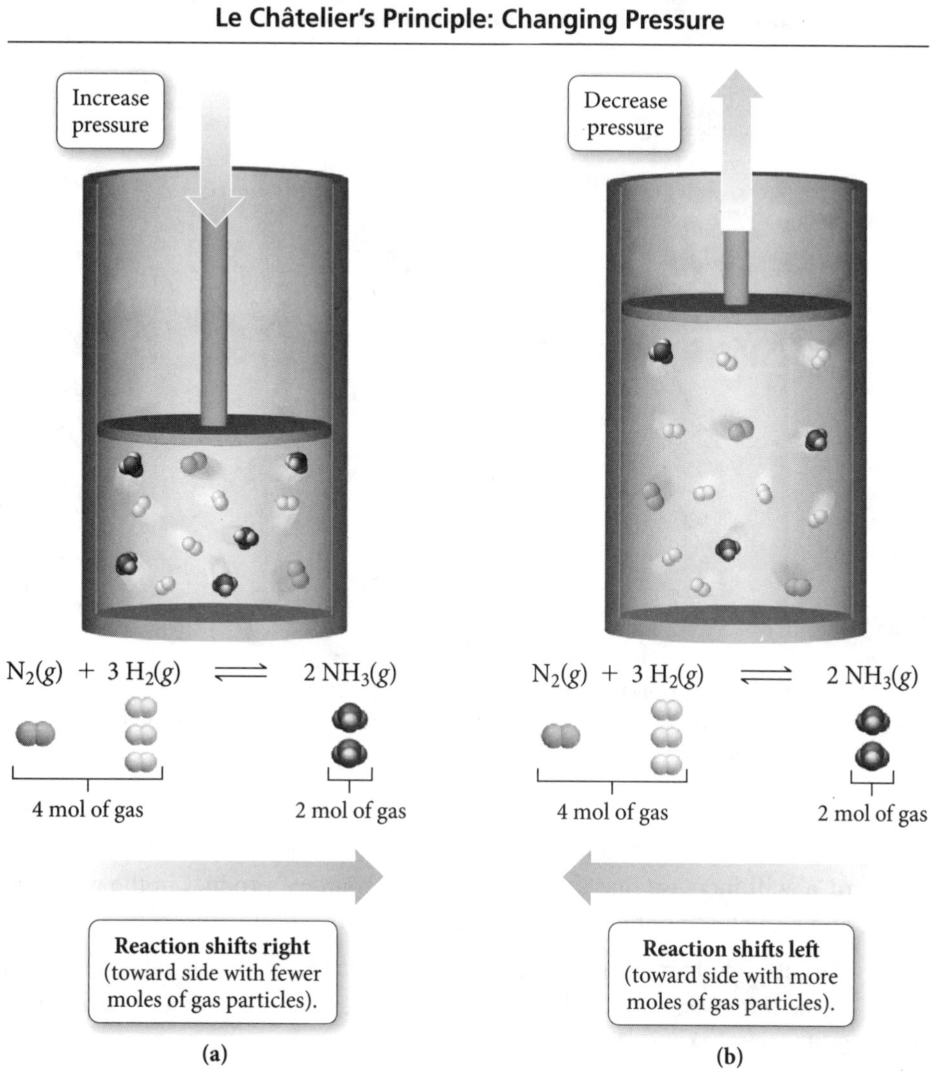

## Le Châtelier's Principle: Changing Pressure

**Figure 14.6  Le Châtelier's Principle: The Effect of a Pressure Change**    **(a)** Decreasing the volume increases the pressure, causing the reaction to shift to the right (fewer moles of gas, lower pressure). **(b)** Increasing the volume reduces the pressure, causing the reaction to shift to the left (more moles of gas, higher pressure).

### Temperature Changes:

Analyzing temperature changes requires knowing if a chemical reaction is endothermic or exothermic. Since equilibrium constants are temperature dependent, increasing or decreasing the temperature changes the equilibrium constant.

- If the reaction is endothermic, heat is being added and can be "treated" as a reactant: For the reaction $A + B \rightleftharpoons C + D$ the reaction would be

## Le Châtelier's Principle: Changing Temperature

**Figure 14.7 Le Châtelier's Principle: The Effect of a Temperature Change**    Because the reaction is endothermic, raising the temperature causes a shift to the right, toward the formation of brown $NO_2$.

A + B + heat $\rightleftharpoons$ C + D. Written this way, increasing the temperature would cause a shift to the products away from the added heat and the value of $K$ will increase due to the increased amount of product in the numerator and a smaller number in the denominator.

- For the endothermic reaction, decreasing the temperature would cause a shift to the left causing the value of $K$ to decrease due to a smaller product value in the numerator and more reactant in the denominator.

- If the reaction is exothermic, heat is being formed and can be "treated" as a product: For the reaction A + B $\rightleftharpoons$ C + D the reaction would be A + B $\rightleftharpoons$ C + D + heat. Written this way, increasing the temperature would cause a shift to the reactants away from the added heat, resulting in a smaller $K$ value.

- Lowering the temperature for an exothermic reaction would cause a shift to the right, resulting in a larger $K$ value.

### Catalyst:

A catalyst has no effect on the equilibrium. A catalyst will increase the rate of reaction so the equilibrium will be reached faster.

## Additional Practice

*Self-Assessment Quiz Questions Q1, Q2, Q3, Q4, Q5, Q6, Q7, Q8, Q9, Q10, Q11, Q12, Q13, Q14, and Q15*

*Problems 3, 4, 5, 6, 7, 9, 12, 14, 17, 21, 22, 23, 24, 25, 297, 29, 31, 37, 44, 46, 47, 49, 51, 56, 62, 63, 65, 69, 71, and 80*

## Practice AP® Test Questions

1.  The graph below is a concentration vs. time plot for a hypothetical reaction $A \rightleftharpoons B$. Estimate the value of the equilibrium constant, $K_c$, for this system.

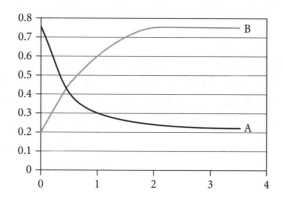

A)  $K_c < 1$

B)  $K_c = 0$

C)  $K_c = 1$

D)  $K_c > 1$

Questions 2, 3, and 4 pertain to the following situation. Automobile exhaust gases often reach a temperature of 1200 K. At this temperature, carbon dioxide can establish the following equilibrium system

$$2\,CO_2\,(g) \rightleftharpoons 2\,CO(g) + O_2(g)\ \Delta H = -514\,kJ$$

2.  If the system occurs at constant volume, the concentration of $O_2$ (g) at equilibrium will decrease if

A)  CO is added to the system

B)  $CO_2$ is added to the system

C)  Ar(g) is added to the system

D)  the temperature of the system decreases

3.  An increase in temperature will

A)  increase the partial pressure of $O_2(g)$

B)  increase the partial pressure of $CO(g)$

C) increase the value of $K_c$

D) decrease the value of $K_c$

4. An equilibrium mixture contains 0.0020 M $CO_2$ and 0.0030 M $O_2$ and $K_c = 1.4 \times 10^2$. Determine the equilibrium concentration of CO.

A) $9.6 \times 10^{-6}$ M

B) $4.4 \times 10^{-3}$ M

C) $1.8 \times 10^{-1}$ M

D) $6.2 \times 10^{-1}$ M

5. At 700 K, carbon tetrachloride decomposes to carbon and chlorine

$$CCl_4\,(g) \rightleftharpoons C(s) + 2Cl_2\,(g)$$

Just before any reaction occurs, initial amounts of $CCl_4(g)$, $C(s)$, and $Cl_2(g)$ are injected into a rigid reaction container at 700 K. For the first 5 seconds, the concentration of $Cl_2$ decreases. Which statement below describes the relationship between $K_c$ and $Q$ during the first 3 seconds of the reaction?

A) $K_c < Q$

B) $K_c = Q$

C) $K_c > Q$

D) more information is needed to determine the status of $K_c$

**Answers**

*1. D); 2. A); 3. D); 4. B); 5. A)*

# ACIDS AND BASES

Acid and bases are covered in Big Idea 6 of the AP Chemistry Framework and include several learning objectives which are listed below. Included in this list are the concepts of equilibrium.

This chapter covers the three theories of acids and bases. Each is useful for different characteristics of acid–base reactions. In the AP curriculum, identification of a Lewis acid or base is not required although understanding the concepts will be beneficial to understanding complex ions and other concepts in the AP curriculum. Although not covered here, Section 15.2 has basic information students should already know about acids and bases.

## Specific Learning Objectives Addressed in This Chapter:

**Learning objective 2.2** The student is able to explain the relative strengths of acids and bases based on molecular structure, interparticle forces, and solution equilibrium. [*See* **SP 7.2**]

**Learning objective 3.1** Students can translate among macroscopic observations of change, chemical equations, and particle views. [*See* **SP 1.5, 7.1**]

**Learning objective 3.7** The student is able to identify compounds as Brønsted-Lowry acids, bases, and/or conjugate acid–base pairs, using proton-transfer reactions to justify the identification. [*See* **SP 6.1**]

**Learning objective 6.1** The student is able to, given a set of experimental observations regarding physical, chemical, biological, or environmental processes that are reversible, construct an explanation that connects the observations to the reversibility of the underlying chemical reactions or processes. [*See* **SP 6.2**]

**Learning objective 6.7** The student is able, for a reversible reaction that has a large or small $K$, to determine which chemical species will have very large versus very small concentrations at equilibrium. [*See* **SP 2.2, 2.3**]

**Learning objective 6.11** The student can generate or use a particulate representation of an acid (strong or weak or polyprotic) and a strong base to explain the species that will have large versus small concentrations at equilibrium. [*See* **SP 1.1, 1.4, 2.3**]

**Learning objective 6.12** The student can reason about the distinction between strong and weak acid solutions with similar values of pH, including the percent ionization of the acids, the concentrations needed to achieve the same pH, and the amount of base needed to reach the equivalence point in a titration. [*See* **SP 1.4**]

**Learning objective 6.14** The student can, based on the dependence of $K_w$ on temperature, reason that neutrality requires $[H^+] = [OH^-]$ as opposed to requiring pH = 7, including especially the applications to biological systems. [*See* **SP 2.2, 6.2**]

**Learning objective 6.15** The student can identify a given solution as containing a mixture of strong acids and/or bases and calculate or estimate the pH (and concentrations of all chemical species) in the resulting solution. [*See* **SP 2.2, 2.3, 6.4**]

**Learning objective 6.16** The student can identify a given solution as being the solution of a monoprotic weak acid or base (including salts in which one ion is a weak acid or base), calculate the pH and concentration of all species in the solution, and/or infer the relative strengths of the weak acids or bases from given equilibrium concentrations. [*See* **SP 2.2, 6.4**]

**Learning objective 6.17** The student can, given an arbitrary mixture of weak and strong acids and bases (including polyprotic systems), determine which species will react strongly with one another (i.e., with $K > 1$) and what species will be present in large concentrations at equilibrium. [*See* **SP 6.4**]

**Learning objective 6.19** The student can relate the predominant form of a chemical species involving a labile proton (i.e., protonated/deprotonated form of a weak acid) to the pH of a solution and the $pK_a$ associated with the labile proton. [*See* **SP 2.3, 5.1, 6.4**]

## Specific Science Practices Addressed in This Chapter:

**Science Practice 1:** The student can use representations and models to communicate scientific phenomena and solve scientific problems.

    1.1  The student can *create representations and models* of natural or man-made phenomena and systems in the domain.

    1.4  The student can *use representations and models* to analyze situations or solve problems qualitatively and quantitatively.

1.5  The student can *re-express key elements* of natural phenomena across multiple representations in the domain.

**Science Practice 2:** The student can use mathematics appropriately.

2.2  The student can *apply mathematical routines* to quantities that describe natural phenomena.

2.3  The student can *estimate numerically* quantities that describe natural phenomena.

**Science Practice 5:** The student can perform data analysis and evaluation of evidence.

5.1  The student can *analyze data* to identify patterns or relationships.

**Science Practice 6:** The student can work with scientific explanations and theories.

6.1  The student can *justify claims with evidence.*

6.2  The student can *construct explanations of phenomena based on evidence* produced through scientific practices.

6.4  The student can *make claims and predictions about natural phenomena* based on scientific theories and models.

**Science Practice 7:** The student is able to connect and relate knowledge across various scales, concepts, and representations in and across domains.

7.1  The student can *connect phenomena and models* across spatial and temporal scales.

7.2  The student can *connect concepts* in and across domain(s) to generalize or extrapolate in and/or across enduring understandings and/or big ideas.

## Concepts and Vocabulary to Review:

# Definitions of Acids and Bases    Section 15.3

The two main theories of acids and bases are in this section. They are the Arrhenius definition and the Brønsted-Lowry definition. The primary definition used in AP is the Brønsted-Lowry since it is more inclusive.

Arrhenius defined acids and bases by ions present and formed when dissociated in water. Acids have $H^+$ ions and dissociate with water to form $H_3O^+$ known as hydronium. The hydronium ion can be simply abbreviated as $H^+(aq)$ and is accepted in AP.

Arrhenius bases are identified by the presence of hydroxide ions $(OH^-)$, which ionize in aqueous solutions.

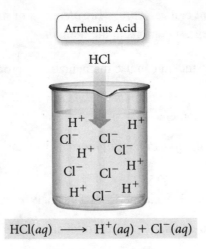

**Figure 15.1 Arrhenius Acid**    An Arrhenius acid produces $H^+$ ions in solution.

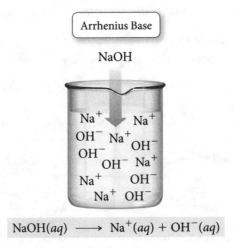

**Figure 15.2 Arrhenius Base**    An Arrhenius base produces $OH^-$ ions in solution.

Brønsted-Lowry defined acids and bases on what occurs in chemical reactions. Acids donate protons and bases accept protons. An $H^+$ is a proton, so when looking at a reaction you can identify the acid as the reactant substance losing an $H^+$ and the base as the reactant substance gaining the $H^+$. This means these reactions have both an acid and a base. In the chemical equation

$$HCl(aq) + H_2O(l) \longrightarrow H_3O^+(aq) + Cl^-(aq),$$

the $H^+$ starts with HCl and is donated to the $H_2O$. HCl donated the proton and is therefore an acid and the water accepted the proton so it is the base. Water can also act as an acid. For instance, in the chemical equation

$$NH_3(aq) + H_2O(l) \rightleftharpoons NH_4^+(aq) + OH^-(aq),$$

the reactant ammonia molecule is accepting a proton to form an ammonium ion while the reactant water donated the proton and formed the hydroxide ion. In this case, ammonia is the base and water is the acid.

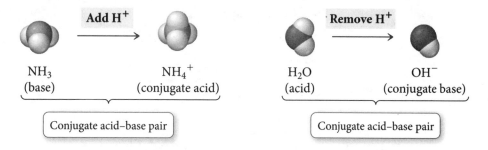

NH$_3$
(base)

NH$_4^+$
(conjugate acid)

H$_2$O
(acid)

OH$^-$
(conjugate base)

Conjugate acid–base pair

Conjugate acid–base pair

**Figure 15.3 Conjugate Acid–Base Pairs**    A conjugate acid–base pair consists of two substances related to each other by the transfer of a proton.

Substances such as water, which can be both an acid and a base depending on the situation, are called amphoteric.

In the chemical equation used above,

$$NH_3(aq) + H_2O(l) \rightleftharpoons NH_4^+(aq) + OH^-(aq),$$

when looking at the reverse reaction an acid and base can also be identified. The ammonium would be the acid and the hydroxide is the base. The acid and base in the reverse reaction are called the conjugate acid and conjugate base. The acid in the forward reaction forms the conjugate base and the base in the forward reaction forms the conjugate acid, so these are called conjugate acid–base pairs.

## Acid Strength and the Acid Ionization Constant ($K_a$)    Section 15.4

Acids are considered weak or strong based on the amount of ionization they undergo in an aqueous solution. If the ions in the acid have a strong attraction to each other, the tendency will be to remain mostly as molecules, although some will ionize. Since both the forward reaction of dissociating into ions, and the reverse reaction of forming ions are ongoing, this reaction will reach equilibrium. For acids, this equilibrium constant is called $K_a$. Problems with $K_a$ are the same as $K_c$, they just refer to being an acid. The less dissociation occurs, the more the backward reaction is favored and the smaller the value of $K_a$, and therefore the weaker the acid.

### A Weak Acid

When HF dissolves in water, only a fraction of the molecules ionize.

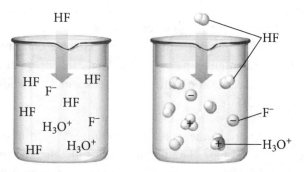

**Figure 15.4 Ionization of a Weak Acid**    When HF dissolves in water, only a fraction of the dissolved molecules ionize to form H$_3$O$^+$ and F$^-$. The solution contains many intact HF molecules.

**A Strong Acid**

When HCl dissolves in water, it ionizes completely.

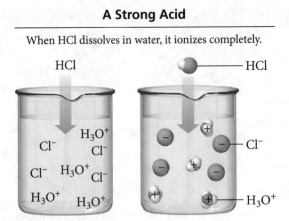

**Figure 15.5 Ionization of a Strong Acid**   When HCl dissolves in water, it completely ionizes to form $H_3O^+$ and $Cl^-$. The solution contains virtually no intact HCl.

If the acid is strong, the attractions between the ions are weaker than the attraction to water molecules and the acid will dissociate completely or close to it. If the acid dissociates completely or close to completely, it is an example of a forward reaction going to completion.

## Section 15.5    Autoionization of Water and pH

Since water is an acid and base, two waters react to form hydronium and hydroxide. This is called the autoionization of water. The reaction is below.

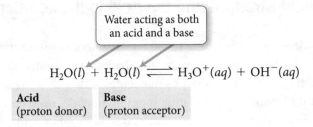

Water acting as both an acid and a base

$$H_2O(l) + H_2O(l) \rightleftharpoons H_3O^+(aq) + OH^-(aq)$$

**Acid**              **Base**
(proton donor)    (proton acceptor)

Writing this reaction in an equilibrium expression results in $K_w = [H_3O^+][OH^-]$. The w for water indicates $K_w$ refers to equilibrium ion product constant of water. $K_w$ at 25°C has a recognized value of $1.0 \times 10^{-14}$. Water is neutral because the hydronium and hydroxide concentrations are equal $(1.0 \times 10^{-7})$ and neutralize each other; $[H_3O^+] = [OH^-]$.

In acidic solutions, the amount of hydronium increases (acid) and the hydroxide decreases (base); $[H_3O^+] > [OH^-]$. The actual amount of each can be calculated using $1.0 \times 10^{-14} = [H_3O^+][OH^-]$. Since the acid and base concentrations multiplied together equal the same number, as one value increases the other must decrease. In basic solutions, the hydroxide concentration increases and the acid concentration decreases; $[H_3O^+] < [OH^-]$.

The pH scale is one way to measure the amount of hydronium ion in solution where the pH $= -\log[H_3O^+]$. The negative log indicates the more acid present, the LOWER the acid number will be. For instance, a hydronium concentration of 0.00010 will equal a pH of 3.00 and a concentration of 0.10 will equal a pH of 1.00.

Therefore, the lower the pH is then the more acidic the solution. Since the scale is logarithmic, the difference between concentrations of a pH of 1 and a pH of 3 is not 2 but $10^2$ or a factor of 100. Another concept about pH values is the number of significant figures present. Since the value is dealing with logs, the number in the front, the mantissa, is not part of the significant figures. The significant figures are the places to the right of the decimal place. A pH of 3.00 has 2 significant figures.

In a solution of pure water at 25 °C, the concentration of hydronium was $1.0 \times 10^{-7}$, which is a pH of 7. Hence, at a pH of 7 the solution is neutral. When the base concentration is greater than the acid concentration, the pH will be greater than 7.

**The pH Scale**

| 0 | 1 | 2 | 3 | 4 | 5 | 6 | 7 | 8 | 9 | 10 | 11 | 12 | 13 | 14 |
|---|---|---|---|---|---|---|---|---|---|----|----|----|----|----|

Acidic                                          pH                                          Basic

| $10^{-0}$ | $10^{-1}$ | $10^{-2}$ | $10^{-3}$ | $10^{-4}$ | $10^{-5}$ | $10^{-6}$ | $10^{-7}$ | $10^{-8}$ | $10^{-9}$ | $10^{-10}$ | $10^{-11}$ | $10^{-12}$ | $10^{-13}$ | $10^{-14}$ |
|---|---|---|---|---|---|---|---|---|---|---|---|---|---|---|

$$[H^+]$$

**Figure 15.6 The pH Scale**   An increase of 1 on the pH scale corresponds to a factor of 10 decrease in $[H_3O^+]$.

If the base concentration is known, a calculation of the hydronium concentration must be done before calculating a pH value. Another way is to convert to pOH and then convert to pH. This requires using the following two equations: $pOH = -\log[OH^-]$ and $pH + pOH = 14$. The pOH scale is just the reverse of the pH scale. The more basic the solution is, the lower the pOH is.

| 0.0 | 1.0 | 2.0 | 3.0 | 4.0 | 5.0 | 6.0 | 7.0 | 8.0 | 9.0 | 10.0 | 11.0 | 12.0 | 13.0 | 14.0 |
|---|---|---|---|---|---|---|---|---|---|----|----|----|----|----|

Acidic                                          pH                                          Basic

| 14.0 | 13.0 | 12.0 | 11.0 | 10.0 | 9.0 | 8.0 | 7.0 | 6.0 | 5.0 | 4.0 | 3.0 | 2.0 | 1.0 | 0.0 |
|---|---|---|---|---|---|---|---|---|---|---|---|---|---|---|

pOH

**Figure 15.7  pH and pOH**

Combining all these equations together, we can see a pattern to help students remember the steps to determining a value.

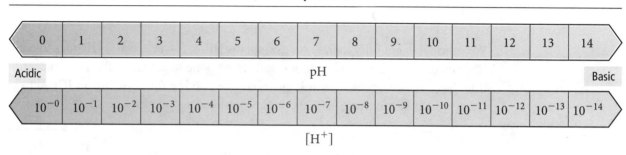

$$pH + pOH = 14$$

$$pH \longleftrightarrow pOH$$

$$pH = [-\log H^+] \qquad\qquad pOH = -\log[OH^-]$$

$$[H^+] \longleftrightarrow [OH^-]$$

$$1.0 \times 10^{-14} = [H_3O^+][OH^-]$$

Other values are $pK_a$ and $pK_b$. In both cases, the $-\log$ is taken. For $pK_a$, the equation is $pK_a = -\log[K_a]$ and for $pK_b$, the equation is $pK_b = -\log[K_b]$. Again the scales are logarithmic and are an indication of the strength of the acid or base.

Section 15.6

## Finding the $[H_3O^+]$ and pH of Strong and Weak Acid Solutions

Since strong acids ionize 100%, the concentrations of the acid will equal the concentration of the hydronium ion. A 1.00 M HCl solution will have 1.00 M $H^+$ and 1.00 M $Cl^-$ concentrations. For weak acids, this is not the case and this is why it is crucial to recognize the differences between strong and weak acids. The first step is to decide if the acid is a strong or weak acid knowing all acids cannot be treated the same in problems.

Weak acids do not fully ionize. An example is $HF \rightleftharpoons H^+ + F^-$. HF goes to equilibrium and therefore a calculation needs to be done to calculate the $H^+$ concentration. Solving this problem will be just like the solving for $K_c$ using an ICE set up. Using a 1.00 M solution of HF, the set up would be as follows:

|   | [HF] | [H⁺] | [F⁻] |
|---|------|------|------|
| I | 1.00 | 0* | 0 |
| C | $-x$ | $+x$ | $+x$ |
| E | $1.00 - x$ | $x$ | $x$ |

*There is some $H^+$ from the autoionization of water, but it is so small it can be ignored.

Solving again is the same as before where $K_a = \dfrac{[H]^+[F]^-}{[HF]}$, which substi-

tuted would be $K_a = \dfrac{[x][x]}{[0.10 - x]}$. The $K_a$ of HF is $3.5 \times 10^{-4}$, therefore,

$3.5 \times 10^{-4} = \dfrac{[x][x]}{[1.00 - x]}$. The $-x$ value in the denominator follows the same 5% rule as before in order to be dropped and not solve the quadratic equation; $x = 0.019$ M.

Percent ionization of an acid is calculated the same as before. % ionization $= \dfrac{[H^+]}{[HA]} \times 100$. The HA concentration is the initial concentration and the $H^+$ is the concentration at equilibrium ($x$ in the ICE set up). In this case, % ionization $= \dfrac{[0.019]}{[1.00]} \times 100$, which is 1.9% ionization. In this case, it was fine to drop the $-x$ value.

As with all equilibrium systems, Le Châtelier's principle also applies to disturbances. If additional HF acid is added to $HF \rightleftharpoons H^+ + F^-$, the system will respond by shifting to the right, which increases the percent ionization.

## Base Solutions   Section 15.7

Basic solutions use the same principles as acids. Bases ionizing 100% are strong and those bases which do not ionize to this extent are weak. Strong base equations have a single forward arrow going to completion; $NaOH(aq) \longrightarrow Na^+(aq) + OH^-(aq)$. The strong bases include all the alkali metal hydroxides. Strong bases can use the concentration in the pOH equation: a 1.0 M NaOH ionizes to 1.0 M $Na^+$ and 1.0 M $OH^-$ so $pOH = -\log[1.0]$ therefore the pH $= 0$.

**A Strong Base**

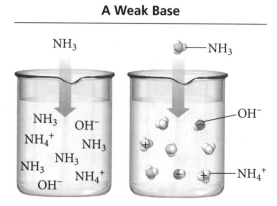

**Figure 15.8 Ionization of a Strong Base**   When NaOH dissolves in water, it dissociates completely into $Na^+$ and $OH^-$. The solution contains virtually no intact NaOH.

**A Weak Base**

**Figure 15.9 Ionization of a Weak Base**   When $NH_3$ dissolves in water, it partially ionizes water to form $NH_4^+$ and $OH^-$. Most of the $NH_3$ molecules in solution remain as $NH_3$.

Weak bases have double arrows going to an equilibrium; $NH_3(aq) + H_2O(l) \rightleftharpoons NH_4^+(aq) + OH^-(aq)$. To find the concentration to use in the pOH equation, a $K$ problem must be solved using an ICE format. Since the substance is a base, the $K$ is a $K_b$.

Using a 1.00 M solution of $NH_3$, the set up would be as follows:

|   | $[NH_3]$ | $[NH_4^+]$ | $[OH^-]$ |
|---|---|---|---|
| I | 1.00 | 0 | 0 |
| C | $-x$ | $+x$ | $+x$ |
| E | $1.00 - x$ | $x$ | $x$ |

$K_b = \dfrac{[NH_4^+][OH^-]}{[NH_3]}$, which substituted would be $K_b = \dfrac{[x][x]}{[1.00 - x]}$. The $K_b$ of $NH_3$ is $1.76 \times 10^{-5}$. The $-x$ value in the denominator follows the same 5% rule as before in order to be dropped and not solve the quadratic equation; $x = 0.00420$ M. In this case, % ionization $= \dfrac{[0.00420]}{[1.00]} \times 100$, which is 0.420% ionization, showing it was fine to subtract the $-x$. Le Châtelier's principle also applies to disturbances of the equilibrium.

## Section 15.8  The Acid–Base Properties of Ions and Salts

The anions of acids and the cations of bases combined together form ionic compounds called salts. Remember in the Brønsted-Lowry definition there are conjugate acid–base pairs. The acid HCl donates the $H^+$ and the anion $Cl^-$ is the conjugate base pair.

$$HCl(aq) + H_2O(l) \longrightarrow H_3O^+(aq) + Cl^-(aq)$$

For the base $NH_3$, the cation $NH_4^+$ is its conjugate acid pair.

$$NH_3(aq) + H_2O(l) \rightleftharpoons NH_4^+(aq) + OH^-(aq)$$

Whether or not these ions will influence the pH of the solution depends on their interaction with water.

If the ions present do not have an interaction with water, the solution will remain neutral. For instance, the salt NaCl is made from the cation $Na^+$ of the base NaOH and the anion $Cl^-$ of the acid HCl. Neither of these ions will undergo hydrolysis with the water and remain as ions in solution. The anions of strong acids are neutral and the cations of strong bases are neutral.

Strong acid anion: $Cl^-(aq) + H_2O(l) \longrightarrow Cl^-(aq) + H_2O(l)$ solution remains neutral

Strong base cation: $Na^+(aq) + H_2O(l) \longrightarrow Na^+(aq) + H_2O(l)$ solution remains neutral

Hence, NaCl is a neutral salt. Neutral salts are formed from the anions of strong acids and the cation from strong bases. Neither ion undergoes a hydrolysis reaction.

Strong Acid-Strong Base Reaction: $HCl(aq) + NaOH(aq) \longrightarrow H_2O(l) + NaCl(aq)$

Neutral salt: $NaCl(aq) \longrightarrow Na^+(aq) + Cl^-(aq)$

$Na^+(aq) + H_2O(l) \rightleftharpoons$ no reaction   $Cl^-(aq) + H_2O(l) \rightleftharpoons$ no reaction

Anions of weak acids in contrast are weak bases and will undergo a hydrolysis reaction with water. Cations of weak bases are weak acids and will also undergo a hydrolysis reaction with water. These reactions can drive the pH to be acidic or basic.

For example, the anion fluoride from the weak acid hydrofluoric acid (HF) reacts with water to form an equilibrium system with the weak hydrofluoric acid and basic hydroxide ions. The hydroxide ions will make the pH basic.

$$F^-(aq) + H_2O(l) \rightleftharpoons HF(aq) + OH^-(aq)$$

The $F^-$ has a strong affinity for $H^+$ and will remove the $H^+$ from the water, leaving $OH^-$ ions behind. The table below indicates the strength of the acid and the base strength of the anion present.

| Acid Strength | Acid | Base | Base Strength |
|---|---|---|---|
| Strong | $HCl$ | $Cl^-$ | Neutral |
| Strong | $H_2SO_4$ | $HSO_4^-$ | Neutral |
| Strong | $HNO_3$ | $NO_3^-$ | Neutral |
| Strong | $H_3O^+$ | $H_2O$ | Weak |
| Weak | $HSO_4^-$ | $SO_4^{2-}$ | Weak |
| Weak | $H_2SO_3$ | $HSO_3^-$ | Weak |
| Weak | $H_3PO_4$ | $H_2PO_4^-$ | Weak |
| Weak | $HF$ | $F^-$ | Weak |
| Weak | $HC_2H_3O_2$ | $C_2H_3O_2^-$ | Weak |
| Weak | $H_2CO_3$ | $HCO_3^-$ | Weak |
| Weak | $H_2S$ | $HS^-$ | Weak |
| Weak | $HSO_3^-$ | $SO_3^{2-}$ | Weak |
| Weak | $H_2PO_4^-$ | $HPO_4^{2-}$ | Weak |
| Weak | $HCN$ | $CN^-$ | Weak |
| Weak | $NH_4^+$ | $NH_3$ | Weak |
| Weak | $HCO_3^-$ | $CO_3^{2-}$ | Weak |
| Weak | $HPO_4^{2-}$ | $PO_4^{3-}$ | Weak |
| Weak | $H_2O$ | $OH^-$ | Strong |
| Negligible | $HS^-$ | $S^{2-}$ | Strong |
| Negligible | $OH^-$ | $O^{2-}$ | Strong |

**Figure 15.10 Strength of Conjugate Acid–Base Pairs** The stronger an acid, the weaker its conjugate base.

The cation of a weak base will affect the pH of the solution. In the example below, ammonium, which is the conjugate acid of ammonia, reacts with water to form an equilibrium system with ammonia and hydronium ions. The hydronium ions will make the pH test acidic.

$$NH_4^+(aq)\ H_2O(l) \rightleftharpoons NH_3(aq) + H_3O^+(l)$$

Knowing the cations and anions will help to determine if the salts will test acidic, basic, or neutral. As mentioned above, cations of strong bases and anions of strong acids will form a neutral salt.

Acidic salts are formed from the anion of a strong acid and the cation of a weak base due to the interaction of the cation with water such as $NH_4Br$.

Basic salts are formed from the anion of a weak acid and the cation of a strong base due to the interaction of the anion with water. Examples include $NaF$, $KNO_2$, and $Ca(C_2H_3O_2)_2$.

One way to find the pH is to use the equation $K_aK_b = K_w$. If the $K_a$ is known of the acid, the $K_b$ of the conjugate base can be calculated. From the $K_b$, the pH can be calculated. We can also use the equation $-\log K_a + -\log K_b = 14$, which can also be written as $pK_a + pK_b = 14$.

**Table 15.1**    pH of Salt Solutions

|  |  | ANION | |
|---|---|---|---|
|  |  | **Conjugate base of strong acid** | **Conjugate base of weak acid** |
| **CATION** | **Conjugate acid of weak base** | *Acidic* | *Depends on relative strengths* |
|  | **Small, highly charged metal ion** | *Acidic* | *Depends on relative strengths* |
|  | **Counterion of strong base** | *Neutral* | *Basic* |

This table summarizes how to predict the pH of a salt.

Section 15.9    **Polyprotic Acids**

Polyprotic acids dissociate in several steps, each with a unique $K_a$. With each step, the $K_a$ values get smaller and smaller, indicating with each successive step ions dissociate less and less. In other words, the majority of the dissociation occurs on the first dissociation. For the most part, by calculating the concentration from the first step, the pH can be calculated as the amounts of $H^+$ from the additional steps is usually insignificant. With dilute sulfuric acid solutions, the actual amounts from each step need to be calculated to determine the pH.

**Dissociation of a Polyprotic Acid**

$$H_2C_6H_6O_6(aq) + H_2O(l) \rightleftharpoons H_3O^+(aq) + HC_6H_6O_6^-(aq)$$

$$\left[H_3O^+\right] = 2.8 \times 10^{-3} \text{ M}$$

$$HC_6H_6O_6^-(aq) + H_2O(l) \rightleftharpoons H_3O^+(aq) + C_6H_6O_6^{2-}(aq)$$

$$\left[H_3O^+\right] = 1.6 \times 10^{-12} \text{ M}$$

$$0.100 \text{ M } H_2C_6H_6O_6$$

$$\text{Total} \left[H_3O^+\right] = 2.8 \times 10^{-3} \text{ M} + 1.6 \times 10^{-12} \text{ M}$$

$$= 2.8 \times 10^{-3} \text{ M}$$

**Figure 15.11  Dissociation of a Polyprotic Acid**    A 0.100 M $H_2C_6H_6O_6$ solution contains an $H_3O^+$ concentration of $2.8 \times 10^{-3}$ M from the first step. The amount of $H_3O^+$ contributed by the second step is only $1.6 \times 10^{-12}$ M, which is insignificant compared to the amount produced by the first step.

# Acid Strength and Molecular Structure    Section 15.10

Two factors affect the strength of binary acids and the ease of dissociation; the polarity of the bond and the strength of the bond in the acid. The $H^+$ must be $\delta^+$ in the bond to end up being dissociated as an $H^+$, so the bond must be polar. In the three cases below, only the HF bond is polar with $\delta^+$ on the H end.

$$\overset{\longleftarrow +}{H—Li} \qquad H—C \qquad \overset{+ \longrightarrow}{H—F}$$

Not acidic    Not acidic    Acidic

In LiH, the H is $\delta^-$ so this is not acidic and H—C is nonpolar so cannot be acidic.

It also makes sense; the stronger the bond, the harder it is to remove the $H^+$ so the less the acid dissociates, the weaker the acid is. If bond energies are known, the stronger acid will have the smaller bond energy.

| Acid | Bond Energy (kJ/mol) | Type of Acid |
|---|---|---|
| H—F | 565 | Weak |
| H—Cl | 431 | Strong |
| H—Br | 364 | Strong |

When combining the effect of bond strength and polarity, the following trend is observed.

Since electronegativities increase from left to right across the periodic table, the bond with hydrogen becomes more polar and the acids get stronger, and as the bond energies decrease down a group, acid strength increases.

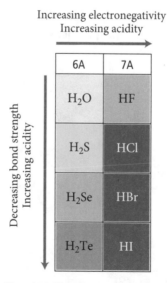

**Figure 15.12 Acidity of the Group 6A and 7A Hydrides** From left to right, the hydrides become more acidic because the H—Y bond becomes more polar. From top to bottom, these hydrides become more acidic because the H—Y bond becomes weaker.

In oxyacids, the more oxygen atoms on the acid, the more the molecule can polarize and pull the electron density away from the H—O bond, weakening the bond and allowing the $H^+$ to be removed more easily. This can be determined by analyzing data in the following table:

| Acid | Structure | $K_a$ |
|---|---|---|
| $HClO_4$ | $\begin{array}{c} O \\ \parallel \\ H-O-Cl=O \\ \parallel \\ O \end{array}$ | Strong |
| $HClO_3$ | $\begin{array}{c} O \\ \parallel \\ H-O-Cl=O \end{array}$ | 1 |
| $HClO_2$ | $H-O-Cl=O$ | $1.1 \times 10^{-2}$ |
| $HClO$ | $H-O-Cl$ | $2.9 \times 10^{-8}$ |

If comparing oxyacids with the same number of oxygen atoms, the electronegativity of the other atom (not the H or O) determines which is stronger. The more electronegative atom will polarize the bond more, making it easier to remove the $H^+$, and is therefore the stronger acid.

| Acid | Electronegativity of Y | $K_a$ |
|---|---|---|
| H—O—I | 2.5 | $2.3 \times 10^{-11}$ |
| H—O—Br | 2.8 | $2.0 \times 10^{-9}$ |
| H—O—Cl | 3.0 | $2.9 \times 10^{-8}$ |

Evaluation of data and accompanying explanations to determine the stronger or weaker acid are included in the science practices students need to master.

## Additional Practice

*Self-Assessment Quiz Questions Q1, Q2, Q3, Q4, Q5, Q6, Q7, Q8, Q9, Q10, Q11, Q12, Q13, Q14, and Q15*

*Problems 2, 4, 5, 6, 7, 8, 9, 12, 13, 15, 16, 17, 18, 19, 25, 33, 35, 37, 41, 43, 47, 48, 51, 54, 57, 66, 69, 73, 81, 87, 89, 94, 95, 96, 99, 101, 109, 110, 117, 119, 127, 128, and 141*

## Practice AP® Test Questions

A student is given 50.0 mL 0.020 M solutions of four acids. Use the data in the following table to help answer Questions 1–5.

| Acid | $K_a$ |
|------|-------|
| HF | $6.8 \times 10^{-4}$ |
| HCOOH | $1.8 \times 10^{-4}$ |
| $CH_3CH_2COOH$ | $1.8 \times 10^{-5}$ |
| HOCl | $3.0 \times 10^{-8}$ |

1. Which is the weakest acid?

   A)  HF

   B)  HCOOH

   C)  $CH_3CH_2COOH$

   D)  HOCl

2. Which 0.020 M acid solution has the highest percentage ionization?

   A)  HF

   B)  HCOOH

   C)  $CH_3CH_2COOH$

   D)  HOCl

3. Determine the pH of an aqueous solution of 0.020 M HOCl?

   A)  1.70

   B)  2.45

   C)  4.61

   D)  9.22

4. The following particulate diagrams are used to represent equal volumes of the acids. Which diagram does not represent any of the four acids?

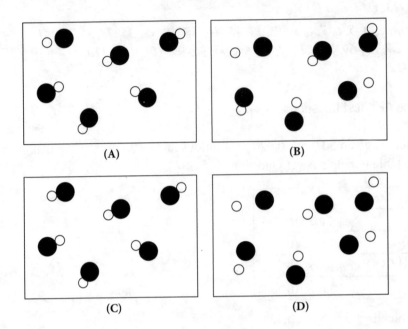

(A)          (B)

(C)          (D)

5. Each acid solution is titrated with 0.020 M NaOH solution until the acid is neutralized. At the equivalence point, the resultant solution from which acid will have the highest pH?

A) HF

B) HCOOH

C) $CH_3CH_2COOH$

D) HOCl

# AQUEOUS IONIC EQUILIBRIUM

CHAPTER

# 16

This chapter has several important sections including those on buffers, precipitation, and acid–base titrations. Learning objectives are from several big ideas but primarily from Big Idea 6. Students should be able to analyze different types of titration curves, data analysis of precipitation, and data analysis of buffers. The following sections should be included in course work:

16.2 **Buffers: Solutions That Resist pH Change**

16.3 **Buffer Effectiveness: Buffer Range and Buffer Capacity**

16.4 **Titrations and pH Curves**

16.5 **Solubility Equilibria and the Solubility Product Constant**

16.6 **Precipitation**

16.7 **Qualitative Chemical Analysis**

## Specific Learning Objectives Addressed in This Chapter:

**Learning objective 1.20** The student can design, and/or interpret data from, an experiment that uses titration to determine the concentration of an analyte in a solution. [*See* **SP 4.2, 5.1**]

**Learning objective 6.1** The student is able to, given a set of experimental observations regarding physical, chemical, biological, or environmental processes that are reversible, construct an explanation that connects the observations to the reversibility of the underlying chemical reactions or processes. [*See* **SP 6.2**]

**Learning objective 6.2** The student can, given a manipulation of a chemical reaction or set of reactions (e.g., reversal of reaction or addition of two reactions), determine the effects of that manipulation on $Q$ or $K$. [*See* **SP 2.2**]

**Learning objective 6.11** The student can generate or use a particulate representation of an acid (strong or weak or polyprotic) and a strong base to explain the species that will have large versus small concentrations at equilibrium. [*See* **SP 1.1, 1.4, 2.3**]

**Learning objective 6.12** The student can reason about the distinction between strong and weak acid solutions with similar values of pH, including the percent ionization of the acids, the concentrations needed to achieve the same pH, and the amount of base needed to reach the equivalence point in a titration. [*See* **SP 1.4**]

**Learning objective 6.13** The student can interpret titration data for monoprotic or polyprotic acids involving titration of a weak or strong acid by a strong base (or a weak or strong base by a strong acid) to determine the concentration of the titrant and the $pK_a$ for a weak acid, or the $pK_b$ for a weak base. [*See* **SP 5.1**]

**Learning objective 6.15** The student can identify a given solution as containing a mixture of strong acids and/or bases and calculate or estimate the pH (and concentrations of all chemical species) in the resulting solution. [*See* **SP 2.2, 2.3, 6.4**]

**Learning objective 6.16** The student can identify a given solution as being the solution of a monoprotic weak acid or base (including salts in which one ion is a weak acid or base), calculate the pH and concentration of all species in the solution, and/or infer the relative strengths of the weak acids or bases from given equilibrium concentrations. [*See* **SP 2.2, 6.4**]

**Learning objective 6.18** The student can design a buffer solution with a target pH and buffer capacity by selecting an appropriate conjugate acid–base pair and estimating the concentrations needed to achieve the desired capacity. [*See* **SP 2.3, 4.2, 6.4**]

**Learning objective 6.20** The student can identify a solution as being a buffer solution and explain the buffer mechanism in terms of the reactions that would occur on addition of acid or base. [*See* **SP 6.4**]

**Learning objective 6.21** The student can predict the solubility of a salt, or rank the solubility of salts, given the relevant $K_{sp}$ values. [*See* **SP 2.2, 2.3, 6.4**]

**Learning objective 6.22** The student can interpret data regarding solubility of salts to determine, or rank, the relevant $K_{sp}$ values. [*See* **SP 2.2, 2.3, 6.4**]

**Learning objective 6.23** The student can interpret data regarding the relative solubility of salts in terms of factors (common ions, pH) that influence the solubility. [*See* **SP 5.1**]

## Specific Science Practices Addressed in This Chapter:

**Science Practice 1:** The student can use representations and models to communicate scientific phenomena and solve scientific problems.

> 1.1  The student can *create representations and models* of natural or man-made phenomena and systems in the domain.

> 1.4  The student can *use representations and models* to analyze situations or solve problems qualitatively and quantitatively.

**Science Practice 2:** The student can use mathematics appropriately.

> 2.2  The student can *apply mathematical routines* to quantities that describe natural phenomena.

> 2.3  The student can *estimate numerically* quantities that describe natural phenomena.

**Science Practice 4:** The student can plan and implement data collection strategies in relation to a particular scientific question.

4.2  The student can *design a plan* for collecting data to answer a particular scientific question.

**Science Practice 5:** The student can perform data analysis and evaluation of evidence.

5.1  The student can *analyze data* to identify patterns or relationships.

**Science Practice 6:** The student can work with scientific explanations and theories.

6.2  The student can *construct explanations of phenomena based on evidence* produced through scientific practices.

6.4  The student can *make claims and predictions about natural phenomena* based on scientific theories and models.

## Concepts and Vocabulary to Review:

## Buffers: Solutions That Resist pH Change     Section 16.2

Buffers resist changes in pH because they have in the solution components acting as both acid and base. They are composed of either a weak acid and its conjugate base or a weak base and its conjugate acid. The acid component neutralizes added base and the base component neutralizes added acid.

Acidic buffers contain acid and a conjugate base.

### Formation of a Buffer

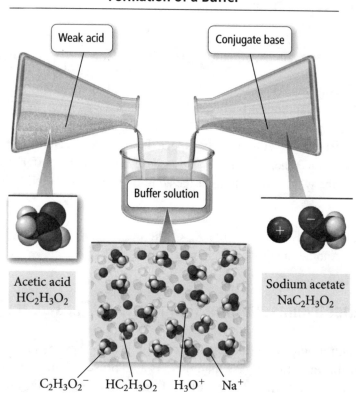

**Figure 16.1  A Buffer Solution**  A buffer typically consists of a weak acid (which can neutralize added base) and its conjugate base (which can neutralize added acid).

Basic buffers contain a base and a conjugate acid.

**Formation of a Buffer**

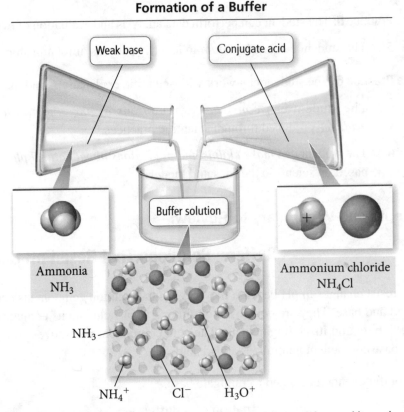

**Figure 16.2  Buffer Containing a Base**    A buffer can also consist of a weak base and its conjugate acid.

The Henderson-Hasselbach equation, $pH = pK_a + \log\dfrac{[base]}{[acid]}$, is provided on the equation pages of the AP exam. Students should anticipate exam questions assess conceptual understanding of buffer solutions. Students can use an ICE chart from an equilibrium approach to solve for concentrations and then use the pH equation to solve for the pH. AP students are only expected to be able to determine the initial pH of a buffer solution. When additional acid or base is added to a buffer, a student only needs to describe what will occur after the addition using Le Châtelier's principle.

If the $K_a$ of an acid is known, the $K_b$ of the conjugate can be calculated using $K_aK_b = K_w$. Another method is using $pK_a + pK_b = 14$.

**Section 16.3**    ## Buffer Effectiveness: Buffer Range and Buffer Capacity

A buffer cannot neutralize more additional acid than there is base present, nor can it neutralize additional base than there is acid present. This amount describes the capacity of a buffer. If 0.10 moles of acid is added to a buffer containing

0.01 moles of base, the buffer capacity (0.01 moles) will be exceeded. Once exceeded, the pH will not stay stable and will become more acidic. The more moles of the buffering components present, the greater the effectiveness of the buffer will be.

The buffering range is the pH range in which the buffer is effective. The most effective range is within one pH unit of $pK_a$ for an acidic buffer. In the titration curve below, notice the pH around this point is fairly stable. A pH near the equivalence point would not work as a buffering region as the pH has a large range.

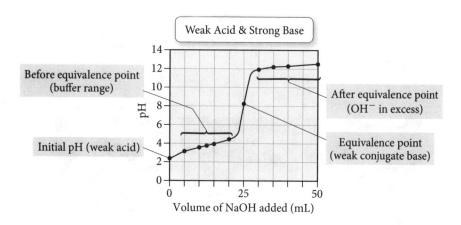

**Titrations and pH Curves**    Section 16.4

Titrations can be done through graphing the pH as the titration is done and then analyzed or an indicator can be used to determine when the titration is complete (see Figure 16.3).

The indicator will visually indicate the endpoint of the titration (equivalence point) by changing color. This means the indicator must change to a different color at the approximate pH. Students are not expected to know the indicator colors except for phenolphthalein, which they should have used during lab. Students should know it is clear in acidic solutions and pink in basic solutions.

When the data collected is graphed, a pH curve of a strong acid, strong base appears like a flattened s. The curve has several points identified by the components of the system. The starting pH of the acid will indicate if the acid is a weak or a strong acid. The pH at the end of the curve will indicate if the base was a weak or a strong base. The pH at the equivalence point will indicate the strength of the acid and base to each other. A strong acid and strong base will reach equivalence at a pH of 7 (see Figures 16.5 and 16.6).

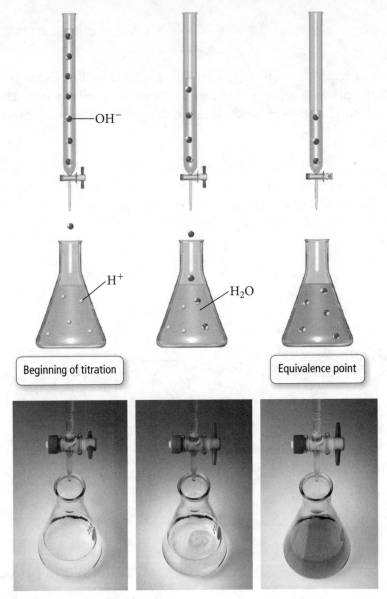

**Figure 16.3 Acid–Base Titration** As OH⁻ is added in a titration, it neutralizes the H⁺, forming water. At the equivalence point, the titration is complete.

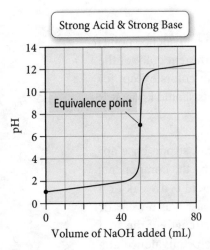

**Figure 16.4 Titration Curve: Strong Acid + Strong Base** This curve represents the titration of 50.0 mL of 0.100 M HCl with 0.100 M NaOH.

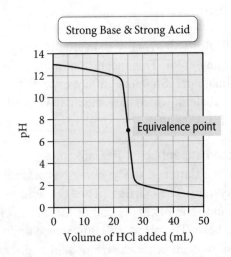

**Figure 16.5 Titration Curve: Strong Base + Strong Acid** This curve represents the titration of 25.0 mL of 0.100 M NaOH with 0.100 M HCl.

A strong base and a weak acid will have a basic equivalence point due to the hydrolysis of the conjugate base of the weak acid.

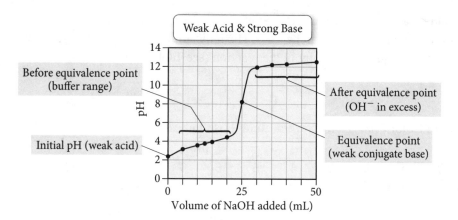

The best buffering region is near the $pK_a$ value, which is located halfway to the equivalence point (also called the half equivalence point).

A weak base and a strong acid will have an acidic equivalence point due to the hydrolysis of the conjugate acid of the weak base (see Figure 16.6).

In this example, the best buffering region is near $pK_b$, which is halfway to equivalence.

For polyprotic acids, the number of equivalence points usually will be equal to the number of hydrogen ions in the acid. For instance, diprotic oxalic acid will have two equivalence points. Each dissociation reaction will have an equation and a $K_a$ although the majority of all $[H^+]$ contributing to the pH comes from the first dissociation (see Figure 16.7).

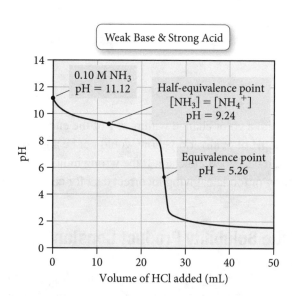

**Figure 16.6  Titration Curve: Weak Base with Strong Acid**   This curve represents the titration of 0.100 M $NH_3$ with 0.100 M HCl.

## Titration of a Polyprotic Acid

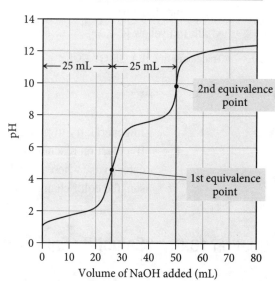

**Figure 16.7  Titration Curve: Diprotic Acid with Strong Base**   This curve represents the titration of 25.0 mL of 0.100 M of a diprotic acid with 0.100 M NaOH.

Another way to determine an end-point while doing a titration is by using an indicator. Indicators are themselves weak acids which turn different colors at different pH levels. The equivalence point (when moles of acid and moles of base are equal) should be located close to the end point (when the indicator changes color) of the titration. Not any indicator can be used. The indicator chosen must change color in the range of the equivalence point in the reaction (see Table 16.1 below).

**Table 16.1**    Ranges of Color Changes for Several Acid–Base Indicators

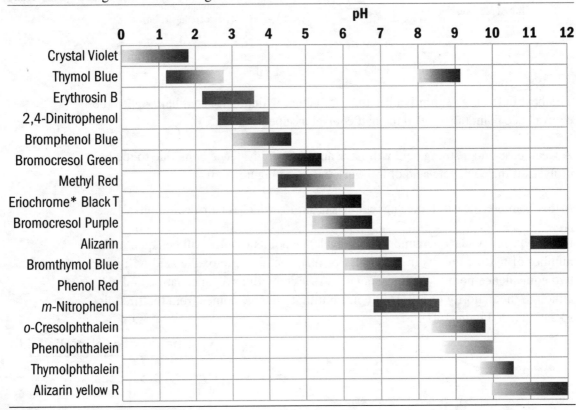

\* Trademark of CIBA GEIGY CORP.

In general, try to pick an indicator with a color change within $\pm 1$ of the end point pH. If a reaction reaches equivalence at a pH of 5, alizarin yellow would not be a good indicator to use whereas methyl red would be a good indicator. If the wrong indicator is chosen, the color change will be too early or too late, giving incorrect data for calculations.

## Section 16.5    Solubility Equilibria and the Solubility Product Constant

Another type of equilibrium is called the solubility product constant $(K_{sp})$. The $K_{sp}$ is a measure of the solubility of a substance. The values of $K_{sp}$ cannot be compared though, unless the species being compared have the same number of ions. Why? This

**Table 16.2**   Selected Solubility Product Constants ($K_{sp}$) at 25°C

| Compound | Formula | $K_{sp}$ | Compound | Formula | $K_{sp}$ |
|---|---|---|---|---|---|
| Barium fluoride | $BaF_2$ | $2.45 \times 10^{-5}$ | Lead(II) chloride | $PbCl_2$ | $1.17 \times 10^{-5}$ |
| Barium sulfate | $BaSO_4$ | $1.07 \times 10^{-10}$ | Lead(II) bromide | $PbBr_2$ | $4.67 \times 10^{-6}$ |
| Calcium carbonate | $CaCO_3$ | $4.96 \times 10^{-9}$ | Lead(II) sulfate | $PbSO_4$ | $1.82 \times 10^{-8}$ |
| Calcium fluoride | $CaF_2$ | $1.46 \times 10^{-10}$ | Lead(II) sulfide* | $PbS$ | $9.04 \times 10^{-29}$ |
| Calcium hydroxide | $Ca(OH)_2$ | $4.68 \times 10^{-6}$ | Magnesium carbonate | $MgCO_3$ | $6.82 \times 10^{-6}$ |
| Calcium sulfate | $CaSO_4$ | $7.10 \times 10^{-5}$ | Magnesium hydroxide | $Mg(OH)_2$ | $2.06 \times 10^{-13}$ |
| Copper(II) sulfide* | $CuS$ | $1.27 \times 10^{-36}$ | Silver chloride | $AgCl$ | $1.77 \times 10^{-10}$ |
| Iron(II) carbonate | $FeCO_3$ | $3.07 \times 10^{-11}$ | Silver chromate | $Ag_2CrO_4$ | $1.12 \times 10^{-12}$ |
| Iron(II) hydroxide | $Fe(OH)_2$ | $4.87 \times 10^{-17}$ | Silver bromide | $AgBr$ | $5.35 \times 10^{-13}$ |
| Iron(II) sulfide* | $FeS$ | $3.72 \times 10^{-19}$ | Silver iodide | $AgI$ | $8.51 \times 10^{-17}$ |

*Sulfide equilibrium is of the type: $MS(s) + H_2O(l) \rightleftharpoons M^{2+}(aq) + HS^-(aq) + OH^-(aq)$

is because the solving of molar solubility uses different exponents depending on the stoichiometry.

Barium sulfate has two ions as does lead(II) sulfate. Looking at the $K_{sp}$ values, barium sulfate is a smaller number and will be more insoluble. To determine the actual molar solubility will require a calculation. When two ions are present, $K_{sp} = s^2$ so the square root of the $K_{sp}$ value indicates the molar solubility. If three ions are present the general formula is $K_{sp} = 4s^3$. The $K_{sp}$ values are temperature dependent.

How molar solubility is affected by common ions and pH can be analyzed using Le Châtelier's principle. Adding a common ion to the ions on the product will cause a shift to the left and decrease solubility. Which way the reaction will shift when adding acid or base depends upon the species in solution. If the solution is basic, adding acid removes base by neutralizing it and the reaction will shift to the right (products side) to replace the lost hydroxide ions. If more base (common ion) is added to the basic solution, the reaction will shift to the left, decreasing solubility. If the solution is acidic, adding base will increase its solubility as the base removes the hydrogen ions, causing a shift to the right to replace the lost ions. If more acid is added to an acidic solution, the reaction will shift to the left and become more insoluble due to the common ion effect.

# Precipitation     Section 16.6

When precipitates form, students often think ALL ions have formed the precipitate. Understanding the solution has both precipitate and ions present at equilibrium is important. If the substance is very insoluble, very few ions will be in solution and the $K_{sp}$ value will be very small. $K_{sp}$ and $Q$ are not only used to determine when precipitates form but also what are the concentrations of the ions still in solution. When two solutions are added together, determining if a precipitate will form can also be determined by using the reaction quotient ($Q$).

Unsaturated solutions will not form a precipitate and data analysis will show $Q < K_{sp}$. When $K_{sp} = Q$, then the solution is saturated. The maximum amount has been dissolved and the addition of any more will form a precipitate. If $Q > K_{sp}$, then the solution is supersaturated and usually excess will precipitate out.

When two or more ions are in solution which will precipitate when a given ion is added, the ions can be isolated from each other. In one method when two precipitate form when the same ion is added, the most insoluble will precipitate first. Another method is to add ions to precipitate one ion and not another. This is called selective precipitation. Adding a chloride anion will precipitate out silver, mercury, and lead cations.

## Section 16.7    Qualitative Chemical Analysis

Qualitative analysis is a method used to identify unknown cations in a sample. The process involves knowing solubility rules and which cations form precipitates with the anions added (see Figure 16.8).

Through this process, cations can be isolated from each other and tested to see what is present. This can be seen in a qualitative analysis flow chart (see Figure 16.9).

AP students are not expected to memorize the flow chart but are expected to be able to look at data and use it as evidence to make a claim about what might be in a solution. Students should do a qualitative analysis lab to understand how the flow chart helps them to identify unknowns.

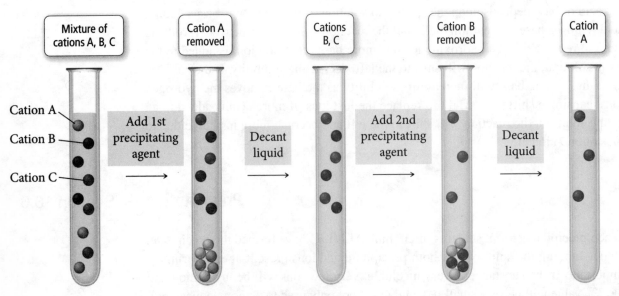

**Figure 16.8  Qualitative Analysis**    In qualitative analysis, specific ions are precipitated successively by the addition of appropriate reagents.

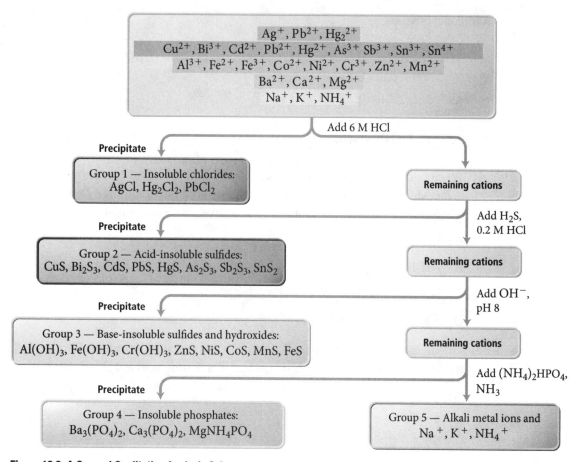

Figure 16.9  A General Qualitative Analysis Scheme

When the only cations left in solution are alkali metals, flame tests can be used to identify the ions.

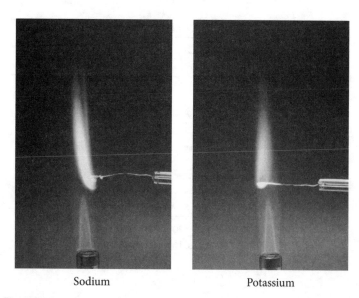

Sodium                    Potassium

Figure 16.10  Flame Tests    The sodium ion produces a yellow-orange flame. The potassium ion produces a violet flame.

### Additional Practice

*Self-Assessment Quiz Questions Q1, Q2, Q3, Q4, Q5, Q6, Q7, Q8, Q9, Q10, Q11, Q12, Q13, Q14, and Q15*
*Problems 1, 3, 17, and 25*

### Practice AP® Test Questions

1. When two solutions, each having a volume of 50.0 mL and concentration of 0.750 M, are mixed, which resultant solution would resist a large change in pH when small amounts of a strong acid or a strong base are added?

   A) $HBr(aq)$ and $KOH(aq)$

   B) $NH_4Br(aq)$ and $NH_3(aq)$

   C) $HBr(aq)$ and $KBr(aq)$

   D) $NH_4Br(aq)$ and $KBr(aq)$

2. Calculate the pH of 40.0 mL of solution that is 0.400 M in sodium formate and 0.800 M in formic acid $(HCO_2H)$. The $K_a$ of formic acid is $1.77 \times 10^{-4}$.

   A) 3.45

   B) 3.75

   C) 4.05

   D) 4.14

3. A volume 30.0 mL of 1.0 M oxalic acid was titrated with 1.00 M NaOH. A graph of pH versus volume of NaOH added was plotted and appears below. At which point can one determine the $pKa_1$ of oxalic acid?

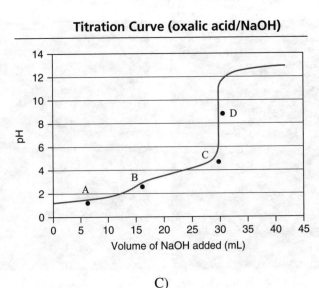

   A)

   B)

   C)

   D)

4. A 50.0 mL sample of 0.300 M nitrous acid ($HNO_2$) is titrated with 50.0 mL of 0.300 M KOH. Determine the pH at the equivalence point using two significant figures. The $K_a$ of nitrous acid is $4.50 \times 10^{-4}$.

A) 3.35

B) 7.00

C) 8.26

D) 11.81

5. The following diagrams represent the molecular level of small volumes of solutions containing various amounts of nitrous acid ($HNO_2$) and potassium nitrite. Water molecules, potassium ions, hydroxide ions, and hydronium ions have been omitted. Which solution has the greatest buffer capacity?

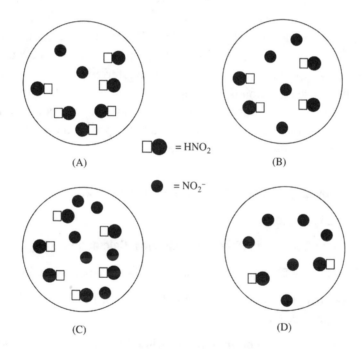

(A)

(B)

$\square\bullet$ = $HNO_2$

$\bullet$ = $NO_2^-$

(C)

(D)

# CHAPTER 17

# FREE ENERGY AND THERMODYNAMICS

Thermodynamics is the focus of Big Idea 5 in the AP Chemistry Framework. Thermodynamics provides the evidence for the driving forces in processes and reactions and is crucial to be understood. There are many misconceptions about thermodynamics. One misconception is spontaneity has to do with speed. Since the word "spontaneous" is commonly used and understood to mean immediate, scientists often use the phrase "thermodynamically favorable" when referring to chemical processes producing products once the reaction starts to occur. Spontaneous occurs naturally but it may be very slow and on the AP test will be referred to as thermodynamically favored. Another misconception is thinking catalysts affect spontaneity. Catalysts affect the speed of the reaction but do not contribute to whether or not the reaction will happen. Nonspontaneous reactions can be made to happen by the addition of energy. The most important sections in this chapter are:

- 17.3 **Entropy and the Second Law of Thermodynamics**

- 17.5 **Gibbs Free Energy**

- 17.6 **Entropy Changes in Chemical Reactions: Calculating $\Delta S^{\circ}_{rxn}$**

- 17.7 **Free Energy Changes in Chemical Reactions: Calculating $\Delta G^{\circ}_{rxn}$**

- 17.8 **Free Energy Changes for Nonstandard States: The Relationship between $\Delta G^{\circ}_{rxn}$ and $\Delta G_{rxn}$**

- 17.9 **Free Energy and Equilibrium: Relating $\Delta G^{\circ}_{rxn}$ to the Equilibrium Constant ($K$)**

## Specific Learning Objectives Addressed in This Chapter:

**Learning objective 5.2** The student is able to relate temperature to the motions of particles, either via particulate representations, such as drawings of particles with arrows indicating velocities, and/or via representations of average kinetic energy and distribution of kinetic energies of the particles, such as plots of the Maxwell-Boltzmann distribution. [*See* **SP 1.1, 1.4, 7.1**]

**Learning objective 5.12** The student is able to use representations and models to predict the sign and relative magnitude of the entropy change associated with chemical or physical processes. [*See* **SP 1.4**]

**Learning objective 5.13**  The student is able to predict whether or not a physical or chemical process is thermodynamically favored by determination of (either quantitatively or qualitatively) the signs of both $\Delta H°$ and $\Delta S°$, and calculation or estimation of $\Delta G°$ when needed. [*See* **SP 2.2**, **2.3**, **6.4**]

**Learning objective 5.14**  The student is able to determine whether a chemical or physical process is thermodynamically favorable by calculating the change in standard Gibbs free energy. [*See* **SP 2.2**]

**Learning objective 5.15**  The student is able to explain how the application of external energy sources or the coupling of favorable with unfavorable reactions can be used to cause processes that are not thermodynamically favorable to become favorable. [*See* **SP 6.2**]

**Learning objective 5.16**  The student can use Le Châtelier's principle to make qualitative predictions for systems in which coupled reactions that share a common intermediate drive formation of a product. [*See* **SP 6.4**]

**Learning objective 5.18**  The student can explain why a thermodynamically favored chemical reaction may not produce large amounts of product (based on consideration of both initial conditions and kinetic effects), or why a thermodynamically unfavored chemical reaction can produce large amounts of product for certain sets of initial conditions. [*See* **SP 1.3**, **7.2**]

## Specific Science Practices Addressed in This Chapter:

**Science Practice 1:** The student can use representations and models to communicate scientific phenomena and solve scientific problems.

    1.1   The student can *create representations and models* of natural or man-made phenomena and systems in the domain.

    1.3   The student can *refine representations and models* of natural or man-made phenomena and systems in the domain.

    1.4   The student can *use representations and models* to analyze situations or solve problems qualitatively and quantitatively.

**Science Practice 2:** The student can use mathematics appropriately.

    2.2   The student can *apply mathematical routines* to quantities that describe natural phenomena.

    2.3   The student can *estimate numerically* quantities that describe natural phenomena.

**Science Practice 6:** The student can work with scientific explanations and theories.

    6.2   The student can *construct explanations of phenomena based on evidence* produced through scientific practices.

    6.4   The student can *make claims and predictions about natural phenomena* based on scientific theories and models.

**Science Practice 7:** The student is able to connect and relate knowledge across various scales, concepts, and representations in and across domains.

7.1  The student can *connect phenomena and models* across spatial and temporal scales.

7.2  The student can *connect concepts* in and across domain(s) to generalize or extrapolate in and/or across enduring understandings and/or big ideas.

### Concepts and Vocabulary to Review:

**Section 17.3**

## Entropy and the Second Law of Thermodynamics

Enthalpy does not in itself determine if a reaction is spontaneous. If it did, all spontaneous reactions would be exothermic, but this is not the case. The other factor to be considered is entropy. For an endothermic process to occur, there must be an increase in the randomness of the particles. In contrast, exothermic reactions or processes may or may not increase in randomness.

The second law of thermodynamics states for any spontaneous process, the entropy of the universe increases ($\Delta S > 0$). The key is the universe is increasing. Entropy ($S$) increases with the number of energetically different (more randomized) ways to arrange a system. Gas particles have the most ways since they are independent from each other compared to a solid.

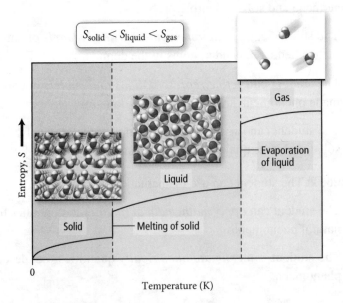

**Figure 17.1 Entropy and State Change**   Entropy increases when matter changes from a solid to a liquid and from a liquid to a gas.

Phase transitions from solid to liquid, liquid to gas, and solid to gas all have positive entropy. In chemical reactions, if the number of moles of gases increases during the reaction, the entropy also increases. There are thermodynamically favorable reactions that decrease in entropy, but meanwhile the surroundings and universe entropy increase.

## Gibbs Free Energy    Section 17.5

For a spontaneous reaction to occur, there must be energy to do work. Gibbs free energy is the measure of this energy or chemical potential. $\Delta G > 0$ is nonspontaneous, $\Delta G = 0$ is at equilibrium, and $\Delta G < 0$ is spontaneous. Gibbs free energy is calculated from the equation

$$\Delta G = \Delta H - T\Delta S$$

All spontaneous processes will have a negative sign but the size of the free energy indicates how spontaneous the process will be. The more negative the number is, the more spontaneous the process will be. The equation also shows both enthalpy and entropy are used to determine $\Delta G$.

When $\Delta H$ is negative (exothermic) and $\Delta S$ is positive, the driving force of spontaneity is both factors, although one may contribute more than the other. Thinking about the equation, a negative number ($\Delta H$) subtracting a positive value ($-T\Delta S$), no matter the temperature, will always be negative. In contrast, when $\Delta H$ is positive (endothermic) and $\Delta S$ is negative, neither is a driving force as, no matter the temperature, the value always comes out positive; $(+) - (-) = (+)$. The question is when both are negative values or positive values. When both are negative, then $(-) - (-) = (?)$; whether or not the final value is spontaneous depends on the size of $T\Delta S$ and is therefore temperature dependent. If the value of $T$ is small, then the value can remain negative and the driving force is the enthalpy, but if $T$ is large then the $\Delta G$ value will become positive. When both are positive values, then $(+) - (+) = (?)$ and again the temperature makes a difference. To be a negative $\Delta G$ value, the $T\Delta S$ must be larger than the $\Delta H$ value. The higher the temperature, the more likely the $\Delta G$ value will be negative. In this case, entropy is the driving force of the spontaneity.

**Table 17.1**  The Effect of $\Delta H$, $\Delta S$, and $T$ on Spontaneity

| $\Delta H$ | $\Delta S$ | Low Temperature | High Temperature | Example |
|---|---|---|---|---|
| $-$ | $+$ | Spontaneous ($\Delta G < 0$) | Spontaneous ($\Delta G < 0$) | $2\,N_2O(g) \rightarrow 2\,N_2(g) + O_2(g)$ |
| $+$ | $-$ | Nonspontaneous ($\Delta G > 0$) | Nonspontaneous ($\Delta G > 0$) | $3\,O_2(g) \rightarrow 2\,O_3(g)$ |
| $-$ | $-$ | Spontaneous ($\Delta G < 0$) | Nonspontaneous ($\Delta G > 0$) | $H_2O(l) \rightarrow H_2O(s)$ |
| $+$ | $+$ | Nonspontaneous ($\Delta G > 0$) | Spontaneous ($\Delta G < 0$) | $H_2O(l) \rightarrow H_2O(g)$ |

The free energy measures the chemical potential of a spontaneous reaction. In the Figure 17.2, the direction of the spontaneous direction can be determined.

## Entropy Changes in Chemical Reactions: Calculating $\Delta S^{\circ}_{rxn}$    Section 17.6

To calculate $\Delta S^{\circ}_{rxn}$, we need to know what the conditions are. The symbol $^{\circ}$ refers to standard state conditions. Standard state for a gas is a pressure of 1 atm, liquids and solids is a temperature of $25\,^{\circ}C$, and a solution is a concentration of 1 M. Individual substance values are reported per mole of substance and are therefore called standard molar

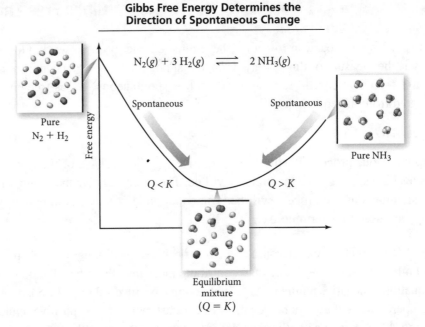

**Figure 17.2 Gibbs Free Energy** Gibbs free energy is also called chemical potential because it determines the direction of spontaneous change for chemical systems.

entropies ($S°$). The values are based on comparison to the third law of thermodynamics saying the entropy of a perfect crystal at absolute zero is zero. Some of the considerations for entropy values are the state of matter, the allotrope present, whether or not it is in solution, molecular complexity, and molar mass. In each case, the freedom for translational motion, rotational motion, and vibrational motion affect the value.

Notice the units are J/mol·K. This is important because when you calculate the standard entropy of the reaction, the balanced equation makes a difference.

$$\Delta S°_{rxn} = \sum n_p S°(\text{products}) - \sum n_r S°(\text{reactants})$$

**Table 17.2** Standard Molar Entropy Values ($S°$) for Selected Substances at 298 K

| Substance | $S°$(J/mol · K) | Substance | $S°$(J/mol · K) | Substance | $S°$(J/mol · K) |
|---|---|---|---|---|---|
| **Gases** | | **Liquids** | | **Solids** | |
| $H_2(g)$ | 130.7 | $H_2O(l)$ | 70.0 | $MgO(s)$ | 27.0 |
| $Ar(g)$ | 154.8 | $CH_3OH(l)$ | 126.8 | $Fe(s)$ | 27.3 |
| $CH_4(g)$ | 186.3 | $Br_2(l)$ | 152.2 | $Li(s)$ | 29.1 |
| $H_2O(g)$ | 188.8 | $C_6H_6(l)$ | 173.4 | $Cu(s)$ | 33.2 |
| $N_2(g)$ | 191.6 | | | $Na(s)$ | 51.3 |
| $NH_3(g)$ | 192.8 | | | $K(s)$ | 64.7 |
| $F_2(g)$ | 202.8 | | | $NaCl(s)$ | 72.1 |
| $O_2(g)$ | 205.2 | | | $CaCO_3(s)$ | 91.7 |
| $Cl_2(g)$ | 223.1 | | | $FeCl_3(s)$ | 142.3 |
| $C_2H_4(g)$ | 219.3 | | | | |

This represents the total of standard entropies of the products which were multiplied by their coefficients minus the total of standard entropies of the reactants which were multiplied by their coefficients.

## Free Energy Changes in Chemical Reactions: Calculating $\Delta G^\circ_{rxn}$

**Section 17.7**

At standard conditions, free energy can be calculated using $\Delta G^\circ_{rxn} = \Delta H^\circ_{rxn} - T\Delta S^\circ_{rxn}$ or by using standard thermodynamic data of free energy of formation values using $\Delta G^\circ_{rxn} = \sum n_p \Delta G^\circ_f(\text{products}) - \sum n_r \Delta G^\circ_f(\text{reactants})$. $\Delta G^\circ_f$ is the free energy of formation and represents the change in free energy when 1 mole of a compound in its standard state forms from its elements in their standard states. The $\Delta G^\circ_f$ of elements in their standard states is zero.

$\Delta G^\circ_{rxn}$ is dependent on the balanced equation. If the equation is doubled, the $\Delta G^\circ_{rxn}$ value doubles. What factor the equation changes by is the same factor $\Delta G^\circ_{rxn}$ will change by. If the reaction is reversed, the free energy sign is changed. If the balanced equation is found by adding a series of reactions together (Hess's Law), the $\Delta G^\circ_{rxn}$ of each equation used can also be added together.

The energy freed during the reaction is available to do work. Therefore, the value of the free energy is the theoretical limit of the maximum possible work. In reality, part of this free energy is converted to heat which is lost to the surroundings. For a reaction with a positive free energy value such as recharging a battery, this value becomes the minimum amount of energy needing to be added to cause the reaction to occur.

## Free Energy Changes for Nonstandard States: The Relationship between $\Delta G^\circ_{rxn}$ and $\Delta G_{rxn}$

**Section 17.8**

When nonstandard conditions are used for a reaction, the free energy can still be calculated: $\Delta G_{rxn} = \Delta G^\circ_{rxn} + RT \ln Q$. $Q$ is the same quotient from equilibrium calculations (products over reactants each raised to the power of their coefficients), $R$ is the gas constant with energy units 8.314 J/mol·K, and as always the temperature ($T$) is in Kelvin. When the reaction is at equilibrium, the value of free energy will be zero. The reaction is going both forward and in reverse with no net change.

## Free Energy and Equilibrium: Relating $\Delta G^\circ_{rxn}$ to the Equilibrium Constant ($K$)

**Section 17.9**

The relationship between free energy and the equilibrium constant is shown in the equation $\Delta G^\circ_{rxn} = -RT \ln K$. Logistically, analyzing each value can indicate the sign of the other value.
The curves in the graphs show graphically the extent of reaction based on the size of $K$.

Other ways to calculate $K$ with thermodynamic data include

$$\ln K = -\frac{\Delta H^{\circ}_{rxn}}{R}\left(\frac{l}{T}\right) + \frac{\Delta S^{\circ}_{rxn}}{R} \text{ and } \ln \frac{K_2}{K_1} = -\frac{\Delta H^{\circ}_{rxn}}{R}\left(\frac{1}{T_2} - \frac{1}{T_1}\right). \text{ Since } \Delta G^{\circ}_{rxn}$$

can be calculated from enthalpy and entropy values, the first equation is substituting them. The second equation is calculating what happens to the equilibrium constant when the reaction is carried out at two different temperatures. Analyzing data of what is occurring during the reaction at two temperatures should indicate if the free energy value is increasing or decreasing.

| $K$ value | ln $K$ | $\Delta G^{\circ}_{rxn}$ | Spontaneous? | graph |
|---|---|---|---|---|
| $K < 1$ | negative | positive | no | |
| $K = 1$ | zero | zero | at equilibrium | |
| $K > 1$ | positive | negative | yes | |

### Additional Practice

*Self-Assessment Quiz Questions Q1, Q2, Q3, Q4, Q5, Q6, Q7, Q8, Q9, Q10, Q11, Q12, Q13, Q14, and Q15*

*Problems 6, 13, 16, 27, 31, 37, 43, 44, 50, 57, 67, 71, 79, 80, 83, 107, 109, 110, 112, and 113*

### Practice AP® Test Questions

1. Of the following, which compound has the largest entropy? All compounds are at some high temperature, *T*.

   A) $H_2O(g)$

   B) $H_2S(g)$

   C) $H_2Se$

   D) $H_2Te$

2. The particulate diagram below represents a view of the sublimation process of iodine in which solid iodine becomes iodine vapor

   $$I_2(s) \rightarrow I_2(g) \quad \Delta G° = 20\ kJ/mol$$

   What are the signs (+ or −) of $\Delta H$, $\Delta S$, and $\Delta G$ for this process at 289K if the partial pressure of the iodine vapor is 1 mmHg?

   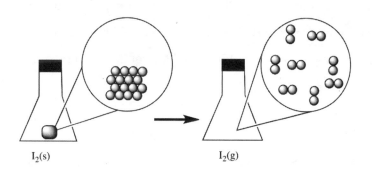

   A) $\Delta H = +, \Delta S = +, \Delta G = +$

   B) $\Delta H = +, \Delta S = +, \Delta G = -$

   C) $\Delta H = -, \Delta S = -, \Delta G = +$

   D) $\Delta H = -, \Delta S = -, \Delta G = -$

3. Consider the reaction: $Ag^+(aq) + Br^-(aq) \longrightarrow AgBr\ (s)$

   | Substance | $\Delta H°_f\,(kJ/mol)$ | $S°(J/mol\ K)$ |
   |-----------|------------------------|----------------|
   | $Ag^+(aq)$ | 105.9 | 73.93 |
   | $Br^-(aq)$ | −120.9 | 80.71 |
   | $AgBr(s)$ | −100.4 | 107.1 |

Determine the temperature (in units of C) above which the reaction is nonspontaneous.

A) Between 50 and 125 °C

B) Between 126 and 175 °C

C) Between 176 and 200 °C

D) Above 200 °C

4. Potassium reacts with water $2 K(s) + 2 H_2O(l) \rightarrow 2 KOH(aq) + H_2(g)$

The temperature of the water is observed to increase as the potassium reacts with water. What occurs with the enthalpy change and the entropy change?

A) The enthalpy change is negative and the entropy change is negative.

B) The enthalpy change is negative and the entropy change is positive.

C) The enthalpy change is positive and the entropy change is negative.

D) The enthalpy change is positive and the entropy change is positive.

5. For the reaction of nitrogen gas with chlorine gas

$$N_2(g) + 3 Cl_2(g) \rightarrow 2 NCl_3(g) \quad \Delta H° = -250\,kJ \text{ and } \Delta S° = -260\,J/K$$

Calculate $\Delta G°$ and indicate if the equilibrium is shifted to reactants or products.

A) $\Delta G°$ is approximately $-300$ kJ and the equilibrium favors the products.

B) $\Delta G°$ is approximately $-300$ kJ and the equilibrium favors the reactants.

C) $\Delta G°$ is approximately $-150$ kJ and the equilibrium favors the products.

D) $\Delta G°$ is approximately $-150$ kJ and the equilibrium favors the reactants.

# ELECTROCHEMISTRY

Most students have little background in electrochemistry and helping students acquire the vocabulary used in electrochemistry is foundational information to cover. Section 18.3 is a crucial section in electrochemistry. Students need to be able to determine if a reaction will be thermodynamically favorable, what positive voltage means, and how to read a standard electrode potentials table. Several learning objectives are addressed across all the big ideas.

18.2 **Balancing Oxidation-Reduction Equations**

18.3 **Voltaic (or Galvanic) Cells: Generating Electricity from Spontaneous Chemical Reactions**

18.4 **Standard Electrode Potentials**

18.5 **Cell Potential, Free Energy, and the Equilibrium Constant**

18.6 **Cell Potential and Concentration**

18.8 **Electrolysis: Driving Nonspontaneous Chemical Reactions with Electricity**

## Specific Learning Objectives Addressed in This Chapter:

**Learning objective 3.1** Students can translate among macroscopic observations of change, chemical equations, and particle views. [*See* **SP 1.5, 7.1**]

**Learning objective 3.8** The student is able to identify redox reactions and justify the identification in terms of electron transfer. [*See* **SP 6.1**]

**Learning objective 3.12** The student can make qualitative or quantitative predictions about galvanic or electrolytic reactions based on half-cell reactions and potentials and/or Faraday's laws. [*See* **SP 2.2, 2.3, 6.4**]

**Learning objective 3.13** The student can analyze data regarding galvanic or electrolytic cells to identify properties of the underlying redox reactions. [*See* **SP 5.1**]

**Learning objective 5.15** The student is able to explain how the application of external energy sources or the coupling of favorable with unfavorable reactions can be used to cause processes that are not thermodynamically favorable to become favorable. [*See* **SP 6.2**]

**Specific Science Practices Addressed in This Chapter:**

**Science Practice 1:** The student can use representations and models to communicate scientific phenomena and solve scientific problems.

> 1.5 The student can *re-express key elements* of natural phenomena across multiple representations in the domain.

**Science Practice 2:** The student can use mathematics appropriately.

> 2.2 The student can *apply mathematical routines* to quantities that describe natural phenomena.

> 2.3 The student can *estimate numerically* quantities that describe natural phenomena.

**Science Practice 5:** The student can perform data analysis and evaluation of evidence.

> 5.1 The student can *analyze data* to identify patterns or relationships.

**Science Practice 6:** The student can work with scientific explanations and theories.

> 6.1 The student can *justify claims with evidence*.

> 6.2 The student can *construct explanations of phenomena based on evidence* produced through scientific practices.

> 6.4 The student can *make claims and predictions about natural phenomena* based on scientific theories and models.

**Science Practice 7:** The student is able to connect and relate knowledge across various scales, concepts, and representations in and across domains.

> 7.1 The student can *connect phenomena and models* across spatial and temporal scales.

## Concepts and Vocabulary to Review:

Section 18.2

## Balancing Oxidation-Reduction Equations

A review from Chapter 4 on assigning oxidation numbers and identifying what is oxidized and what is reduced is a good review. From these steps, it will be easy to finish balancing the reaction.

> 1. Assign oxidation states to all atoms and identify what is being oxidized and what is being reduced.

> 2. Separate into two half-reactions. Balance each half-reaction to have the same number of each atom on both sides of the equation and the

required number of electrons for the change in oxidation state. If in acidic solution, add $H^+$ as a reactant to the half-reaction with O atoms.

- What is oxidized frees up electrons (product) and what is reduced uses the electrons (reactant).

3. Balance the charge in both half-reactions so when added, the electrons will cancel.

4. Add the two half-reactions together.

When first looking at this equation, if only looking at numbers of atoms it appears to be balanced $Al(s) + Ni^{2+}(aq) \rightarrow Al^{3+}(aq) + Ni(s)$. The equation is not balanced due to unbalanced charge. Following the above steps to balance the equation, the steps would be as follows:

1. $Al = 0$, $Ni^{2+} = +2$, $Al^{3+} = +3$, $Ni = 0$; Al is being oxidized to $+3$ and $Ni^{2+}$ is being reduced to 0.

2. $Al(s) \rightarrow Al^{3+}(aq) + 3\,e^-$ and $Ni^{2+}(aq) + 2\,e^- \rightarrow Ni(s)$

3. $2(Al(s) \rightarrow Al^{3+}(aq) + 3\,e^-)$ and $3(Ni^{2+}(aq) + 2\,e^- \rightarrow Ni(s))$
   - $2\,Al(s) \rightarrow 2\,Al^{3+}(aq) + 6\,e^-$
   - $3\,Ni^{2+}(aq) + 6\,e^- \rightarrow 3\,Ni(s)$

4. $2\,Al(s) + 3\,Ni^{2+}(aq) \rightarrow 2\,Al^{3+}(aq) + 3\,Ni(s)$

The half-reactions will be important in subsequent sections and need to be a mastered skill.

## Voltaic (or Galvanic) Cells: Generating Electricity from Spontaneous Chemical Reactions

Section 18.3

This section is full of vocabulary for students to understand. While definitions will not be tested on the AP Test, students need to know what the words mean to understand the questions asked. For instance, if asked to identify the anode on a diagram of an electrochemical cell and draw the direction of electron flow, students need to know what an anode is. The evidence to support a student's claim needs to be analyzed.

In Figure 18.1 zinc electrode is plated with copper, providing evidence the copper is precipitating from the solution. The color of the solution will go from the color of the copper(II) cation to the colorless solution of the zinc cation, indicating the copper was reduced and the zinc was oxidized.

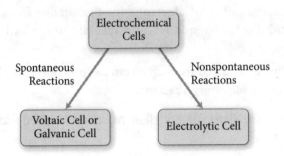

Spontaneous reactions produce electrical current while nonspontaneous reactions use electrical current.

In the galvanic cell (see Figure 18.2), the anode is the half-cell where oxidation occurs. Oxidation frees the electrons which then travel across the wire to the cathode where the electrons are used in the reduction half-cell at the cathode. The anode electrode will lose mass as it converts to cations. This will cause a buildup of cations or positive charge in the half-cell. To keep the cell neutralized, the anion in the salt bridge will flow toward the anode. At the cathode, there will be an increase of mass although if an inert electrode is present, the mass will be in gas form. As cations

**A Spontaneous Redox Reaction: Zn + Cu²⁺**

Zinc strip

Copper(II) sulfate solution

Zn atoms (solid)

Cu²⁺ ions in solution

e⁻

Zn²⁺ ion

Cu atom

$$Zn(s) + Cu^{2+}(aq) \longrightarrow Zn^{2+}(aq) + Cu(s)$$

**Figure 18.1 A Spontaneous Oxidation-Reduction Reaction**   When zinc is immersed in a solution containing copper ions, the zinc atoms transfer electrons to the copper ions. The zinc atoms are oxidized and dissolve in the solution. The copper ions are reduced and are deposited on the electrode.

## A Voltaic Cell

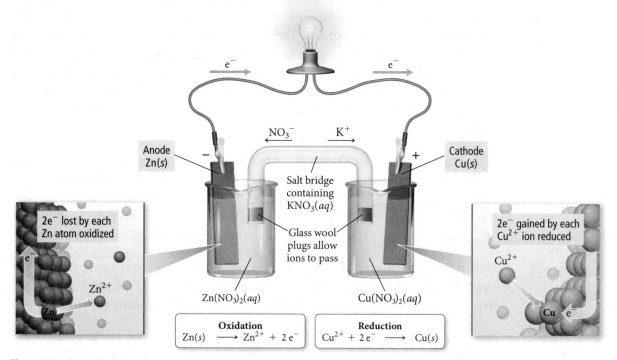

**Figure 18.2  A Voltaic Cell**   The tendency of zinc to transfer electrons to copper results in a flow of electrons through the wire that lights the bulb. The movement of electrons from the zinc anode to the copper cathode creates a positive charge buildup at the zinc half-cell and a negative charge buildup at the copper half-cell. The flow of ions within the salt bridge neutralizes this charge buildup, allowing the reaction to continue.

leave solution and are reduced, a buildup of negative charge occurs. To neutralize the buildup, cations in the salt bridge will travel toward the cathode.

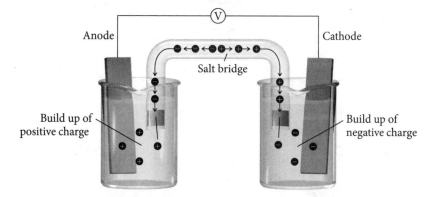

What causes the spontaneous or thermodynamically favored reaction? For a simple galvanic cell with a zinc electrode in 1.0 M $Zn(NO_3)_2(aq)$ and a nickel electrode in $Ni(NO_3)_2(aq)$, the zinc metal is more active compared to the nickel metal. Zinc gives up electrons easier compared to nickel. The electrons in zinc are subjected to a slightly greater push compared to the electrons in nickel. When two metals are connected in a circuit, electrons are pushed out of the more active metal electrode and they flow toward the least active metal electrode. In this situation, zinc serves as the anode.

In order for zinc to have electrons pushed out of the metal and into a wire, a zinc atom must lose two electrons and $Zn^{2+}$ cations are released into the solution. We can represent this process by the following half-equation $Zn \rightarrow Zn^{2+} + 2\,e^-$. Hence, oxidation occurs at the anode. In order for the nickel metal to receive two electrons, some of the $Ni^{2+}$ ions in solution will each gain two electrons $Ni^{2+} + 2\,e^- \rightarrow Ni$. Reduction occurs at the cathode. Electrons are neither created nor destroyed in a galvanic cell. The nickel electrode has a greater tendency to be reduced compared to the zinc electrode. The electrons in the wire will flow toward the cathode. The ions in the salt bridge will migrate to balance the charge in the two compartments. Together electrons flowing in the wire and ions migrating in the aqueous solution creates an electrical current.

The difference in potential between the two cells is measured in volts. This difference in potential energy is referred to as electromotive force (emf). In a voltaic cell, this is cell potential $(E_{cell})$. One volt is a joule per coulomb (J/C) and one coulomb per second (C/s) is an ampere (A). If standard conditions are present, then the label will be $E^\circ_{cell}$ or standard emf. The conditions are 1 atm of pressure, 25 °C, and 1 M solutions.

When comparing the cell potentials, if the potential difference is small, the less the tendency there is for the reaction to occur, but it will occur. If the potential is negative, the forward reaction is nonspontaneous or thermodynamically unfavored.

Instead of drawing an electrochemical cell, a shorthand cell notation can be used. For the cell with the balanced equation $2\,Al(s) + 3\,Ni^{2+}(aq) \rightarrow 2\,Al^{3+}(aq) + 3\,Ni(s)$, the

### Inert Platinum Electrode

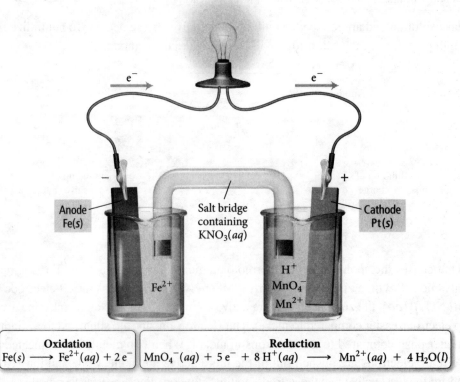

| Oxidation | Reduction |
|---|---|
| $Fe(s) \longrightarrow Fe^{2+}(aq) + 2\,e^-$ | $MnO_4^-(aq) + 5\,e^- + 8\,H^+(aq) \longrightarrow Mn^{2+}(aq) + 4\,H_2O(l)$ |

**Figure 18.3 Inert Platinum Electrode**   When the participants in a half-reaction are all in the aqueous phase, a conductive surface is needed for electron transfer to take place. In such cases an inert electrode of graphite or platinum is often used. In this electrochemical cell, an iron strip acts as the anode and a platinum strip acts as the cathode. Iron is oxidized at the anode and $MnO_4^-$ is reduced at the cathode.

notation is $Al(s)|Al^{3+}||Ni^{2+}(aq)|Ni(s)$. The first part is the anode reaction with a single vertical line|indicating a phase boundary, in this case metal in an aqueous solution. The double vertical lines $||$ indicate a salt bridge or other media supporting an exchange of ions. The double vertical lines indicate the break between the anode reaction (electrode and the ion it forms) and the cathode reaction with the cathode reaction following the lines. Again a single vertical line separates the ion from the electrode it plates or uses as a surface with an inert electrode.

The cell notation for the reaction depicted in the above diagram of an electrochemical cell is $Fe(s)|Fe^{2+}(aq)||MnO_4^-(aq),H^+(aq),Mn^{2+}(aq)|Pt(s)$.

## Standard Electrode Potentials    Section 18.4

Electrode potentials are determined by comparing them to the standard hydrogen electrode (SHE), which is assigned a value of zero.

All the potentials are measured relative to the SHE.

The difference between the final state (cathode) and the initial state (anode) determines $E^{\circ}_{cell}$.

$$E^{\circ}_{cell} = E^{\circ}_{cathode} - E^{\circ}_{anode}$$

If the forward reaction is spontaneous, the value of $E^{\circ}_{cell}$ is positive. When using a standard electrode potentials chart, the oxidation half-reaction at the anode (which will be written in reverse on a reductions chart) must be below the cathode half-reaction to end up being thermodynamically favorable.

Looking at the table on page 255, the oxidation reaction $Zn(s) \rightarrow Zn^{2+}(aq)+2\,e^-$ written as a reduction is $Zn^{2+}(aq)+2\,e^- \rightarrow Zn(s)$ and is below

**Standard Hydrogen Electrode (SHE)**

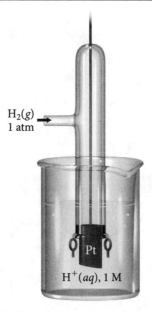

**Figure 18.4  The Standard Hydrogen Electrode**    The standard hydrogen electrode (SHE) is arbitrarily assigned an electrode potential of zero. All other electrode potentials are then measured relative to the SHE.

**Measuring Half-Cell Potential with the SHE**

0.76

Voltmeter

$e^-$

$e^-$

$NO_3^-$     $Na^+$

H$_2$(g)

Anode
Zn(s)

−

$NO_3^-$

$Zn^{2+}$

$NO_3^-$

Cl$^-$

H$^+$

Cathode
(standard
hydrogen
electrode)

H$_2$(g)

Pt
surface

H$_2$

$e^-$

$e^-$

$Zn^{2+}$

Zn

| Oxidation | Reduction |
|---|---|
| Zn(s) $\longrightarrow$ Zn$^{2+}$(aq) + 2 e$^-$ | 2 H$^+$(aq) + 2 e$^-$ $\longrightarrow$ H$_2$(g) |

2 H$^+$

**Figure 18.5 Measuring Electrode Potential**   Because the electrode potential of the SHE is zero, the electrode potential for the oxidation of Zn is equal to the cell potential.

$Cu^{2+}(aq) + 2\ e^- \rightarrow Cu(s)$, so when calculated, this should have positive voltage and be spontaneous. Using $E°_{cell} = E°_{cathode} - E°_{anode}$; $E°_{cell} = 0.34V - -0.76V$ or $1.10\ V$.

Another indicator on the table is the ability of an acid to react with a metal. Any metal below the SHE on the table will dissolve in acid and generate hydrogen gas.

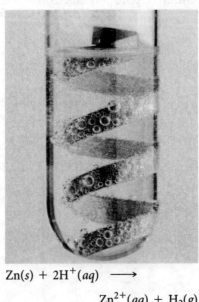

$$Zn(s) + 2H^+(aq) \longrightarrow$$
$$Zn^{2+}(aq) + H_2(g)$$

This holds true for all but nitric acid, which will dissolve copper.

**Table 18.1**  Standard Electrode Potentials at 25 °C

| Reduction Half-Reaction | | $E°$ (V) | |
|---|---|---|---|
| Stronger oxidizing agent | $F_2(g) + 2\,e^-$ → $2\,F^-(aq)$ | 2.87 | Weaker reducing agent |
| | $H_2O_2(aq) + 2\,H^+(aq) + 2\,e^-$ → $2\,H_2O(l)$ | 1.78 | |
| | $PbO_2(s) + 4\,H^+(aq) + SO_4^{2-}(aq) + 2\,e^-$ → $PbSO_4(s) + 2\,H_2O(l)$ | 1.69 | |
| | $MnO_4^-(aq) + 4\,H^+(aq) + 3\,e^-$ → $MnO_2(s) + 2\,H_2O(l)$ | 1.68 | |
| | $MnO_4^-(aq) + 8\,H^+(aq) + 5\,e^-$ → $Mn^{2+}(aq) + 4\,H_2O(l)$ | 1.51 | |
| | $Au^{3+}(aq) + 3\,e^-$ → $Au(s)$ | 1.50 | |
| | $PbO_2(s) + 4\,H^+(aq) + 2\,e^-$ → $Pb^{2+}(aq) + 2\,H_2O(l)$ | 1.46 | |
| | $Cl_2(g) + 2\,e^-$ → $2\,Cl^-(aq)$ | 1.36 | |
| | $Cr_2O_7^{2-}(aq) + 14\,H^+(aq) + 6\,e^-$ → $2\,Cr^{3+}(aq) + 7\,H_2O(l)$ | 1.33 | |
| | $O_2(g) + 4\,H^+(aq) + 4\,e^-$ → $2\,H_2O(l)$ | 1.23 | |
| | $MnO_2(s) + 4\,H^+(aq) + 2\,e^-$ → $Mn^{2+}(aq) + 2\,H_2O(l)$ | 1.21 | |
| | $IO_3^-(aq) + 6\,H^+(aq) + 5\,e^-$ → $\frac{1}{2}I_2(aq) + 3\,H_2O(l)$ | 1.20 | |
| | $Br_2(l) + 2\,e^-$ → $2\,Br^-(aq)$ | 1.09 | |
| | $VO_2^+(aq) + 2\,H^+(aq) + e^-$ → $VO^{2+}(aq) + H_2O(l)$ | 1.00 | |
| | $NO_3^-(aq) + 4\,H^+(aq) + 3\,e^-$ → $NO(g) + 2\,H_2O(l)$ | 0.96 | |
| | $ClO_2(g) + e^-$ → $ClO_2^-(aq)$ | 0.95 | |
| | $Ag^+(aq) + e^-$ → $Ag(s)$ | 0.80 | |
| | $Fe^{3+}(aq) + e^-$ → $Fe^{2+}(aq)$ | 0.77 | |
| | $O_2(g) + 2\,H^+(aq) + 2\,e^-$ → $H_2O_2(aq)$ | 0.70 | |
| | $MnO_4^-(aq) + e^-$ → $MnO_4^{2-}(aq)$ | 0.56 | |
| | $I_2(s) + 2\,e^-$ → $2\,I^-(aq)$ | 0.54 | |
| | $Cu^+(aq) + e^-$ → $Cu(s)$ | 0.52 | |
| | $O_2(g) + 2\,H_2O(l) + 4\,e^-$ → $4\,OH^-(aq)$ | 0.40 | |
| | $Cu^{2+}(aq) + 2\,e^-$ → $Cu(s)$ | 0.34 | |
| | $SO_4^{2-}(aq) + 4\,H^+(aq) + 2\,e^-$ → $H_2SO_3(aq) + H_2O(l)$ | 0.20 | |
| | $Cu^{2+}(aq) + e^-$ → $Cu^+(aq)$ | 0.16 | |
| | $Sn^{4+}(aq) + 2\,e^-$ → $Sn^{2+}(aq)$ | 0.15 | |
| | $2\,H^+(aq) + 2\,e^-$ → $H_2(g)$ | 0 | |
| | $Fe^{3+}(aq) + 3\,e^-$ → $Fe(s)$ | −0.036 | |
| | $Pb^{2+}(aq) + 2\,e^-$ → $Pb(s)$ | −0.13 | |
| | $Sn^{2+}(aq) + 2\,e^-$ → $Sn(s)$ | −0.14 | |
| | $Ni^{2+}(aq) + 2\,e^-$ → $Ni(s)$ | −0.23 | |
| | $Cd^{2+}(aq) + 2\,e^-$ → $Cd(s)$ | −0.40 | |
| | $Fe^{2+}(aq) + 2\,e^-$ → $Fe(s)$ | −0.45 | |
| | $Cr^{3+}(aq) + e^-$ → $Cr^{2+}(aq)$ | −0.50 | |
| | $Cr^{3+}(aq) + 3\,e^-$ → $Cr(s)$ | −0.73 | |
| | $Zn^{2+}(aq) + 2\,e^-$ → $Zn(s)$ | −0.76 | |
| | $2\,H_2O(l) + 2\,e^-$ → $H_2(g) + 2\,OH^-(aq)$ | −0.83 | |
| | $Mn^{2+}(aq) + 2\,e^-$ → $Mn(s)$ | −1.18 | |
| | $Al^{3+}(aq) + 3\,e^-$ → $Al(s)$ | −1.66 | |
| | $Mg^{2+}(aq) + 2\,e^-$ → $Mg(s)$ | −2.37 | |
| | $Na^+(aq) + e^-$ → $Na(s)$ | −2.71 | |
| | $Ca^{2+}(aq) + 2\,e^-$ → $Ca(s)$ | −2.76 | |
| | $Ba^{2+}(aq) + 2\,e^-$ → $Ba(s)$ | −2.90 | |
| | $K^+(aq) + e^-$ → $K(s)$ | −2.92 | |
| Weaker oxidizing agent | $Li^+(aq) + e^-$ → $Li(s)$ | −3.04 | Stronger reducing agent |

Section 18.5

# Cell Potential, Free Energy, and the Equilibrium Constant

Several indictors are used to determine if a reaction is spontaneous. These include, $K$, $\Delta G°$, and $E°_{cell}$. The values can be converted to other values in the equations below. It is important to recognize signs: if a reaction is spontaneous, then $E°_{cell}$ is positive, $K$ is larger than one since products are favored, and $\Delta G°$ is negative since free energy will be available to do work. At equilibrium $E°_{cell}$ is zero, $K$ is one, and $\Delta G°$ is zero since both the forward and backward reactions are equally favored.

| $E°_{cell}$ | $K$ | $\Delta G°$ | Spontaneous? |
|---|---|---|---|
| $<0$ | $<1$ | $>0$ | no |
| $0$ | $1$ | $0$ | at equilibrium |
| $>0$ | $>1$ | $<0$ | yes |

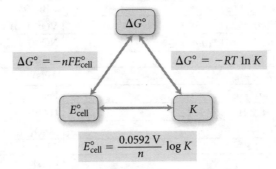

$$\Delta G° = -nFE°_{cell}$$

$$\Delta G° = -RT \ln K$$

$$E°_{cell} = \frac{0.0592\ \text{V}}{n}\ \log K$$

Section 18.6

# Cell Potential and Concentration

The expectation is students can explain what will happen to voltage using Le Châtelier's principle.

- $Q = 1$; $E_{cell} = E°_{cell}$ at standard conditions of 1 M solutions.

- $Q < 1$; $E_{cell} > E°_{cell}$ as the concentration of the reactants is greater and the reaction will move forward to make additional product and thereby increase the voltage.

- $Q = K$; $E_{cell} = 0$ The reaction is at equilibrium so no net change is occurring and voltage is zero.

- $Q > 1$; $E_{cell} < E°_{cell}$ since the product concentration is larger, the reactions will shift toward the products side, decreasing voltage (see Figure 18.6 on the next page.).

Concentration cells are driven by a difference in concentration. For instance, the Figure 18.7 has both copper as the anode and cathode but the concentrations in the cells are different. The cells will try to reach the same concentrations. To do this, the more concentrated ion concentration solution must reduce by forming reducing ions at the cathode and the dilute solution ion concentration must increase from oxidation of the anode. The electrons freed at the anode in oxidation flow toward the cathode where they are used in reduction.

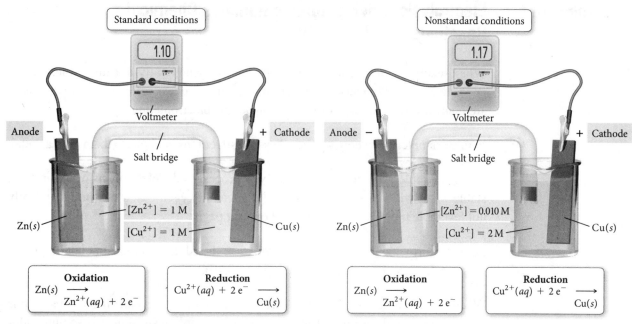

**Figure 18.6  Cell Potential and Concentration**    This figure compares the $Zn/Cu^{2+}$ electrochemical cell under standard and nonstandard conditions. In this case, the nonstandard conditions consist of a higher $Cu^{2+}$ concentration ($[Cu^{2+}] > 1\,M$) at the cathode and a lower $Zn^{2+}$ concentration at the anode ($[Zn^{2+}] < 1\,M$). According to Le Châtelier's principle, the forward reaction has a greater tendency to occur, resulting in a greater overall cell potential than the potential under standard conditions.

## A Concentration Cell

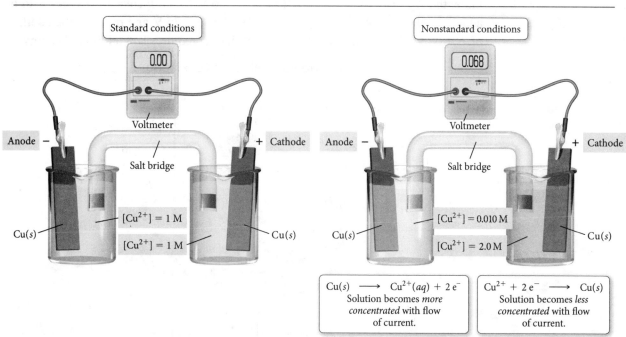

**Figure 18.7  Cu/Cu²⁺ Concentration Cell**    If two half-cells have the same $Cu^{2+}$ concentration, the cell potential is zero. If one half-cell has a greater $Cu^{2+}$ concentration than the other, a spontaneous reaction occurs. In the reaction, $Cu^{2+}$ ions in the more concentrated cell are reduced (to solid copper), while $Cu^{2+}$ ions in the more dilute cell are formed (from solid copper). The concentration of copper ions in the two half-cells tends toward equality.

Section 18.8

## Electrolysis: Driving Nonspontaneous Chemical Reactions with Electricity

When reactions are nonspontaneous or thermodynamically not favorable, energy needs to be added to cause the reaction to go in a process called electrolysis. There are many uses for this type of process, including electroplating.

In this example, the energy source takes free silver ions, and plates them onto a metal.

Another simple example of an electrolysis process is the electrolysis of water. Here stable water will actually split into hydrogen and oxygen gas, a thermodynamically not favorable process (see Figure 18.9 on next page).

For reactions with negative voltage, it will take the addition of this amount of voltage to cause the reaction to happen (see Figure 18.10).

When predicting the product of electrolysis reactions, it depends if the substance is molten (hot liquid) or in aqueous solution. If the molten substance is sodium chloride, the cation will reduce and the anion will oxidize. In this case, the sodium ion ($Na^+$) will form the metal Na and chloride ion ($Cl^-$) will form chlorine gas ($Cl_2$) (see Figure 18.11).

If there is a mixture of salts, then the metal ion being reduced first will be the one requiring the least amount of energy. This can be determined from a table of reduction potentials. For instance, in a mixture of calcium chloride and aluminum bromide, the $Al^{3+}(aq) + 3\,e^- \rightarrow Al(s)$ is $-1.66$ V which means 1.66 V needs to be added, while the $Ca^{2+}(aq) + 2\,e^- \rightarrow Ca(s)$ is $-2.76$ V and requires the addition of 2.76 V. The Al reaction will reduce first since it requires less additional energy.

**Electrolytic Cell for Silver Plating**

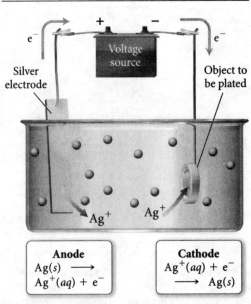

**Figure 18.8 Silver Plating**    Silver can be plated from a solution of silver ions onto metallic objects in an electrolytic cell.

## Electrolysis of Water

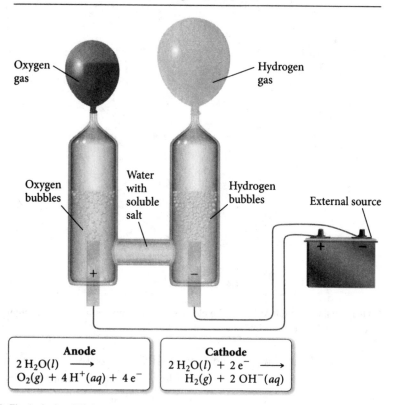

Oxygen gas

Hydrogen gas

Oxygen bubbles

Water with soluble salt

Hydrogen bubbles

External source

**Anode**
$2 H_2O(l) \longrightarrow$
$O_2(g) + 4 H^+(aq) + 4 e^-$

**Cathode**
$2 H_2O(l) + 2 e^- \longrightarrow$
$H_2(g) + 2 OH^-(aq)$

**Figure 18.9  Electrolysis of Water**  Electrical current can decompose water into hydrogen and oxygen gas.

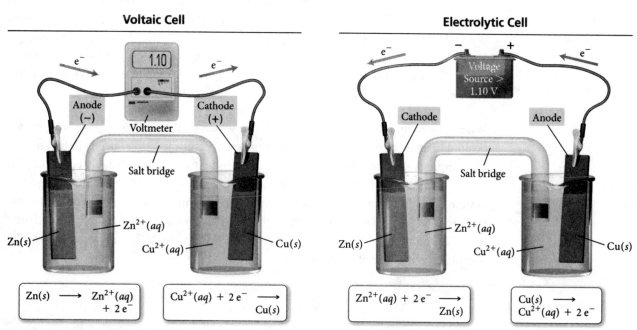

## Voltaic Cell

$e^-$

1.10

Anode (−)

Voltmeter

Cathode (+)

Salt bridge

Zn(s)

Zn²⁺(aq)

Cu²⁺(aq)

Cu(s)

$Zn(s) \longrightarrow Zn^{2+}(aq) + 2 e^-$

$Cu^{2+}(aq) + 2 e^- \longrightarrow Cu(s)$

## Electrolytic Cell

$e^-$     −   +     $e^-$

Voltage Source > 1.10 V

Cathode

Anode

Salt bridge

Zn(s)

Zn²⁺(aq)

Cu²⁺(aq)

Cu(s)

$Zn^{2+}(aq) + 2 e^- \longrightarrow Zn(s)$

$Cu(s) \longrightarrow Cu^{2+}(aq) + 2 e^-$

**Figure 18.10  Voltaic versus Electrolytic Cells**  In a $Zn/Cu^{2+}$ voltaic cell, the reaction proceeds in the spontaneous direction. In a $Zn^{2+}/Cu$ electrolytic cell, electrical current drives the reaction in the nonspontaneous direction.

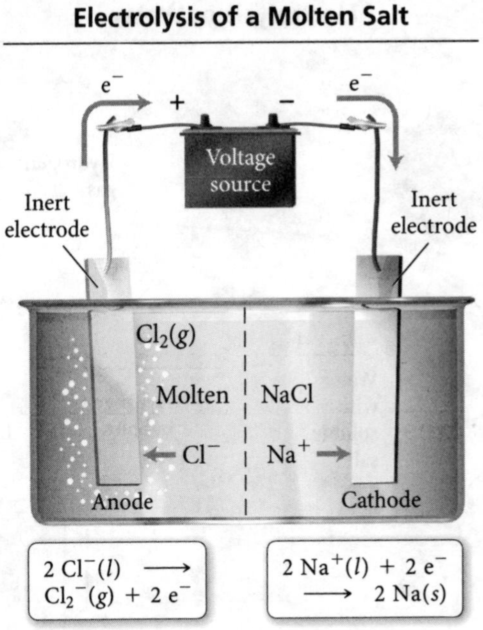

## Electrolysis of a Molten Salt

**Figure 18.11 Electrolysis of Molten NaCl**   In the electrolysis of a pure molten salt, the anion (in this case $Cl^-$) is oxidized and the cation (in this case $Na^+$) is reduced.

The same is true of the anion; the one more easily oxidized will occur first. Again simply compare voltage numbers. The chloride reaction takes more energy than the bromide reaction, so the bromide reaction will occur first.

If the substance is in a water solution, a reaction with water must also be considered. In the case of the molten sodium iodide, sodium ions will be reduced and iodide ions will be oxidized. If the sodium iodide is in solution with water, this is not the case! Instead water is reduced to hydrogen gas and hydroxide ions while the iodide is still oxidized. Why? The amount of energy needed to reduce the water ($-0.41V$) is less than what is needed to reduce the sodium ($-2.71V$) while the amount of energy to oxidize the iodide ($0.54 V$) is less than oxidizing the water ($0.82 V$). In general, very active metal cations are not reduced in aqueous solution in electrolysis reactions ($Li^+$, $K^+$, $Na^+$, $Mg^{2+}$, $Ca^{2+}$, and $Al^{3+}$) (see Figure 18.12).

When calculating the amount of a substance which could be plated, generated, or deposited in an electrolysis reaction, the number of electrons added needs to be known. This requires knowing the current added, the time it ran, and Faraday's constant ($F$); Faraday's constant ($F$) represents the energy to move 1 mole of electrons through the system. The current is measured in amperes (A), which is the number of coulombs per second. The Faraday constant is 96,485 coulombs (C) per mole of electrons, which is rounded to 96,500 C/mol e$^-$ for the AP Exam. If 2.5 amperes ran for 20 minutes, the number of electrons moving through the system would be

$$2.5 \text{ A} \times 1200 \text{ s} \times \frac{1 \text{ C}}{\text{A} \cdot \text{s}} \times \frac{1 \text{ mol e}^-}{96,500 \text{ C}} = 0.31 \text{ moles of electrons.}$$

Then, knowing the substance and the number of electrons (stoichiometry), the final calculations can be made. For instance, if the metal silver was to be plated, then

## Electrolysis of an Aqueous Salt Solution

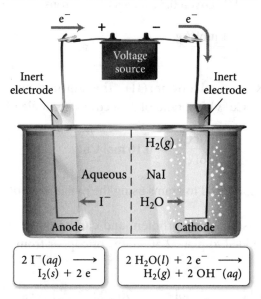

$$2\ I^-(aq) \longrightarrow I_2(s) + 2\ e^-$$

$$2\ H_2O(l) + 2\ e^- \longrightarrow H_2(g) + 2\ OH^-(aq)$$

**Figure 18.12  Electrolysis of Aqueous NaI**    In this cell, $I^-$ is oxidized to $I_2$ at the anode and $H_2O$ is reduced to $H_2$ at the cathode. Sodium ions are not reduced, because their electrode potential is more negative than the electrode potential of water.

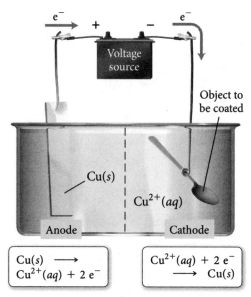

$$Cu(s) \longrightarrow Cu^{2+}(aq) + 2\ e^-$$

$$Cu^{2+}(aq) + 2\ e^- \longrightarrow Cu(s)$$

**Figure 18.13  Electrolytic Cell for Copper Plating**    In this cell, copper ions are plated onto other metals. It takes two moles of electrons to plate one mole of copper atoms.

$Ag^+(aq) + 1\,e^- \rightarrow Ag(s)$ and one mole of electrons are needed to plate 1 mole of silver. This is a ratio of 1/1. Given 0.31 moles of electrons:

$$0.31\text{ mol }e^- \times \frac{1\text{ mol Ag}}{1\text{ mol }e^-} = 0.31\text{ mol Ag.}$$

If the cation was instead copper(II), the amount would change since $Cu^{2+}(aq) + 2\,e^- \rightarrow Cu(s)$ is a ratio of 2 electrons per mole of copper.

$$0.31\text{ mol }e^- \times \frac{1\text{ mol Cu}}{2\text{ mol }e^-} = 0.16\text{ mol Cu.}$$

These could then be converted to grams using the molar mass of the substance.

These can be done as one long problem and can be done in reverse; how does current needs to be added to plate 2.50 grams of copper from copper(II) cations in 10.0 minutes?

$$2.50\text{ g Cu} \times \frac{1\text{ mol Cu}}{63.55\text{ g}} \times \frac{2\text{ mol }e^-}{1\text{ mol Cu}} \times \frac{96.500\text{ C}}{1\text{ mol }e^-} \times \frac{1\text{ A}\cdot\text{s}}{1\text{ C}} \times \frac{x\text{A}}{600\text{ s}} = 12.7\text{ A}$$

Electrolysis is a very common process done in industry. Due to its stability, gold plating is one of the substances used on the space shuttle!

## Additional Practice

*Self-Assessment Quiz Questions Q1, Q2, Q3, Q4, Q5, Q6, Q7, Q8, Q9, Q10, Q11, Q12, Q13, Q14, and Q15*

*Problems 12, 13, 18, 31, 36, 37, 38, 41, 43, 51, 53, 55, 56, 57, 61, 65, 72, 73, 88, 89, 92, 95, 99, 100, 103, 104, 105, 106, 114, 117, 118, 136, 138, and 139*

## Practice AP® Test Questions

Questions 1 and 2 pertain to the following diagrams situation: Consider Cell X and Cell Y, both operating at 25 °C and 1.0 atm pressure.

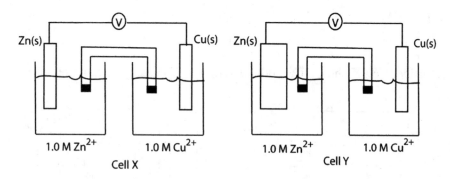

1. The $E°$ generated by Cell Y is _____ the $E°$ generated by Cell X.

    A) less than

    B) the same as

    C) greater than

    D) unknown compared to

2. Which statement is true as Cell X operates?

    A) Oxidation occurs at the copper electrode.

    B) The concentration of the $Cu^{2+}$ ions in the $Cu^{2+}$ solution will increase.

    C) The mass of the copper electrode will decrease.

    D) Electrons will migrate in the wire from the zinc electrode to the copper electrode.

3. An electrochemical cell Z is constructed using a silver electrode in 1.0 M silver nitrate and a copper electrode in 1.0 M copper(II) nitrate.

| Half-cell reaction | $E°$ |
|---|---|
| $Ag^+(aq) + e \rightarrow Ag(s)$ | +0.800 V |
| $Cu^{2+}(aq) + 2\,e^- \rightarrow Cu(s)$ | +0.340 V |

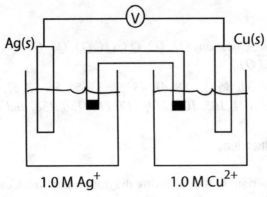

Cell Z

A)  0.46 V                          C)  1.26 V

B)  1.14 V                          D)  1.94 V

4.  Consider Cell X and Cell Y, both operating at 25 °C and 1.0 atm pressure.

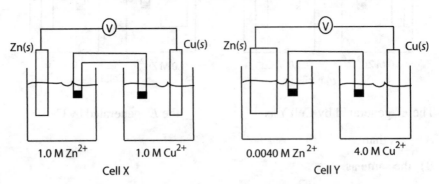

The emf, $E$, generated by Cell Y is _____ the emf, $E$, generated by Cell X.

A)  less than                       C)  greater than

B)  the same as                     D)  unknown compared to

Questions 5, 6, and 7 pertain to the following description and diagram. The diagram below shows an electrolytic cell in which an electric current passes through hot liquid calcium bromide, $CaBr_2(l)$, using inert electrodes.

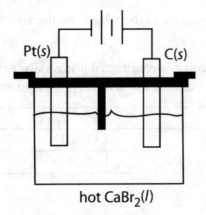

hot $CaBr_2(l)$

5. At the carbon electrode, bromide ions are oxidized.

   A) True

   B) False

6. The reason for my answer in 5:

   A) Copper(II) ions move to the carbon electrode and accept electrons.

   B) Copper(II) ions move to the carbon electrode and donate electrons.

   C) Bromide ions move to the carbon electrode and accept electrons.

   D) Bromide ions move to the carbon electrode and donate electrons.

7. Calculate the mass of calcium metal, in units of grams, produced by electrolysis when a current of 15.0 amps is passed through the liquid calcium bromide for 10.0 hours.

   A) 0.0311 g

   B) 11.2 g

   C) 61.0 g

   D) 112 g

**Answers**

*1. B); 2. D); 3. A); 4. C); 5. B); 6. D); 7. D)*

# CHAPTER 19

# RADIOACTIVITY AND NUCLEAR CHEMISTRY

The AP Chemistry Framework no longer includes nuclear chemistry. The topics are considered to be prior knowledge for the course or covered in a later course in chemistry. The one section pertaining to the AP exam is on kinetics.

### 19.6  The Kinetics of Radioactive Decay and Radiometric Dating

## Specific Learning Objectives Addressed in This Chapter:

**Learning objective 4.2** The student is able to analyze concentration vs. time data to determine the rate law for a zero-, first-, or second-order reaction. [*See* **SP 5.1**]

**Learning objective 4.3** The student is able to connect the half-life of a reaction to the rate constant of a first-order reaction and justify the use of this relation in terms of the reaction being a first-order reaction. [*See* **SP 2.1, 2.2**]

## Specific Science Practices Addressed in This Chapter:

**Science Practice 2:** The student can use mathematics appropriately.

2.1  The student can *justify the selection of a mathematical routine* to solve problems.

2.2  The student can *apply mathematical routines* to quantities that describe natural phenomena.

**Science Practice 5:** The student can perform data analysis and evaluation of evidence.

5.1  The student can *analyze data* to identify patterns or relationships.

Section 19.6  ## The Kinetics of Radioactive Decay and Radiometric Dating

All radioactive decay follows first-order kinetics. Nuclear reactions therefore use the first-order integrated rate law and half-life equations.

$$t_{1/2} = \frac{0.693}{k}$$

$$\ln\frac{N_t}{N_0} = -kt$$

The only difference is instead of concentrations in the integrated rate law the number of nuclides ($N$) are used.

Nuclides with short half-lives will have large rate constants compared to those with long half-lives and small rate constants. Looking at a graph with atoms and time, when half the sample is gone is one half-life.

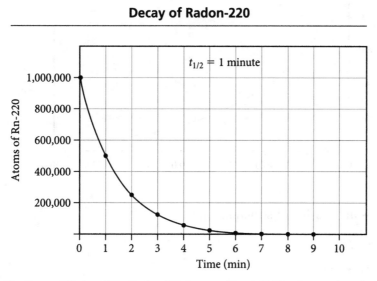

**Decay of Radon-220**

**Figure 19.1 The Decay of Radon-220**    Radon-220 decays with a half-life of approximately 1 minute.

The next half-life is when half of the remaining sample is gone. This would drop the sample to ¼ of the original sample. Radioactive dating can be used to estimate the age of materials.

## Additional Practice

*Self-Assessment Quiz Questions Q5 and Q6*
*Problems 14, 45, 47, and 106*

## Practice AP® Test Questions

Questions 1–5 refer to the following information and graph. The decay of a 10.0 gram sample of strontium-90 is represented by plotting mass versus time in the graph below.

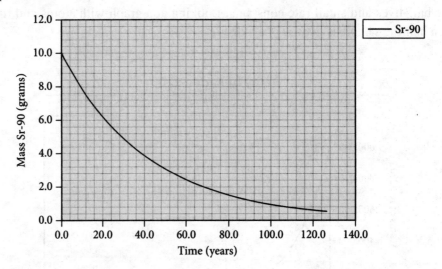

1.  What is the half-life of strontium-90?

    A)  14.4 years

    B)  20.0 years

    C)  28.8 years

    D)  50.0 years

2.  How much Sr-90 remains after three half-lives?

    A)  7.25 grams

    B)  5.00 grams

    C)  2.50 grams

    D)  1.25 grams

3.  Strontium-90 decays to yttrium-90 by what decay process?

    A)  alpha emission

    B)  beta emission

    C)  gamma emission

    D)  electron capture or positron emission

4. Which of the following will slow down the radioactive decay process of a sample of strontium-90?

    A) lower the temperature

    B) decrease the pressure

    C) place the sample in a lead box

    D) nothing will slow down the radioactive decay process

5. The number of neutrons in strontium-90 is

    A) 38

    B) 52

    C) 76

    D) 90

# CHAPTER

# 20

# ORGANIC CHEMISTRY

Many sections of this chapter go into more detail than the AP curriculum requires. Although there are no specific learning objectives, students are expected to look at data and structures including organic compounds and analyze properties such as polarity, intermolecular forces, and boiling points. There are many organic molecules discussed during the year, such as weak organic acids like ethanoic (acetic) acid, where it will be helpful if the students can draw the structure although on the AP exam students are usually given the structure. The major sections to understand are the naming systems, functional groups, and general characteristics of organic families.

## Specific Learning Objectives Addressed in This Chapter:

**Learning objective 2.20** The student is able to explain how a bonding model involving delocalized electrons is consistent with macroscopic properties of metals (e.g., conductivity, malleability, ductility, and low volatility) and the shell model of the atom. [*See* **SP 6.2, 7.1**]

**Learning objective 5.11** The student is able to identify the noncovalent interactions within and between large molecules, and/or connect the shape and function of the large molecule to the presence and magnitude of these interactions. [*See* **SP 7.2**]

## Specific Science Practices Addressed in This Chapter:

**Science Practice 6:** The student can work with scientific explanations and theories.

6.2  The student can *construct explanations of phenomena based on evidence* produced through scientific practices.

**Science Practice 7:** The student is able to connect and relate knowledge across various scales, concepts, and representations in and across domains.

7.1  The student can *connect phenomena and models* across spatial and temporal scales.

7.2  The student can *connect concepts* in and across domain(s) to generalize or extrapolate in and/or across enduring understandings and/or big ideas.

## Concepts and Vocabulary to Review:

### Carbon: Why It Is Unique          Section 20.2

Carbon has four valence electrons and can form four bonds. These can be all single bonds or combinations of single, double, and triple bonds. This allows for a wide variety of compounds since carbon can also bond to itself and form chains, branches, and ringed structures.

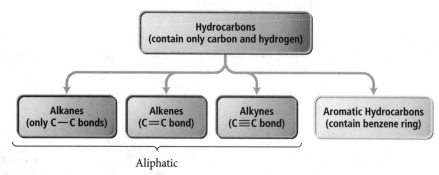

| Propane | Isobutane | Cyclohexane |

Silicon, which sits below carbon in the periodic table, does not have all these properties. The size of silicon is larger, making it more difficult to form double and triple bonds. Also, in the atmosphere, silicon will bond more readily to oxygen than to itself.

### Hydrocarbons: Compounds Containing          Section 20.3
### Only Carbon and Hydrogen

Hydrocarbon compounds are classified into four main groups.

```
              Hydrocarbons
     (contain only carbon and hydrogen)

   Alkanes      Alkenes      Alkynes      Aromatic Hydrocarbons
(only C—C bonds) (C=C bond)  (C≡C bond)   (contain benzene ring)

   |_____Aliphatic_____|
```

**Figure 20.1  Four Types of Hydrocarbons**

**Table 20.1**  Alkanes, Alkenes, Alkynes

| Type of Hydrocarbon | Type of Bonds | Generic Formula* | Example |
|---|---|---|---|
| Alkane | All single | $C_nH_{2n+2}$ | 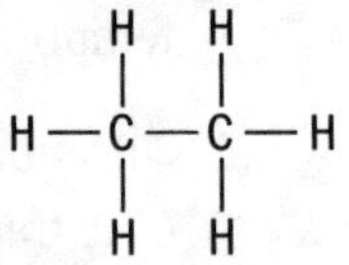 Ethane |
| Alkenes | One (or more) double | $C_nH_{2n}$ | 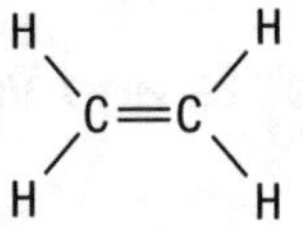 Ethene |
| Alkynes | One (or more) triple | $C_nH_{2n-2}$ | $H-C\equiv C-H$ Ethyne |

*n is the number of carbon atoms. These formulas apply only to noncyclic structures containing no more than one multiple bond.

Knowing the formula of the compound alone does not indicate the structure of the compound since isomers, compounds having the same molecular formula but different arrangement of atoms, can form. Even though isomers have the same formula, they have different names and different physical and chemical properties. The simplest example is butane and isobutane, which can also be called 2-methylpropane. These compounds with the same formulas but different structures are called structural isomers.

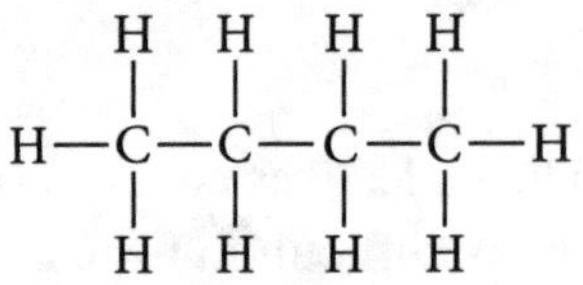

Butane

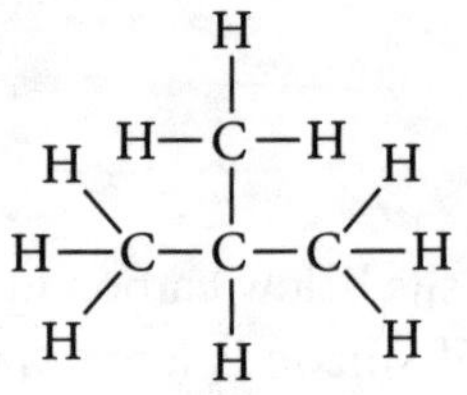

Isobutane

The same structure can be represented in different formats. The structures often seen are the full structural formulas showing all the atoms, condensed formulas showing what is located on each carbon in the chain, and the skeletal formula only showing the bonds between the carbons.

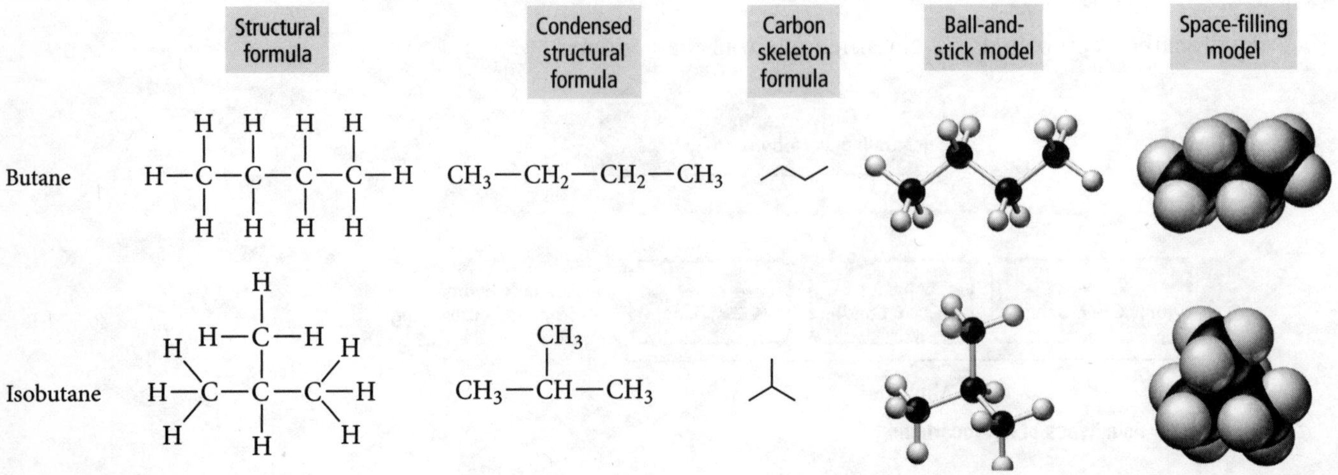

| | Structural formula | Condensed structural formula | Carbon skeleton formula | Ball-and-stick model | Space-filling model |
|---|---|---|---|---|---|
| Butane | | $CH_3-CH_2-CH_2-CH_3$ | | | |
| Isobutane | | $CH_3-CH-CH_3$ | | | |

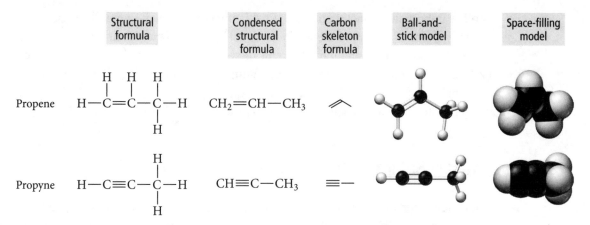

|  | Structural formula | Condensed structural formula | Carbon skeleton formula | Ball-and-stick model | Space-filling model |
|---|---|---|---|---|---|
| Propene | | $CH_2{=}CH{-}CH_3$ | | | |
| Propyne | | $CH{\equiv}C{-}CH_3$ | | | |

One important property of some of these isomers is whether or not they are stereoisomers. There are two types of stereoisomers; geometric and optical. Geometric isomers are also called *cis-trans* isomers (see Section 20.5 for more detail). The geometric isomer will have a double bond. The chain will either be continued on the same side (up or down) or on the opposite side (up and then down or down then up).

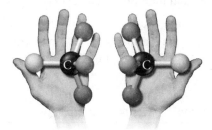

*cis*-2-Butene                    *trans*-2-Butene

In this example of *cis*-2-butene, the chain is staying on the top side of the molecule, while in *trans*-2-butene it starts up and then goes across and down.

Optical isomers (also called enantiomers) are not superimposable on each other. For instance, your hands look alike but you cannot place them on top of each other and have them look the same.

**Figure 20.2  Mirror Images**    The left and right hand are nonsuperimposable mirror images, just as are optical isomers.

Molecules which do this are said to be chiral. This is very important in biological organisms as many body systems and enzymes will only recognize one of the isomers.

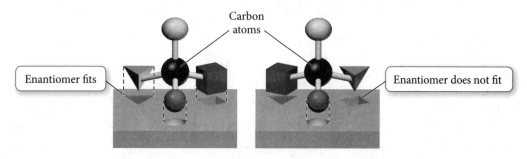

Another important characteristic of optical isomers is the way they will rotate plane polarized light. One form of the isomer will rotate light clockwise and is called the *d* isomer (dextrorotatory) and the other will rotate light counterclockwise and is called the *l* isomer (levorotatory). If there is an equimolar mixture of both, the light will not rotate and the mixture is called a racemic mixture. Interestingly, in the human body the recognized form of amino acids are *l* isomers and the carbohydrates are the *d* isomers.

## Section 20.4    Alkanes: Saturated Hydrocarbons

When the carbon atoms in the chain have only single bonds between them, the compound is called an alkane. If all the other atoms are hydrogen atoms, the compound is also called a saturated hydrocarbon. The chain can be straight, branched, or ringed (cycloalkanes are not covered in the chapter and will not be addressed here although they do exist). The straight-chained alkanes are called normal alkanes and may be designated with an *n-* in front of the name such as *n*-heptane.

**Table 20.2** Prefixes for Base Names of Alkane Chains

| Number of Carbon Atoms | Prefix |
|---|---|
| 1 | meth- |
| 2 | eth- |
| 3 | prop- |
| 4 | but- |
| 5 | pent- |
| 6 | hex- |
| 7 | hept- |
| 8 | oct- |
| 9 | non- |
| 10 | dec- |

Naming the alkanes requires looking at their structural formulas, knowing the prefix for the number of carbons in the chain, and the names of any branched groups called substituent groups.

- Find the longest continuous chain and count the number of carbons in the chain. Use the prefix for this number of carbons followed by –ane.
- If any substituent groups are added, write the names of the groups in alphabetical order if there is more than one type added in front of the name.
- Number the carbons in the chain so the groups are on the lowest numbered carbon. For each group added, put the number of the carbon it is located on in front of its name and then place a dash between the number and the name.
- If more than one of a particular group is present, also add a prefix in front of the group name such as di-(2), tri-(3), or tetra-(4). The prefix does not change the order of the substituent groups.

**Table 20.3**   Common Alkyl Groups

| Condensed Structural Formula | Name | Condensed Structural Formula | Name |
|---|---|---|---|
| $-CH_3$ | Methyl | $-CHCH_3$<br>    \|<br>   $CH_3$ | Isopropyl |
| $-CH_2CH_3$ | Ethyl | $-CH_2CHCH_3$<br>      \|<br>     $CH_3$ | Isobutyl |
| $-CH_2CH_2CH_3$ | Propyl | $-CHCH_2CH_3$<br>   \|<br> $CH_3$ | *sec*-Butyl |
| $-CH_2CH_2CH_2CH_3$ | Butyl | $CH_3$<br> \|<br>$-CCH_3$<br> \|<br>$CH_3$ | *tert*-Butyl |

**Table 20.4**   *n*-Alkanes

| *n* | Name | Molecular Formula $C_nH_{2n+2}$ | Structural Formula | Condensed Structural Formula |
|-----|------|------------------|--------------------|------------------------------|
| 1 | Methane | $CH_4$ | H—C—H (with H above and H below) | $CH_4$ |
| 2 | Ethane | $C_2H_6$ | H—C—C—H | $CH_3CH_3$ |
| 3 | Propane | $C_3H_8$ | H—C—C—C—H | $CH_3CH_2CH_3$ |
| 4 | *n*-Butane | $C_4H_{10}$ | H—C—C—C—C—H | $CH_3CH_2CH_2CH_3$ |
| 5 | *n*-Pentane | $C_5H_{12}$ | H—C—C—C—C—C—H | $CH_3CH_2CH_2CH_2CH_3$ |
| 6 | *n*-Hexane | $C_6H_{14}$ | H—C—C—C—C—C—C—H | $CH_3CH_2CH_2CH_2CH_2CH_3$ |
| 7 | *n*-Heptane | $C_7H_{16}$ | H—C—C—C—C—C—C—C—H | $CH_3CH_2CH_2CH_2CH_2CH_2CH_3$ |
| 8 | *n*-Octane | $C_8H_{18}$ | H—C—C—C—C—C—C—C—C—H | $CH_3CH_2CH_2CH_2CH_2CH_2CH_2CH_3$ |
| 9 | *n*-Nonane | $C_9H_{20}$ | H—C—C—C—C—C—C—C—C—C—H | $CH_3CH_2CH_2CH_2CH_2CH_2CH_2CH_2CH_3$ |
| 10 | *n*-Decane | $C_{10}H_{22}$ | H—C—C—C—C—C—C—C—C—C—C—H | $CH_3CH_2CH_2CH_2CH_2CH_2CH_2CH_2CH_2CH_3$ |

The simplest alkanes to name are the straight-chain hydrocarbons without branches. Only the length of chain has to be counted.

Following the steps for the branched compounds requires more of the steps since substituent groups have been added and must be accounted for in the name.

**Example 20.1**

**Naming Alkanes**

*Name this alkane.*

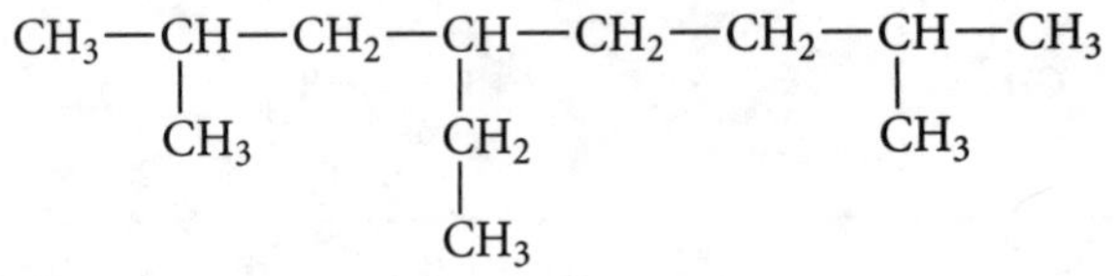

$$CH_3-CH-CH_2-CH-CH_2-CH_2-CH-CH_3$$
$$\phantom{CH_3-}CH_3 \qquad\quad CH_2 \qquad\qquad\quad CH_3$$
$$\phantom{CH_3-CH-CH_2-CH-}CH_3$$

**Solution**

*This compound has eight carbon atoms in its longest continuous chain.*

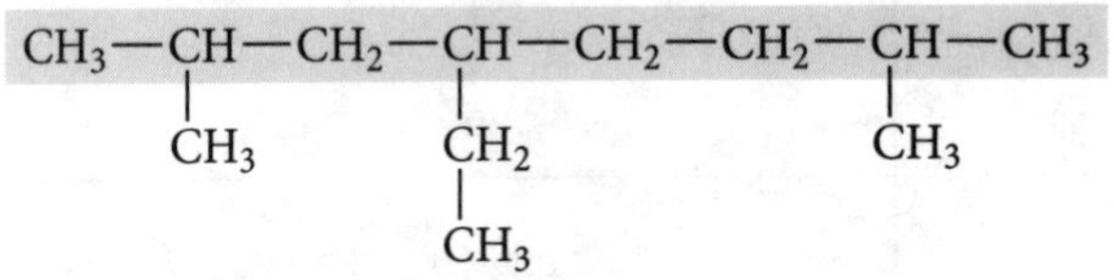

$$CH_3-CH-CH_2-CH-CH_2-CH_2-CH-CH_3$$
$$\phantom{CH_3-}CH_3 \qquad\quad CH_2 \qquad\qquad\quad CH_3$$
$$\phantom{CH_3-CH-CH_2-CH-}CH_3$$

*The correct prefix from Table 20.5 is oct-. The base name is octane.*

*This compound has one substituent named* ethyl *and two named* methyl.

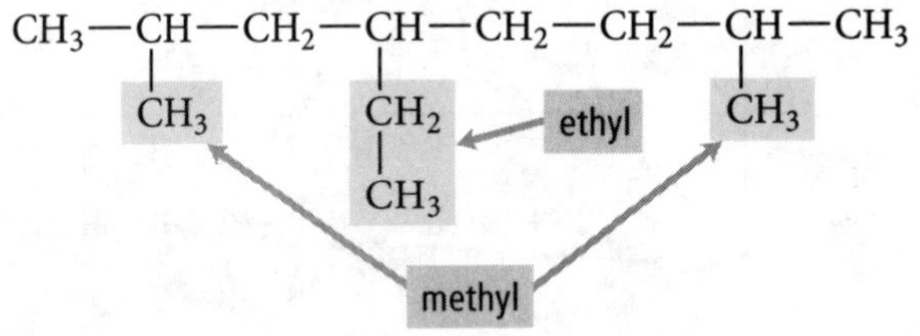

$$CH_3-CH-CH_2-CH-CH_2-CH_2-CH-CH_3$$
$$\phantom{CH_3-}CH_3 \qquad\quad CH_2 \quad\text{ethyl} \quad CH_3$$
$$\phantom{CH_3-CH-CH_2-CH-}CH_3$$
$$\text{methyl}$$

*Number the base chain as follows:*

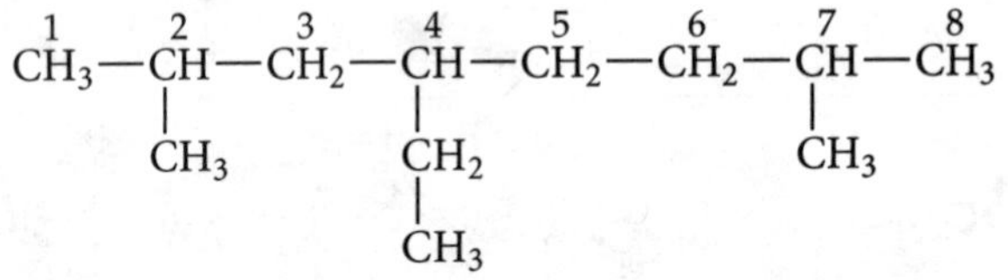

$$\overset{1}{C}H_3-\overset{2}{C}H-\overset{3}{C}H_2-\overset{4}{C}H-\overset{5}{C}H_2-\overset{6}{C}H_2-\overset{7}{C}H-\overset{8}{C}H_3$$
$$\phantom{CH_3-}CH_3 \qquad\quad CH_2 \qquad\qquad\quad CH_3$$
$$\phantom{CH_3-CH-CH_2-CH-}CH_3$$

*Assign the number 4 to the ethyl substituent and the numbers 2 and 7 to the two methyl substituents.*

*The basic form of the name of the compound is:*

*4-ethyl-2,7-methyloctane*

*List ethyl before methyl because substituents are listed in alphabetical order.*

*This compound has two methyl substituents; therefore, the final name of the compound is:*

*4-ethyl-2,7-dimethyloctane*

Although no questions will be "name this compound," being familiar with names can reduce "panic" when students see these types of structures of data from organic compounds.

The questions students will be expected to be able to answer are questions asking to explain trends such as boiling points of organic compounds or to explain the different models of representation of the same compound.

**Table 20.5**    *n*-Alkane Boiling Points

| *n*-Alkane | Boiling Point (°C) |
|------------|--------------------|
| Methane    | −161.5             |
| Ethane     | −88.6              |
| Propane    | −42.1              |
| *n*-Butane | −0.5               |
| *n*-Pentane| 36.0               |
| *n*-Hexane | 68.7               |
| *n*-Heptane| 98.5               |
| *n*-Octane | 125.6              |

Since these compounds are all have a straight chain arrangement and only have carbon-carbon single bonds and carbon-hydrogen single bonds, these compounds are non-polar. The difference in boiling points between each compound is due to the amount of London dispersion forces occurring between the molecules in the liquid state.

## Alkenes and Alkynes    Section 20.5

Alkenes have at least one double bond and alkynes have at least one triple bond. Take the following steps to name these types of compounds:

- Name the compound by identifying the longest chain which includes the multiple bond(s).

- Number the carbons in the chain so the multiple bond is on the lowest numbered carbon.

- Change the ending to -ene for alkenes (double bond) and -yne for alkynes (triple bond).

- Put a number before the base name to indicate the numbered carbon the multiple bond is on. See the examples in the Tables 20.6 and 20.7 on the next page.

## Aromatic Hydrocarbons    Section 20.7

Benzene is the base of many aromatic compounds.

**Table 20.6** Alkenes

| $n$ | Name | Molecular Formula $C_nH_{2n}$ | Structural Formula | Condensed Structural Formula |
|---|---|---|---|---|
| 2 | Ethene | $C_2H_4$ | 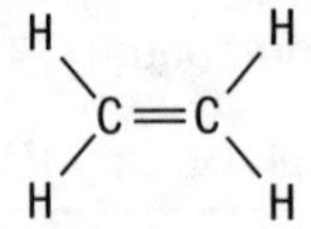 | $CH_2{=}CH_2$ |
| 3 | Propene | $C_3H_6$ | 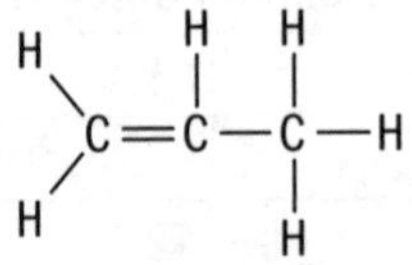 | $CH_2{=}CHCH_3$ |
| 4 | 1-Butene* | $C_4H_8$ | 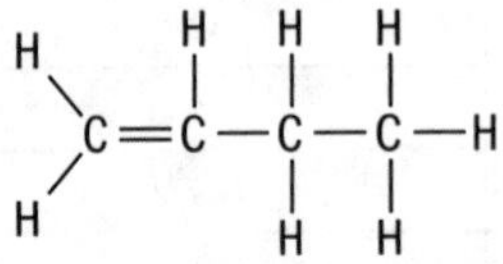 | $CH_2{=}CHCH_2CH_3$ |
| 5 | 1-Pentene* | $C_5H_{10}$ | 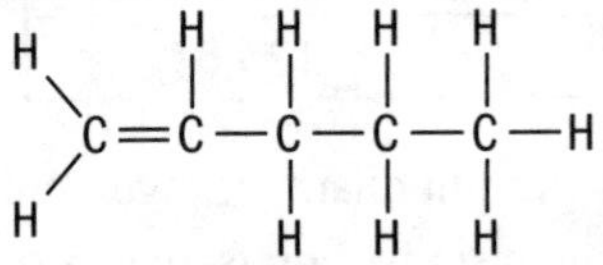 | $CH_2{=}CHCH_2CH_2CH_3$ |
| 6 | 1-Hexene* | $C_6H_{12}$ | 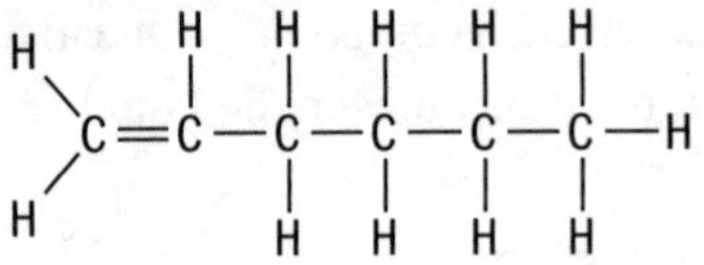 | $CH_2{=}CHCH_2CH_2CH_2CH_3$ |

*These alkenes have one or more isomers depending on the position of the double bond. The isomers shown here have the double bond in the 1 position, meaning the first carbon–carbon bond of the chain.

**Table 20.7** Alkynes

| $n$ | Name | Molecular Formula $C_nH_{2n-2}$ | Structural Formula | Condensed Structural Formula |
|---|---|---|---|---|
| 2 | Ethyne | $C_2H_2$ | $H{-}C{\equiv}C{-}H$ | $CH{\equiv}CH$ |
| 3 | Propyne | $C_3H_4$ | 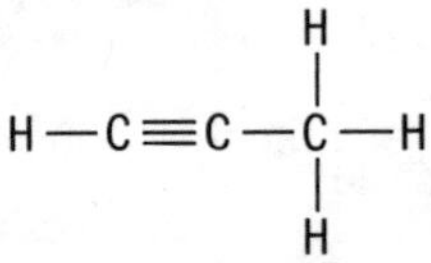 | $CH{\equiv}CCH_3$ |
| 4 | 1-Butyne* | $C_4H_6$ | 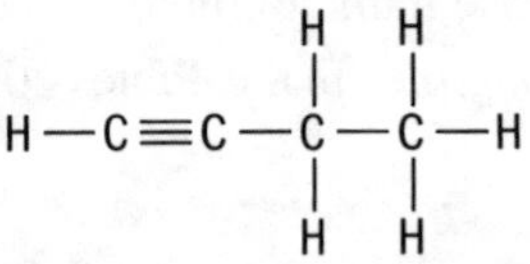 | $CH{\equiv}CCH_2CH_3$ |
| 5 | 1-Pentyne* | $C_5H_8$ | 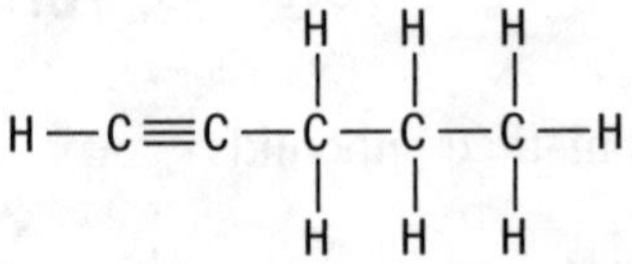 | $CH{\equiv}CCH_2CH_2CH_3$ |
| 6 | 1-Hexyne* | $C_6H_{10}$ | 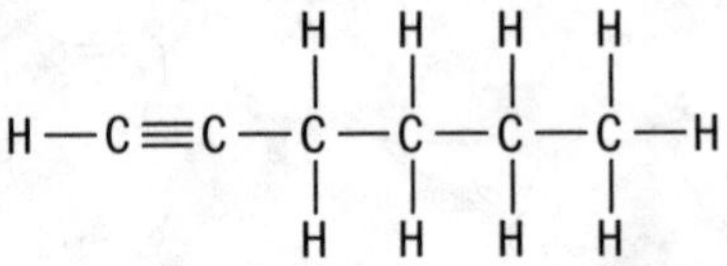 | $CH{\equiv}CCH_2CH_2CH_2CH_3$ |

*These alkynes have one or more isomers depending on the position of the triple bond. The isomers shown here have the triple bond in the 1 position, meaning the first carbon–carbon bond of the chain.

It has two resonance structures. For simplification the structure is written as

The delocalized electrons are indicated by the circle inside. These rings can be combined together and substitutions can be made for the hydrogen atoms creating new compounds. If the benzene itself is added as a functional group, it is called phenyl.

# Functional Groups    Section 20.8

Hydrogen atoms can be substituted with other atoms. Functional groups identify families of organic compounds. For instance, alcohols all have a —OH substituted in the formula. This is not hydroxide, since this is not attached to a cation and hence, it does not affect pH. Students do not need to memorize the functional groups, but should be able to look at a structure and determine if it is polar, will form hydrogen bonds with water, or analyze a trend of given properties.

**Table 20.8**  Some Common Functional Groups

| Family | General Formula* | Condensed General Formula | Example | Name |
|---|---|---|---|---|
| Alcohols | R — OH | ROH | $CH_3CH_2OH$ | Ethanol (ethyl alcohol) |
| Ethers | R — O — R | ROR | $CH_3OCH_3$ | Dimethyl ether |
| Aldehydes | $R - \overset{\overset{\displaystyle O}{\|\|}}{C} - H$ | RCHO | $CH_3 - \overset{\overset{\displaystyle O}{\|\|}}{C} - H$ | Ethanal (acetaldehyde) |
| Ketones | $R - \overset{\overset{\displaystyle O}{\|\|}}{C} - R$ | RCOR | $CH_3 - \overset{\overset{\displaystyle O}{\|\|}}{C} - CH_3$ | Propanone (acetone) |
| Carboxylic acids | $R - \overset{\overset{\displaystyle O}{\|\|}}{C} - OH$ | RCOOH | $CH_3 - \overset{\overset{\displaystyle O}{\|\|}}{C} - OH$ | Ethanoic acid (acetic acid) |
| Esters | $R - \overset{\overset{\displaystyle O}{\|\|}}{C} - OR$ | RCOOR | $CH_3 - \overset{\overset{\displaystyle O}{\|\|}}{C} - OCH_3$ | Methyl acetate |
| Amines | $R - \overset{\overset{\displaystyle R}{\|}}{N} - R$ | $R_3N$ | $CH_3CH_2 - \overset{\overset{\displaystyle H}{\|}}{N} - H$ | Ethylamine |

*In ethers, ketones, esters, and amines, the R groups may be the same or different.

## Additional Practice

*Self-Assessment Quiz Questions Q1, Q2, Q3, Q4, Q5, Q6, Q9, and Q10,*
*Problems 6, 8, 12, 35, 39, 41, 43, 45, 53, 55, 57, 63, 73, 74, 77, 78, 81, 82, 85, 86,*
*87, 88, 95, 96, 97, 98, and 99*

## Practice AP® Test Questions

Questions 1–5 refer to the following information and structure

$$H-C\equiv \overset{*}{C}-\underset{\underset{\displaystyle H}{|}}{\overset{\overset{\displaystyle H}{|}}{C}}-H$$

1. Hydrocarbons containing a carbon-carbon triple bond are called _____.

   A) alkanes

   B) alkenes

   C) alkynes

   D) aldehydes

2. The hybridization of the carbon atom indicated by a (*) in the above structure is

   A) sp          B) $sp^2$          C) $sp^3$          D) $dsp^2$

3. What is the name of the compound?

   A) propane

   B) propene

   C) propyne

   D) 1-methylethyne

4. For the structure above, identify the hybrid orbital(s) used by the carbon atom indicated by a (*) for bonding with the carbon atom in the $CH_3$ group.

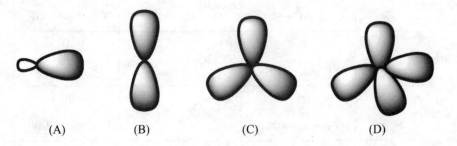

(A)          (B)          (C)          (D)

5. The compound represented by the structure above is not soluble in water.

   A) It is not soluble because it is less dense than water

   B) It is not soluble because it has a higher molar mass higher in molar mass

   C) It is not soluble because it is a polar molecule

   D) It is not soluble because it is a nonpolar molecule

# BIOCHEMISTRY

This chapter focuses on compounds with biological functions. Most of this material is not in the AP curriculum but is referenced in understanding using concepts in and across domains.

21.1  **Diabetes and the Synthesis of Human Insulin**

21.2  **Lipids**

21.3  **Carbohydrates**

21.4  **Proteins and Amino Acids**

21.5  **Protein Structure**

21.6  **Nucleic Acids: Blueprints for Proteins**

21.7  **DNA Replication, the Double Helix, and Protein Synthesis**

## Specific Learning Objectives Addressed in This Chapter:

**Learning objective 3.8** The student is able to identify redox reactions and justify the identification in terms of electron transfer. [*See* **SP 6.1**]

**Learning objective 5.11** The student is able to identify the noncovalent interactions within and between large molecules, and/or connect the shape and function of the large molecule to the presence and magnitude of these interactions. [*See* **SP 7.2**]

## Specific Science Practices Addressed in This Chapter:

**Science Practice 6:** The student can work with scientific explanations and theories.

 6.1 The student can *justify claims with evidence*.

**Science Practice 7:** The student is able to connect and relate knowledge across various scales, concepts, and representations in and across domains.

 7.2 The student can *connect concepts* in and across domain(s) to generalize or extrapolate in and/or across enduring understandings and/or big idea.

**Concepts and Vocabulary to Review:**

## Diabetes and the Synthesis of Human Insulin    Section 21.1

Many biological molecules are macromolecules such as DNA. They are created as the components hook together in long chains called polymers.

## Lipids    Section 21.2

Lipids, which include fats and oils, are nonpolar so do not dissolve in water but dissolve in nonpolar solvents. Intermolecular forces between molecules can affect their melting points, determining whether certain fats are solids or liquids at room temperature.

## Carbohydrates    Section 21.3

Polysaccharides are long chains of monosaccharides linked together. Examples include cellulose and starch.

## Proteins and Amino Acids    Section 21.4

Proteins are polymers of amino acids linked together. Specific types of proteins are enzymes which act as catalysts. The shape of a protein is important to its function.

## Protein Structure    Section 21.5

A protein's structure will determine its function.

## Nucleic Acids: Blueprints for Proteins    Section 21.6

Nucleic acids are also polymers. They contain a sugar, base, and a phosphate group. The bases determine which nuclei acid is present.

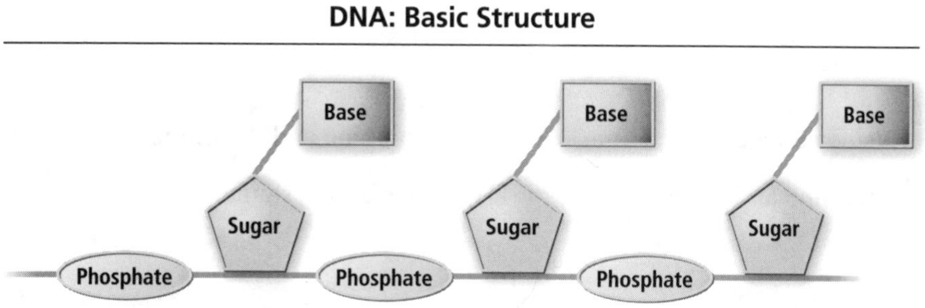

### DNA: Basic Structure

**Figure 21.1  DNA Structure**   DNA is composed of repeating units called nucleotides. Each nucleotide contains a sugar, a base, and a phosphate group.

## Additional Practice

*Self-Assessment Quiz Questions Q1, Q2, Q3, Q4, Q7, Q8, and Q9*
*Problems 4, 14, and 75*

## Practice AP® Test Question

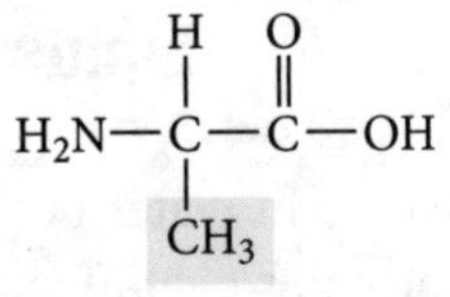

Alanine (Ala)

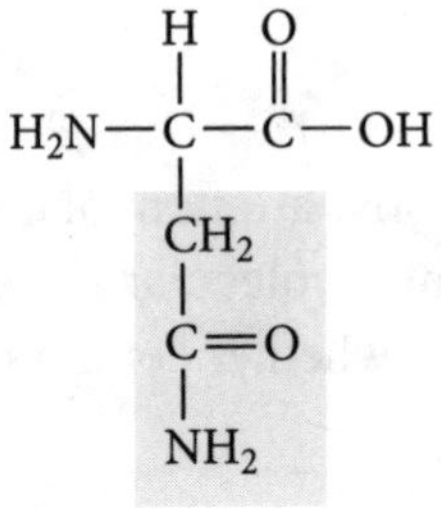

Asparagine (Asn)

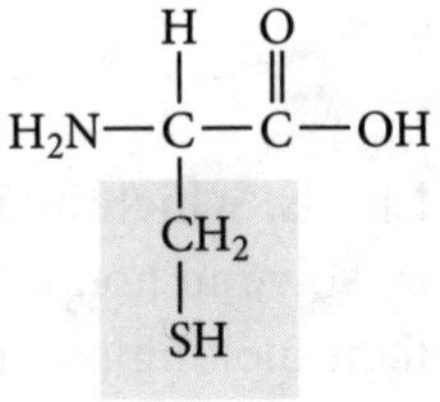

Cysteine (Cys)

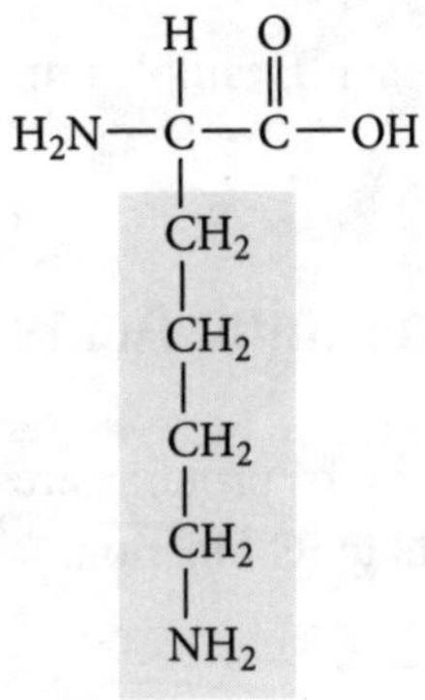

Lysine (Lys)

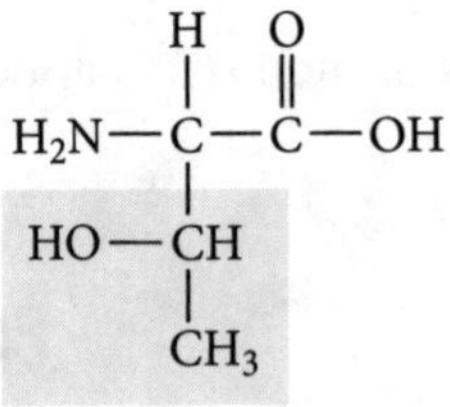

Threonine (Thr)

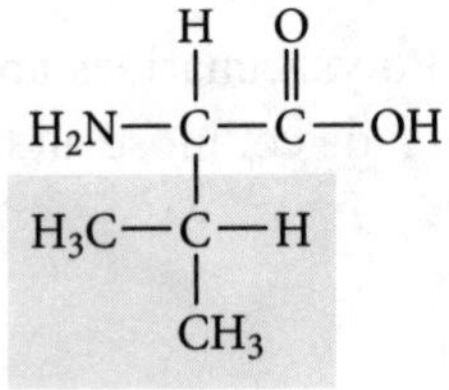

Valine (Val)

1. From the structures above, which two amino acids form the following dipeptide?

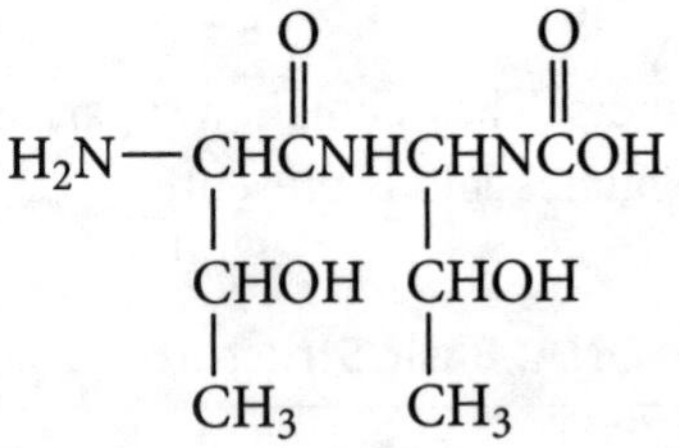

A) lysine and alanine
B) asparagine and threonine
C) threonine and valine
D) valine and cysteine

**Answer**

*1. C)*

# CHEMISTRY OF NONMETALS

Science Practice Seven asks students to see how chemistry principles apply across domains in science and in their everyday life. This chapter and the following chapters give many good examples of these connections. These are good reading chapters for students in terms of background knowledge about applications and do have some review from earlier chapters. Although noble gases are nonmetals, they are not covered in this chapter. Only a few examples are mentioned from the sections below:

22.2 **The Main-Group Elements: Bonding and Properties**

22.4 **Boron and Its Remarkable Structures**

22.5 **Carbon, Carbides, and Carbonates**

22.6 **Nitrogen and Phosphorus: Essential Elements for Life**

22.7 **Oxygen**

22.8 **Sulfur: A Dangerous but Useful Element**

22.9 **Halogens: Reactive Elements with High Electronegativity**

## Specific Learning Objectives Addressed in This Chapter:

**Learning objective 2.29** The student can create a representation of a covalent solid that shows essential characteristics of the structure and interactions present in the substance. [*See* **SP 1.1**]

**Learning objective 2.30** The student is able to explain a representation that connects properties of a covalent solid to its structural attributes and to the interactions present at the atomic level. [*See* **SP 1.1**, **6.2**, **7.1**]

## Specific Science Practices Addressed in This Chapter:

**Science Practice 1:** The student can use representations and models to communicate scientific phenomena and solve scientific problems.

    1.1 The student can *create representations and models* of natural or man-made phenomena and systems in the domain.

**Science Practice 6:** The student can work with scientific explanations and theories.

> 6.2 The student can *construct explanations of phenomena based on evidence* produced through scientific practices.

**Science Practice 7:** The student is able to connect and relate knowledge across various scales, concepts, and representations in and across domains.

> 7.1 The student can *connect phenomena and models* across spatial and temporal scales.

### Concepts and Vocabulary to Review

Section 22.2

## The Main-Group Elements: Bonding and Properties

The nonmetals with the exception of hydrogen and helium are all filling *p* orbitals in their electron configurations.

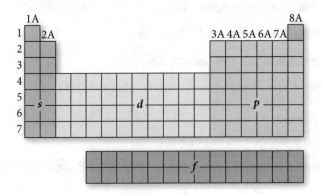

Nonmetals can form ionic bonds with metals and covalent bonds with other nonmetals. Nonmetals such as carbon and silicon can form network covalent bonds. The most electronegative elements like fluorine are nonmetals.

Section 22.4

## Boron and Its Remarkable Structures

Boron is added to glass so it does not crack. An example is Pyrex, which is used in beakers in the chemistry lab.

Section 22.5

## Carbon, Carbides, and Carbonates

Graphite and diamond structures and properties vary due to their structures.

Graphite has covalent bonds in the horizontal plane but has weak interaction between the layers. This allows graphite to slide one layer over another, making it a good lubricant. In contrast, diamond has covalent bonds in all four directions as each carbon is bonded to four other carbon atoms. As a result, diamond is very hard and is used in cutting tools.

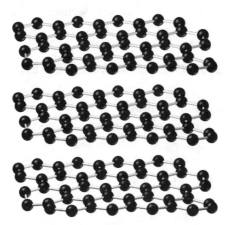

**Figure 22.1  Graphite Structure**    The carbon atoms in graphite bond strongly within the plane of the carbon atoms but bond weakly between the sheets.

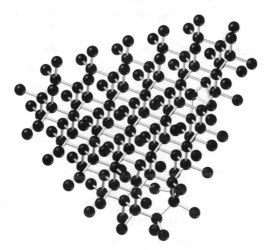

**Figure 22.2  Diamond Structure**    The diamond structure has carbon atoms at the corners of a tetrahedron, each connected to four other carbon atoms.

Carbon also has other forms such as coal, charcoal, fullerenes, and carbon black. Carbon forms many compounds including carbides. Carbon can form ionic carbides and covalent carbides, but they are both hard and have high melting points. An example of an ionic carbide is $CaC_2$ where carbon combines with a less electronegative metallic atom. In covalent carbides, carbon combines with another nonmetal, to form compounds such as SiC. If a metal alloy such as steel has a lattice with space to add carbon atoms, it will form a metallic carbide; the result is a harder, less malleable metal.

Carbon also combines with oxygen to form carbon dioxide, carbon monoxide, and carbonates.

$$CO_2(aq) + H_2O(l) \rightleftharpoons H_2CO_3(aq)$$
carbonic acid

$$H_2CO_3(aq) \rightleftharpoons H^+(aq) + HCO_3^-(aq) \rightleftharpoons 2H^+(aq) + CO_3^{2-}(aq)$$

carbonic acid                    hydrogen corbonate                      corbonate

If you are asked to write an equation where carbonic acid forms, remember the species in the greatest concentration is the species written in the equation.

## Section 22.6    Nitrogen and Phosphorus: Essential Elements for Life

The strength of the triple bond in nitrogen gas makes it very stable. With the ending configuration of $2s^2 2p^3$, nitrogen can form many compounds since it can show a variety of oxidation states including $+2, +3, +5$, and $-3$.

An equilibrium reaction where Le Châtelier's principle is observed is when colorless $N_2O_4$ is heated to form the reddish brown $NO_2$.

$$N_2O_4(g) \xrightarrow{\text{heat}} 2\,NO_2(g)$$

When cooled, the reaction goes back to the colorless $N_2O_4$. The change in color provides evidence of which part of the reaction is favored when heating and cooling.

Phosphorus is very similar to nitrogen since it has a similar ending electron configuration. When nitrogen bonds with hydrogen, polar ammonia molecules are formed, but because phosphorus is less electronegative, when it bonds with nitrogen, the phosphine that results is not as polar as ammonia.

## Section 22.7    Oxygen

With an electron configuration ending in $2s^2 2p^4$, oxygen shows a primary oxidation state of $-2$. Oxygen has the second highest electronegativity of all elements and is found in ionic, covalent, and network covalent compounds. To separate oxygen from the air, fractionation is used. The air is cooled until it all liquefies. Then it is warmed and the other gases will vaporize before the oxygen so the oxygen can be collected.

An allotrope of oxygen is ozone, $O_3$. Ozone is denser than oxygen gas and unlike oxygen gas, is diamagnetic.

## Section 22.8    Sulfur: A Dangerous but Useful Element

With the same outer electron configuration as oxygen, $s^2 p^4$, sulfur is larger due to the additional energy level added. Sulfur also forms the $-2$ oxidation state and has several allotropes, including a $S_8$ ring structure.

While $H_2S$, is bent in shape like water, it is less polar, as sulfur is not as electronegative as oxygen. Water also has larger bond angles than $H_2S$. Water forms hydrogen bonds between molecules while $H_2S$ does not, which results in $H_2S$ having a lower melting point than water.

## Halogens: Reactive Elements with High Electronegativity    Section 22.9

All halogens are the most electronegative atoms in their period and the smallest atom in their period. Within the halogens, the atomic radius increases regularly due to the additional energy level added. All have the outer configuration of $s^2p^5$ and show a primary oxidation state of $-1$. When combined with metals, the small size of fluorine and its large electronegativity result in ionic bonds with high lattice energies. Halogens can also combine with nonmetals to form covalent bonds and can combine with other halogens to form interhalide compounds.

## Additional Practice

*Self-Assessment Quiz Questions Q3, Q4, Q5, Q6, Q7, Q8, Q9, and Q10*
*Problems 4, 11, 14, 35, 36, 38, 45, 62, 69, 100, and 102*

## Practice AP® Test Questions

1. Which element exists as a diatomic molecule at 298K?

   A) B                          C) N

   B) C                          D) Ne

2. Ozone, $O_3$, is the upper atmosphere is important to life on the surface of the Earth because

   A) $O_3$ provides a shield against incoming X-rays and gamma rays from solar radiation.

   B) $O_3$ reacts with chlorofluorocarbons to create a hole in the ozone layer.

   C) $O_3$ plays a role in helping plants undergo photosynthesis.

   D) $O_3$ absorbs UV solar radiation.

3. Which of the following substances is being tested as a replacement for gasoline as the fuel for medium combustion engines?

   A) $NO_2$                     C) $H_2$

   B) $CO_2$                     D) $BF_3$

4. When nonmetal oxides are placed in water, the resultant solution is _____.

   A) acidic

   B) basic

   C) amphoteric

   D) neutral

5. The major source of the element sulfur is

   A) evaporation of seawater

   B) mining underground deposits of sulfur

   C) extraction from minerals containing sulfates

   D) reduction of sulfuric acid

**Answers**

1. C); 2. D); 3. C); 4. B); 5. B)

# METALS AND METALLURGY

This chapter provides background material about metals and their properties. As mentioned in Chapter 22, while very interesting material, it is not the focus of the AP curriculum. Most of the material mentioned was previously mentioned in other chapters. Sections which are AP material include

23.1 **Vanadium: A Problem and an Opportunity**

23.2 **The General Properties and Natural Distribution of Metals**

23.5 **Sources, Properties, and Products of Some of the 3d Transition Metals**

## Specific Learning Objectives Addressed in This Chapter:

**Learning objective 2.25** The student is able to compare the properties of metal alloys with their constituent elements to determine if an alloy has formed, identify the type of alloy formed, and explain the differences in properties using particulate level reasoning. [*See* **SP 1.4, 7.2**]

**Learning objective 2.26** Students can use the electron sea model of metallic bonding to predict or make claims about the macroscopic properties of metals or alloys. [*See* **SP 6.4, 7.1**]

**Learning objective 2.27** The student can create a representation of a metallic solid that shows essential characteristics of the structure and interactions present in the substance. [*See* **SP 1.1**]

**Learning objective 2.28** The student is able to explain a representation that connects properties of a metallic solid to its structural attributes and to the interactions present at the atomic level. [*See* **SP 1.1, 6.2, 7.1**]

## Specific Science Practices Addressed in This Chapter:

**Science Practice 1:** The student can use representations and models to communicate scientific phenomena and solve scientific problems.

    1.1  The student can *create representations and models* of natural or man-made phenomena and systems in the domain.

      1.4   The student can *use representations and models* to analyze situations or solve problems qualitatively and quantitatively.

**Science Practice 6:** The student can work with scientific explanations and theories.

      6.2   The student can *construct explanations of phenomena based on evidence* produced through scientific practices.

      6.4   The student can *make claims and predictions about natural phenomena* based on scientific theories and models.

**Science Practice 7:** The student is able to connect and relate knowledge across various scales, concepts, and representations in and across domains.

      7.1   The student can *connect phenomena and models* across spatial and temporal scales.

      7.2   The student can *connect concepts* in and across domain(s) to generalize or extrapolate in and/or across enduring understandings and/or concepts.

**Concepts and Vocabulary to Review:**

Section 23.1

# Vanadium: A Problem and an Opportunity

Metallurgy includes all processes associated with mining and processes of metal production. Alloys are mixtures of metals.

Section 23.2

# The General Properties and Natural Distribution of Metals

Properties of metals include being a good conductor of heat and electricity, hammered into sheets (malleability), drawn into wires (ductility), and are generally silver in color. They have delocalized electrons found in an electron "sea." Properties vary as lead is very soft while chromium is very brittle.

Very few metals actually are found in their elemental form on earth, due to their reactivity. The metals found in their elemental form are called the noble metals. They include gold, platinum, silver, palladium, copper, and nickel.

Section 23.5

# Sources, Properties, and Products of Some of the 3d Transition Metals

Titanium is highly resistant to corrosion because it reacts with oxygen, forming a coating on the outside of the metal. Titanium is very strong and light, so it is used in airline jet engines. White paints often include $TiO_2$, which was substituted for toxic $PbO_2$ in older paints.

Chromium is a hard white, brittle metal, yet its compounds are colored. Colors range from anions in orange in dichromate and yellow in chromate to compounds that are violet in chrome alum to red in chromium(II) acetate. Chromium is often used in steel.

Cobalt, iron, and nickel are ferromagnetic. They are attracted to magnets.

Copper replaced lead in piping due to lead's toxicity. Bronze is an alloy of copper and tin, while brass is an alloy of copper and zinc.

Zinc is also used in galvanizing steel. The zinc coating protects the metal underneath from oxidizing.

## Additional Practice

*Self-Assessment Quiz Questions Q1, Q7, Q8, Q9, and Q10*
*Problems 15, 16, and 18*

### Practice AP® Test Questions

Questions 1–3 refer to the following information. Nickel sulfide is abundant in Ontario, Canada. To produce nickel metal, the nickel sulfide is roasted in air then the product reacted with carbon monoxide to form nickel carbonyl. When the nickel carbonyl is heated it decomposes to nickel metal.

$$Ni(CO)_4(g) \rightleftharpoons Ni(s) + 4\,CO\,(g) \qquad \Delta S = -320\,JK^{-1} \cdot mol^{-1}\,and$$

$$\Delta H = -160.7\,kJ$$

|                 | $\Delta G_f^\circ\,(kJ/mol)$ |
| --------------- | ---------------------------- |
| $CO(g)$         | $-137$                       |
| $Ni(CO)_4(g)$   | $-587.4\,kJ/mol$             |

1. The molecular geometry of nickel carbonyl is

    A) square planar

    B) trigonal pyramidal

    C) tetrahedral

    D) distorted tetrahedron

2. In order to maximize the production of nickel,

    A) temperature must be increased

    B) pressure must be increased

    C) volume must be decreased

    D) catalyst must be added

3. Assume $\Delta G_f^\circ$ is independent of temperature; estimate the equilibrium constant, $K_p$, for the reaction at $60.0\,°C$.

    A) less than $1.0 \times 10^{-5}$

    B) greater than $1.0 \times 10^{-5}$ but less than 1

    C) greater than 1 but less than 100,000

    D) greater than 100,000

4. The process of arc-melting is used to facilitate the production of which pure metal?

   A) Ag

   B) Al

   C) Pt

   D) Ti

5. Which of the following elements is most likely to be found on Earth as an oxide?

   A) Fe

   B) Zn

   C) Pt

   D) Hg

**Answers**

*1. C); 2. A); 3. D); 4. D); 5. A)*

# TRANSITION METALS AND COORDINATION COMPOUNDS

This chapter goes into detail about coordination compounds and crystal field splitting. These will not be tested in the AP curriculum. There are a few details about transition metals which are good foundational information to be aware of.

24.1 **The Colors of Rubies and Emeralds**

24.2 **Properties of Transition Metals**

24.3 **Coordination Compounds**

## Specific Learning Objectives Addressed in This Chapter:

**Learning objective 1.9** The student is able to predict and/or justify trends in atomic properties based on location on the periodic table and/or the shell model. [*See* **SP 6.4**]

**Learning objective 2.1** Students can predict properties of substances based on their chemical formulas, and provide explanations of their properties based on particle views. [*See* **SP 6.4, 7.1**]

**Learning objective 2.25** The student is able to compare the properties of metal alloys with their constituent elements to determine if an alloy has formed, identify the type of alloy formed, and explain the differences in properties using particulate level reasoning. [*See* **SP 1.4, 7.2**]

## Specific Science Practices Addressed in This Chapter:

**Science Practice 1:** The student can use representations and models to communicate scientific phenomena and solve scientific problems.

    1.4  The student can *use representations and models* to analyze situations or solve problems qualitatively and quantitatively.

**Science Practice 6:** The student can work with scientific explanations and theories.

    6.4  The student can *make claims and predictions about natural phenomena* based on scientific theories and models.

**Science Practice 7:** The student is able to connect and relate knowledge across various scales, concepts, and representations in and across domains.

> 7.1  The student can *connect phenomena and models* across spatial and temporal scales.
>
> 7.2  The student can *connect concepts* in and across domain(s) to generalize or extrapolate in and/or across enduring understandings and/or concepts.

## Concepts and Vocabulary to Review:

## The Colors of Rubies and Emeralds    Section 24.1

This is background information only. The color of both rubies and emeralds is due to the chromium III ion. Rubies are red and emeralds are green, so how can this be? In both, the $Cr^{3+}$ is replacing some of the $Al^{3+}$ in the host crystal, but in rubies it is in $Al_2O_3$ while in emeralds it is $Be_3Al_2(SiO_6)$. The red of garnet and yellow-green of peridot are both caused by $Fe^{2+}$ substitutions while the blue of turquoise is caused by $Cu^{2+}$ substitutions in their host crystals. The color seen is the color absorbed by the crystal.

## Properties of Transition Metals    Section 24.2

The transition metals are adding electrons in *d* orbitals, have the outermost electrons in the next level of *s*, and have metallic bonding. Remember when looking at the following diagram, AP students will not be expected to memorize the configuration exceptions of chromium and copper. Students will be expected though to explain why these exceptions occur.

Atomic size remains relatively the same in each period of the transition metals since the outer valence electrons remain the same for the period.

**Table 24.1**   First-Row Transition Metal Orbital Occupancy

| | 4s | 3d | | | | |
|---|---|---|---|---|---|---|
| Sc | ⇅ | ↑ | | | | |
| Ti | ⇅ | ↑ | ↑ | | | |
| V | ⇅ | ↑ | ↑ | ↑ | | |
| Cr | ↑ | ↑ | ↑ | ↑ | ↑ | ↑ |
| Mn | ⇅ | ↑ | ↑ | ↑ | ↑ | ↑ |
| Fe | ⇅ | ⇅ | ↑ | ↑ | ↑ | ↑ |
| Co | ⇅ | ⇅ | ⇅ | ↑ | ↑ | ↑ |
| Ni | ⇅ | ⇅ | ⇅ | ⇅ | ↑ | ↑ |
| Cu | ↑ | ⇅ | ⇅ | ⇅ | ⇅ | ⇅ |
| Zn | ⇅ | ⇅ | ⇅ | ⇅ | ⇅ | ⇅ |

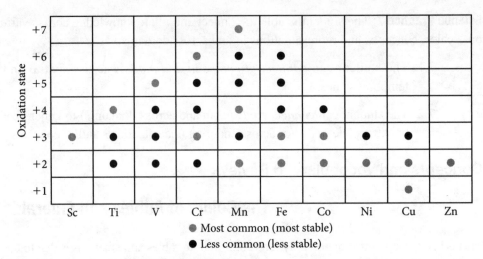

Figure 24.1  **First-Row Transition Metal Oxidation States**   The transition metals exhibit many more oxidation states than the main-group elements. These oxidation states range from +7 to +1.

The oxidation states of the transition metals vary, but most can form a +2 ion due to the loss of the outer $s$ electrons in the valence level.

## Section 24.3    Coordination Compounds

Complex ions have a central atom bound to one or more ligands. When naming a complex ion, the ligands with a prefix for the number added are named first, then the central atom and the charge of the central atom follows. For instance $[Ag(NH_3)_2]^+$ is the diamine silver(I) complex. Complex ions are placed inside a bracket with the overall charge outside the bracket. The number of ligands added is called a coordination number. Usually, this number is 2, 4, or 6.

Some common ligands are in the following table:

**Table 24.2**   Name and Formulas of Common Ligands

| Ligand | Name in Complex Ion |
|---|---|
| **Anions** | |
| Bromide, $Br^-$ | Bromo |
| Chloride, $Cl^-$ | Chloro |
| Hydroxide, $OH^-$ | Hydroxo |
| Cyanide, $CN^-$ | Cyano |
| Nitrite, $NO_2^-$ | Nitro |
| Oxalate, $C_2O_4^{2-}$ (ox) | Oxalato |
| Ethylenediaminetetraacetate ($EDTA^{4-}$) | Ethylenediaminetetraacetato |
| **Neutral molecules** | |
| Water $H_2O$ | Aqua |
| Ammonia, $NH_3$ | Ammine |
| Carbon monoxide, CO | Carbonyl |
| Ethylenediamine (en) | Ethylenediamine |

## Additional Practice

*Self-Assessment Quiz Questions Q1 and Q4*
*Problems 1, 3, 17, and 25*

## Practice AP® Test Questions

Given the following substances

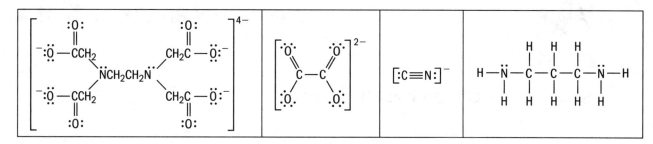

1.  Which is a monodentate ligand?

    A)  EDTA

    B)  $C_2O_4^-$

    C)  $CN^-$

    D)  $H_2NCH_2CH_2CH_2NH_2$

2.  Which is a bidentate ligand?

    A)  EDTA

    B)  $C_2O_4^-$

    C)  $CN^-$

    D)  $H_2NCH_2CH_2CH_2NH_2$

3.  Which substance is a coordination compound and not a complex ion?

    A)  $[Fe(CN)_3]$

    B)  $[Pt(NH_3)_2Cl_2]$

    C)  $[Fe(CN)_6]^{4-}$

    D)  $PtO_2 2H_2O$

4.  $Ti^{3+}$ has _____ electrons in the $3d$ orbital

    A)  1          B)  2          C)  3          D)  4

5.  Square planar complexes can be formed with metals having a _____electron configuration. Such species are diamagnetic.

    A)  $d^6$          B)  $d^8$          C)  $d^9$          D)  $d^{10}$

TEST

A

# CHEMISTRY PRACTICE TEST A

Section I **Multiple-Choice Questions**

(Time–90 minutes)

You may not use your calculator for Section I

**Note:** For all questions, assume that the temperature is 298 K, the pressure is 1.00 atmosphere, and the solutions are aqueous unless otherwise specified.

**Directions:** Each of the questions or incomplete sentences in Section I are followed by four suggested answers or completions. Select the answer that is best in each case and fill in the circle on the answer sheet.

**Given the following table containing information about elements, answer questions 1–3.**

| Element | Atomic number | Atomic mass | Ionization energy (kJ/mol) |
|---------|---------------|-------------|----------------------------|
| H | 1 | 1 | 1312 |
| Li | 3 | 6 | 520 |
| C | 6 | 12 | 1086 |
| N | 7 | 14 | 1402 |
| O | 8 | 16 | 1314 |
| F | 9 | 19 | 1681 |
| Na | 11 | 23 | 496 |

1. Which of the following statements about 1 gram of pure hydrogen gas, $H_2$, is correct?

    A) 1 gram of hydrogen gas has fewer atoms than 7 grams of pure nitrogen gas.

    B) 1 gram of hydrogen gas has the same number of atoms as 44 grams of pure carbon dioxide, $CO_2$.

    C) 1 gram of hydrogen gas has the same number of hydrogen atoms as 18 grams of water, $H_2O$.

    D) 1 gram of hydrogen gas has the same number of atoms as 16 grams of oxygen gas, $O_2(g)$.

2. Which of the following statements about ionization energies can be deduced?

   A) Ionization energies generally increase as atomic number increases.
   B) Ionization energies generally increase in a period in the periodic table from left to right.
   C) Ionization energies generally decrease as atoms increase in number of electrons.
   D) Ionization energies are generally similar if the number of valence electrons is the same.

3. Which statement is correct about the electron being removed when the ionization energy was measured?

   A) It must be closer to the nucleus in nitrogen than for the other elements.
   B) It must be further from the nucleus in carbon than for the other elements.
   C) It is more strongly attracted to the nucleus as the number of protons increases.
   D) Its attraction to the nucleus depends on both distance and atomic number.

## Questions 4 and 5 use the following information.

The values of electron affinities for some elements are shown in the table below.

### ELectron Affinities (KJ/mol)

| H | | | | | | He |
|---|---|---|---|---|---|---|
| -73 | | | | | | >0 |
| Li | Be | C | N | O | F | Ne |
| -60 | >0 | -122 | >0 | -141 | -328 | >0 |
| Na | Mg | Si | P | S | Cl | Ar |
| -53 | >0 | -134 | -72 | -200 | -349 | >0 |
| K | Ca | Ge | As | Se | Br | Kr |
| -48 | -2 | -119 | -78 | -195 | -325 | >0 |
| Rb | Sr | Sn | Sb | Te | I | Kr |
| -47 | -6 | -107 | -103 | -190 | -295 | >0 |

4. Based on the table and your knowledge of periodic properties, which elements would be expected to be found as negative ions ($X^-$) in compounds, and why?

   A) F and Cl as they have the largest energy released when forming compounds, making the process thermodynamically favorable.
   B) Ca and Sr as they have the least energy released when forming a negative ion.
   C) Be, Mg, He, Ne, Ar, Kr, and Xe as they are listed as > 0 in the table.
   D) Br and I as they have high energy releases, and are the largest ions.

5. Fluorine reacts with Group 1 metals and forms an anion. Potassium reacts with the halogens and forms a cation. One reason for this is

A) a fluorine atom is larger compared to a potassium atom.
B) fluorine has a greater ionization energy compared to potassium.
C) fluorine has a greater electron affinity compared to potassium.
D) at room temperature, fluorine is a diatomic gas and potassium is a solid.

**Question 6 uses information in the following table.**

The table below lists atomic properties of size and ionization energy across the first period.

| Element | Atomic radius (pm) | First ionization Energy (kJ/mol) |
|---------|--------------------|-----------------------------------|
| Li | 152 | 520 |
| Be | 112 | 899 |
| B | 85 | 801 |
| C | 77 | 1086 |
| N | 70 | 1402 |
| O | 73 | 1314 |
| F | 72 | 1681 |
| Ne | 70 | 2081 |

6. Which of the following best explains the data in the table?

A) Both radius and ionization energy generally increase uniformly across the period, consistent with the shell model of atomic structure.
B) Radius generally increases uniformly across the period, but subshells in the quantum model are needed to explain the inconsistencies in the trend of ionization energies.
C) As the number of protons increases in the nucleus, the valence electrons are pulled closer to the nucleus. The atomic radius decreases and the force of attraction on the valence electrons increases.
D) The values of ionization energy for N and O are out of line with the general trend predicted by the shell model because these atoms form unusually strong diatomic molecules ($O_2$ and $N_2$) and influence the measurement of ionization energy.

7. A chemist carries out a reaction to form a gaseous chemical which could have either one of the formulas drawn below.

$$H_3C \diagdown \qquad CH_3$$
$$\qquad C{=}C$$
$$H \diagup \qquad \diagdown H$$

$$H_2C{-}CH_2$$
$$\vert \qquad \vert$$
$$H_2C{-}CH_2$$

Which of the following describes how the chemist might best find out which is the formula of the compound made?

A) Infra-red absorption spectrometry to look at vibrations of the carbon to carbon bonds.

B) Visible light absorption spectrometry to look at electronic transitions.

C) Mass spectrometry to examine the exact mass of the two compounds.

D) Gas diffusion measurements to determine the speeds of the gas molecules.

8. The concentration of bromide ion in a solution can be found by precipitating the bromide ion as silver bromide (AgBr). Assuming a complete reaction, if the amount of silver bromide collected from 500.0 mL of solution is 0.188 grams, what was the concentration, in moles per liter of bromide ion (Br$^-$)? The following table is given for your use:

| Element | Atomic Mass |
|---------|-------------|
| Ag | 108 |
| Br | 80 |

A) $1.0 \times 10^{-3}$ M

B) $2.0 \times 10^{-3}$ M

C) $3.7 \times 10^{-3}$ M

D) 2.0 M

9. The most familiar acids are compounds containing hydrogen and are classified as strong or weak. Which of the following best describes the basis for the classification of strong acid when it is dissolved in water?

A) The acid has the most H atoms in its formula to react when a base is added.

B) The maximum amount of heat is produced when the acid is dissolved in water.

C) The acid contains one of the halogen atoms (F, Cl, Br, or I) in addition to H atoms.

D) The acid transfers at least one H atom as a proton completely to water as it dissolves.

The diagram below represents the gas molecules in a sealed flask filled with methane gas at room temperature (20 °C). The boiling point of methane is −164 °C.

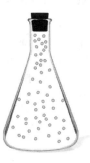

10. Which best represents the same flask when placed in a freezer at a temperature of $-20°C$?

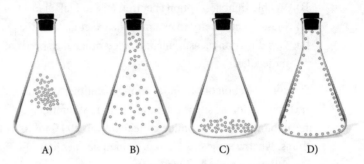

A)          B)          C)          D)

**Question 11 can best be answered by referring to the following information.**

The diagram below shows the results, after 4 minutes, from placing spots of three different dyes on paper strips 1 cm from the bottom of the strip and placing the paper in a small amount of solvent at the base in an enclosed container.

**Paper Chromatography Results from Three Dye Samples**

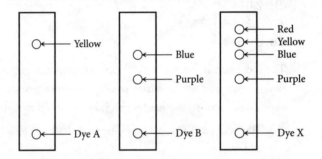

11. Which of the following best explains the results.

A) The red dye has the strongest interactions with paper and with the solvent.

B) The yellow dye has the weakest interactions with the solvent but the strongest interactions with the paper.

C) Dye X is a mixture of dye A and dye B in equivalent amounts.

D) The purple dye has the strongest interactions with paper, but the weakest with the solvent.

12. Which of the following parameters is the most useful in predicting the polarity of a bond between two atoms.

A) The relative electronegativities of the two atoms.

B) The relative atomic radius of each of the two atoms.

C) The relative ionization energies of the two atoms.

D) The relative electron affinities of the two atoms.

13. Which of the following has the correct order of bond polarity from smallest to largest of the C—X bond, where X is the atom bonded to C in each case?

A) F, O, N, C

B) N, C, F, O

C) C, N, O, F

D) O, F, C, N

14. FeO can be prepared by heating iron(II) oxalate in a vacuum. A gas mixture consisting of a mixture of carbon monoxide gas and carbon dioxide gas also forms.

$$FeC_2O_4(s) \rightleftharpoons FeO(s) + CO(g) + CO_2(g)$$

How many grams of $FeC_2O_4(s)$ (molar mass 144) are needed to produce a total volume of 2.24 L of gas at 1.00 atm and 273 K, assuming the reaction goes to completion? The gas is collected in a rigid container.

A) 1.8 g

B) 3.6 g

C) 7.2 g

D) 14.4 g

15. Ammonia is frequently produced by the Haber process in which nitrogen gas, $N_2$, and hydrogen gas, $H_2$, are combined to form ammonia gas, $NH_3$. If 2 moles of nitrogen gas and 3 moles of hydrogen gas are reacted, what is the **maximum** amount of ammonia gas that could be produced?

A) 2 mol

B) 3 mol

C) 4 mol

D) 5 mol

16. If a 22.4 L volume of a sample of gas has a density of 0.900 grams/L at 1.00 atm and 0.00°C. Given the following gases, which could it be?

A) Ne

B) CO

C) $CO_2$

D) Kr

**Questions 17 and 18 can be answered using the following information.**

The properties of two solid substances are examined to determine their structure and suitability of forming an alloy with iron.

| Substance | Radius | Electrical Conductivity of solid | Melting Point | Electrical Conductivity of liquid | Solubility in water | Hardness |
|---|---|---|---|---|---|---|
| X | 182 pm 172 pm | not | 690°C | high | very | brittle |
| Y | 128 pm | high | 1907°C | high | not | very hard, brittle |
| Fe | 126 pm | high | 1538°C | high | not | soft |

17. Which type of structure is most likely associated with substance X?

A) Molecular Covalent

B) Network Covalent

C) Ionic

D) Metal

18. What substance can best be mixed with iron to form an alloy and why?

    A) Substance Y because of their similar electrical conductivity in the liquid phase allows for an interstitial alloy to form.

    B) Substance Y because the radius of atoms are similar allowing a substitutional alloy to form.

    C) Substance X because of their similar electrical conductivity in the solid phase allows for an interstitial alloy to form.

    D) Substance X because the larger size of particles allowing a substitutional alloy to form.

### Questions 19 and 20 use the following information.

The following diagram is a representation of a solid structure.

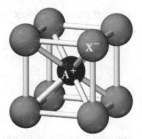

19. Which two attributes contribute most to the value of lattice energy of this solid?

    A) Electronegativity values of each of the component elements.

    B) Radius and charge of each of the component ions.

    C) Electron affinity of the anion and ionization energy of the cation.

    D) Effective nuclear charges on valence electrons of each component element.

20. Which of the following properties are most likely for this compound?

    A) soft, low melting, non-conducting as a liquid

    B) hard, high melting, conducts as a liquid

    C) hard, high melting, non-conducting as a liquid

    D) soft, low melting, conducts as a liquid

### The following information is useful to help answer Question 21.

In order to measure the composition of a compound formed by reacting magnesium with oxygen gas, a student places a weighed strip of cleaned magnesium metal into a clean crucible and heats it until it burns to form a white powder. Being careful to make sure no powder is lost, the student lets the crucible cool and places it on a balance to obtain its mass. From the measured mass, the student calculates the formula of the oxide, using the known atomic masses of magnesium and oxygen.

21. What important step has the student omitted in this procedure?

    A) cutting the magnesium strip into small pieces.

    B) determining the volume of the crucible

    C) dissolving the magnesium metal in acid

    D) weighing the empty crucible.

22. A class was presented with the following list of substances and asked to order the substances according to increasing acidity.

HOOH, CH₃COOH: H₂CO₃: CH₃OCH₃; HOOCCH₂COOH

What feature of these molecules is most helpful to know in predicting acidity?

A) the number of —COOH functional groups
B) the total number of hydrogen atoms
C) the total number of oxygen atoms
D) the number of C—C bonds.

23. Which of the following represents a conjugate acid–base pair?

A) $HNO_3$; $H_2SO_4$
B) $H_2O_2$; $H_3O^+$
C) $HCO_3^-$; $H_2CO_3$
D) $H_2SO_4$; $SO_4^{2-}$

24. Students in a lab were investigating how much heat was given off by a "hot pack" that was triggered by snapping a small metal disk inside the pack.

Students observed the following:

i) the pack got hot
ii) its appearance changed from clear liquid to white crystals
iii) when placed in boiling water it went back to a clear liquid
iv) through all the changes, its total mass was unchanged

Based on this evidence, was the exothermic process they observed a physical or chemical change?

A) physical because no change in mass was observed
B) chemical because this involved a change in appearance
C) physical because this process can be reversed to give the original substance
D) chemical because a disk snap was needed

25. Which of the following graphs show the energy change resulting from the burning of a wood log?

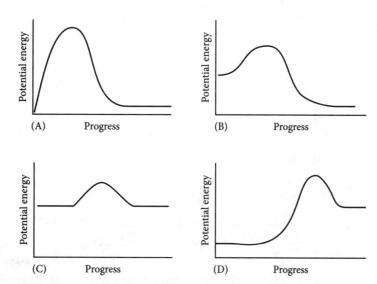

26. Technetium-99m is a metastable nuclear isomer of technetium-99, symbolized as $^{99m}T_c$. A hospital buys a sample of $^{99m}T_c$, a radioactive isotope used to perform kidney scans of patients. The half-life of $^{99m}T_c$ is 6.0 hours. A technician needs to determine the rate constant for $^{99m}T_c$ to ensure the patient will receive enough of the isotope to produce a good scan. Which is the correct expression for calculating the rate constant for $^{99m}T_c$ in units of $min^{-1}$? $\ln 2 = 0.693$.

   A) $6.0 \times 60$
   B) $6.0/60$
   C) $0.693 \times (6.0 \times 60)$
   D) $0.693/(6.0 \times 60)$

### Question 27 and 28 relate to the following information.

The graph below was drawn for a reaction between chemicals X and Y to form a product Z.

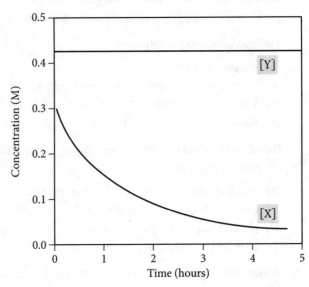

27. Assuming there are no complications, and under these conditions, what is the rate law for this reaction?

   A) Rate $= k[X][Y]$
   B) Rate $= k[X]$
   C) Rate $= k[Y]$
   D) Rate $= k[X][Y]/[Z]$

28. What is the half-life for this reaction?

   A) 0.5 hours
   B) 1 hour
   C) 2 hours
   D) 5 hours

29. In a test tube, a student placed 20 drops of 0.10 M hydrochloric acid and 2 drops of phenolphthalein solution. She then added, drop by drop, barium hydroxide solution until the solution just turned pink. 10 drops of base had been added. What was the approximate concentration of the barium hydroxide solution?

A) 0.05 M

B) 0.10 M

C) 0.20 M

D) 0.40 M

The diagram below represents energy changes for the reaction

A $\longrightarrow$ B

Use this diagram in answering questions 30 and 31.

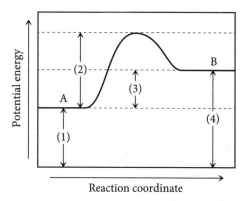

Reaction coordinate

30. If the temperature of the reaction is increased, the magnitude of which energy change will determine the rate of reaction when the temperature increases?

A) (1)

B) (2)

C) (3)

D) (4)

31. If a catalyst is added, the expected change on the diagram will be to

A) increase energy (1)

B) decrease energy (2)

C) increase energy (3)

D) decrease energy (4)

## Use the following graph to help answer questions 32 and 33.

The graph shows the distribution of speeds of gas particles for four different noble gases.

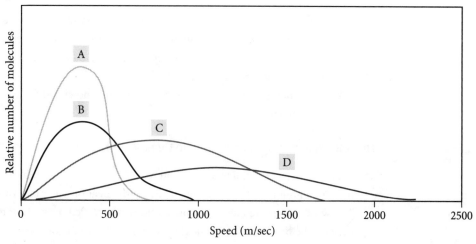

32. The plots are different for the different gases because

   A) the gases are at different temperatures

   B) speeds are directly proportional to square root of mass

   C) speeds are inversely proportional to square root of mass

   D) the kinetic energies of the gases are different

33. If the curves represented one gas at 4 different temperatures, which curve would represent the highest temperature?

   A) A

   B) B

   C) C

   D) D

**The following information may be helpful to answer Question 34.**

The gases described in this problem were confined in a cylinder with a movable piston as represented in the diagram below. Atmospheric pressure holds the piston in the cylinder. If the cylinder is heated, the piston can move and a volume change will occur.

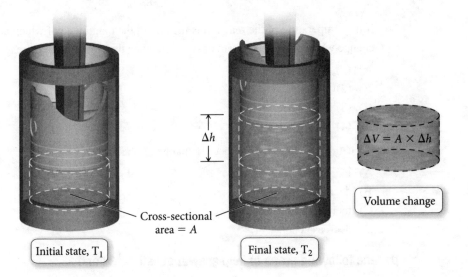

Initial state, $T_1$        Final state, $T_2$        $\Delta V = A \times \Delta h$

Cross-sectional area = $A$        Volume change

34. Which gas will do the greatest amount of work for a given temperature change, where $T_2 > T_1$?

   A) Xenon because it is the heaviest, so more energy transfer per collision.

   B) Helium because it is the lightest so more collisions to transfer energy.

   C) All the gases will do the same work as they have the same average kinetic energy.

   D) The actual temperature and pressure must be known before this question can be answered.

**The following information relates to Question 35.**

35. A 20.0 g piece of metal at a temperature of 62°C was dropped into a calorimeter containing 40.0 g of water. The specific heat of water is 4.18 J/g°C. The water was stirred and its temperature was recorded over a four minute period. The data table on the next page shows the results of water:

| Time (min) | Temperature (°C) |
|------------|------------------|
| 0.0 | 24.0 |
| 1.0 | 24.8 |
| 1.4 | 25.2 |
| 1.8 | 25.8 |
| 2.0 | 26.0 |
| 2.4 | 26.0 |
| 3.0 | 25.8 |
| 3.4 | 25.6 |

Which of the following is the most probable approximate value for the specific heat of the metal in units of J/g°C?

A)  0.148

B)  0.450

C)  0.615

D)  8.00

**For Questions 36, 37, and 38 use the graph below which shows the temperature change as a function as a sample of pure solid ethanol is heated at a constant rate (50 J/minute).**

The melting point of ethanol is −115°C and the boiling point is +78°C. The line segments are numbered I through V.

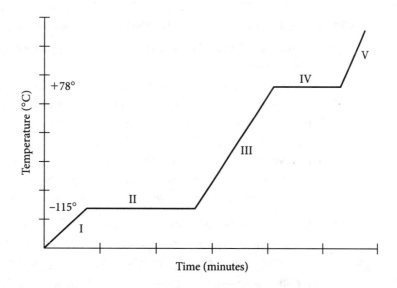

36. The slope of which line can be used, with other information, to calculate the heat capacity of solid ethanol?

A)  I

B)  II

C)  III

D)  V

37. In which region of the graph is both solid and liquid ethanol present?

    A) I

    B) II

    C) III

    D) IV

38. Which of the following can be deduced about the substance from the graph?

    A) It takes more energy to vaporize all of the liquid compared to melt all of the solid.

    B) The melting point can change as a function of the amount of substance to be heated.

    C) The heat capacity of the liquid is smaller than that of the solid.

    D) The heat of fusion is smaller than the heat of vaporization.

**Use the following information to help answer questions 39 and 40.**

Glucose can react with oxygen according to the following equation:

$$C_6H_{12}O_6(s) + 6O_2(g) \longrightarrow 6CO_2(g) + 6H_2O(l)$$

Standard Enthalpies of formation for three substances are given in the following table

| Compound | $\Delta H^{\circ}_{formation}$ (kJ/mol) |
|---|---|
| $CO_2(g)$ | −393.5 |
| $H_2O$ (l) | −285.8 |
| $C_6H_{12}O_6(s)$(glucose) | −1273.3 |

39. Which of the following best explains how cells in most living system obtain energy?

    A) Glucose has strong bonds that store lots of energy. Cells use glucose to make important biochemicals.

    B) Carbon dioxide and water have stronger bonds than in glucose. Energy is released in cells when glucose is converted to $CO_2$ and $H_2O$.

    C) Glucose has stronger bonds than carbon dioxide and water, so energy is released when plants make glucose in the photosynthesis process.

    D) Oxygen, $O_2$, is a reactant in the conversion of glucose to carbon dioxide and water. Its heat of formation must be larger than that of glucose in order that cells can gain positive energy from this reaction.

40. Unless glucose is burned in a flame, a sample of glucose can remain stable in a bottle for a long time, but living cells can convert it to carbon dioxide and water at room temperature. Which of the following best explains how this is possible?

    A) Cells use other forms of energy, such as light, to create the activation energy needed to start the reaction.

    B) Cells contain lithium, which speeds up the reduction half-reaction compared to the sample in the bottle, where the reaction is taking place very slowly.

    C) Cells carry out the reaction in a series of small intermediate steps, each requiring only small activation energy to start them.

    D) Cells have a high oxygen concentration so the reaction goes at a faster rate. The oxygen concentration in air is lower.

**The following information can be used to help answer Questions 41–45.**

The following spontaneous reaction occurs when the cell represented in the diagram below operates

$$Mg(s) + 2 Ag^+(aq) \longrightarrow 2 Ag(s) + Mg^{2+}(aq)$$

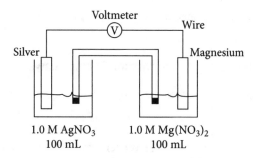

Four separate but identical electrochemical cells, W, X, Y and Z, are prepared. Cells W, X, Y, and Z all look like the diagram above,

| Half-reaction | $E°(V)$ |
|---|---|
| $Mg^{2+}(aq) + 2e^- \longrightarrow Mg(s)$ | −2.37 |
| $Ag^+(aq) + e^- \longrightarrow Ag(s)$ | +0.80 |

41.  Calculate $E°$ for cell W when it first starts to operate.

   A)  −3.17 V
   B)  −1.57 V
   C)  +1.57 V
   D)  +3.17 V

42.  In cell W, the salt bridge is replaced by a magnesium wire.

   A)  The voltage increases.
   B)  The voltage decreases.
   C)  The voltage becomes zero.
   D)  No change in the voltage occurs

43.  In cell X, a 50 mL sample of 2.0 M $Mg(NO_3)_2(aq)$ is added to the 1.0 M $Mg(NO_3)_2(aq)$.

   A)  The voltage increases.
   B)  The voltage decreases.
   C)  The voltage becomes zero.
   D)  No change in the voltage occurs.

44.  In electrochemical cell Y, the magnesium electrode is replaced by one twice as large and the solution is 200 mL of 1.0 M $Mg(NO_3)_2(aq)$.

   A)  The voltage increases.
   B)  The voltage decreases.
   C)  The voltage becomes zero.
   D)  No change in the voltage occurs.

45. In electrochemical cell Z, a 20 mL sample of 3 M $AgNO_3(aq)$ is added to the 1.0 M $AgNO_3(aq)$ and 20 mL of deionized water are added to the 1.0 M $Mg(NO_3)_2(aq)$.

   A) The voltage increases.
   B) The voltage decreases.
   C) The voltage becomes zero.
   D) No change in the voltage occurs.

## Use the following information to help answer questions 46–49.

$C_4H_9Br$ and water react to form $C_4H_9OH$ and two other products.

$$CH_4H_9Br + 2H_2O \longrightarrow CH_4H_9OH + \underline{\quad} + \underline{\quad}$$

A three-step mechanism has been proposed for this reaction.

Step 1.  $C_4H_9Br \rightleftharpoons C_4H_9Br^+ + Br^-$      Slow
Step 2.  $C_4H_9Br^+ + H_2O \longrightarrow C_4H_9OH_2^+$      Fast
Step 3.  $C_4H_9OH_2^+ + H_2O \longrightarrow C_4H_9OH + H_3O^+$      Fast

46. Which species is an intermediate in the mechanism?

   A) $Br^-$
   B) $CH_4H_9Br^+$
   C) $CH_4H_9OH_2^+$
   D) $CH_4H_9Br^+$ and $CH_4H_9OH_2^+$

47. What is the molecularity of the rate-determining step?

   A) unimolecular
   B) bimolecular
   C) termolecular
   D) tetramolecular

48. The rate law that is consistent with the proposed mechanism is

   A) rate $= k[C_4H_9Br^+][Br^-]$
   B) rate $= k[C_4H_9Br^+][H_2O]$
   C) rate $= k[C_4H_9OH_2^+]$
   D) rate $= k[C_4H_9Br]$

49. What are the two other products in this reaction?

   A) $HBrO_4$ and HBr
   B) $C_2H_5Br$ and $C_2H_4OH$
   C) $Br^-$ and $H_3O^+$
   D) HBrO and $2H^+$

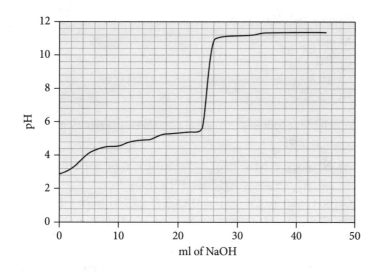

ml of NaOH

**Questions 50–53 refer to the following graph and information.**

The titration curve of 25.0 mL of 0.10 M weak acid, HA, with 0.10 M sodium hydroxide, NaOH, is shown in the graph below.

50. Estimate the value of acid dissociation constant $K_a$.

   A) $2 \times 10^{-3}$
   B) $2 \times 10^{-5}$
   C) $2 \times 10^{-7}$
   D) $2 \times 10^{-9}$

51. At the equivalence point, which of the following species has the highest concentration?

   A) HA
   B) $A^-$
   C) $OH^-$
   D) $H_3O^+$

52. What is the percent dissociation of the weak acid when pH = 4.74?

   A) 100%
   B) 80%
   C) 50%
   D) 10%

53. Which of the following chemical equations best represents the predominate reaction occurring as 4.0 mL of NaOH(*aq*) were added?

   A) $H^+(aq) + OH^-(aq) \longrightarrow H_2O(l)$
   B) $H^+(aq) + NaOH(aq) \longrightarrow H_2O(l) + Na^+(aq)$
   C) $OH^-(aq) + HA(aq) \longrightarrow H_2O(aq) + A^-(aq)$
   D) $HA(aq) + CH_3NH_2(aq) \longrightarrow A^-(aq) + CH_3NH_3^+(aq)$

**Questions 54–57 refer to the following information.**

A solution with initial concentrations of 0.10 M $NH_3$ and 1.00 M $NH_4Cl$ is prepared. The $K_b$ for $NH_3$ is $1.8 \times 10^{-5}$. The $pK_b$ for ammonia is 4.74.

54. Estimate the pH of the resultant solution.

A) 4.7

B) 8.2

C) 10.8

D) 12.2

55. Which of the following chemical equations best represents the system at equilibrium?

A) $NH_3(aq) + NH_4Cl(aq) \rightleftharpoons NH_3Cl^-(aq) + NH_4^+(aq)$

B) $NH_4Cl(aq) \rightleftharpoons NH_3(aq) + HCl(aq)$

C) $NH_4^+(aq) + Cl^-(aq) + H_2O(l) \rightleftharpoons NH_3(aq) + HClO(aq) + H^+(aq)$

D) $NH_3(aq) + H_2O(l) \rightleftharpoons NH_4^+(aq) + OH^-(aq)$

56. Which reaction best represents predominately what happens when 0.5 mL of 0.1 M HCl(aq) is added to the resultant solution described above?

A) $NH_4Cl(aq) + HCl(aq) \longrightarrow NH_3(aq) + 2HCl(aq)$

B) $NH_3(aq) + H^+(aq) \longrightarrow NH_4^+(aq)$

C) $OH^-(aq) + HCl(aq) \longrightarrow H_2O(l) + Cl^-(aq)$

D) $H_2O(l) + H^+(aq) \longrightarrow H_3O^+(aq)$

57. Which statement is true for the solution described in the initial statement?

A) The solution consists of a strong base and a weak acid.

B) The pH solution will not change at all when a small amount of acid is added.

C) The pH of the solution will change slightly when a small amount of acid is added.

D) The pH of the solution will increase when 2.0 grams of solid $NH_4Cl$ is added.

## Questions 58–59 refer to the following information.

A student prepares a solution of calcium fluoride by mixing just enough solid $CaF_2$ in deionized water to show some solid $CaF_2$ remaining in the bottom of the flask. The following equation represents the system at equilibrium.

$$CaF_2(s) \overset{H_2O(l)}{\rightleftharpoons} Ca^{2+}(aq) + 2F^-(aq) \qquad K_{sp} = 4.0 \times 10^{-11}$$

58. What is the solubility product constant, $K_{sp}$, expression for this slightly soluble salt?

A) $K_{sp} = \dfrac{[Ca^{2+}][F^-]^2}{[CaF_2][H_2O]}$

B) $K_{sp} = \dfrac{[Ca^{2+}][F^-]^2}{[CaF_2]}$

C) $K_{sp} = \dfrac{1}{[Ca^{2+}][F^-]^2}$

D) $K_{sp} = [Ca^{2+}][F^-]^2$

The following particulate diagram represents a small volume of the saturated $CaF_2$ solution. Open circles represent $Ca^{2+}$ ions, grey circles represent $F^-$ ions and open squares represent $Na^+$ ions.

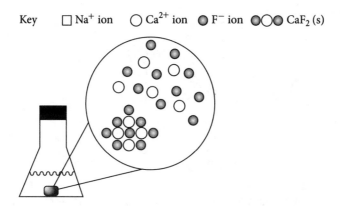

59. Which of the following particulate diagrams represent the small volume of solution after a small amount of 0.10 M sodium fluoride is added, the solution is stirred, and equilibrium is restored?

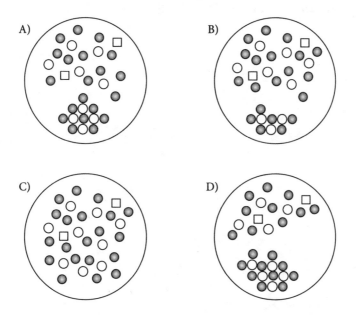

60. The following particulate drawings represent an initial state and an equilibrium state of the reaction $2Cl(g) \rightleftharpoons Cl_2(g)$. Grey spheres represent chlorine atoms. Double grey spheres represent a chlorine molecule.

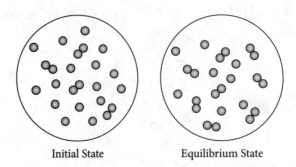

Initial State              Equilibrium State

What are the signs (+ or −) of $\Delta H$, $\Delta S$, and $\Delta G$ for the reaction when the
system goes from the initial state to the equilibrium state?

A)  $\Delta H = +, \Delta S = +, \Delta G = +$
B)  $\Delta H = +, \Delta S = +, \Delta G = -$
C)  $\Delta H = -, \Delta S = -, \Delta G = +$
D)  $\Delta H = -, \Delta S = -, \Delta G = -$

# CHEMISTRY PRACTICE TEST A

## 7 Constructed-Response Questions

Section II

(Time–90 minutes)

You May Use Your Calculator for Section II

**Directions:** Questions 1, 2, and 3 are long constructed response questions that should take a student about 20 minutes each to answer. Questions 4, 5, and 6 are short constructed-response questions that should take a student about seven minutes each to answer. You must show all of your work, the steps involved in arriving at your answer, follow the rules for working with significant figures, and include units when appropriate to receive full credit. Your responses to these questions will be scored on the basis of the accuracy and relevance of the information displayed.

1. Students place blue crystals in a test tube and then strongly heat it. The blue crystals are observed to turn to a white powder, and a clear liquid (water) is seen at the mouth of the test tube. The liquid eventually turns to steam (water vapor) as the tube is further heated. Before and after each heating the student allows the tube to cool to room temperature and measures the mass on a sensitive balance. Students were told that the molar mass of the white powder was 159.5. The mass data are given in the table below:

| Sample Information | Mass (gram) |
|---|---|
| 1. Test tube empty | 15.25 |
| 2. Test tube and blue crystals | 20.18 |
| 3. After first heating—tube and powder | 19.35 |
| 4. After second heating—tube and crystals | 18.45 |
| 5. After third heating—tube  +  crystals | 18.45 |

    a) Calculate the mass of the blue crystals at the start of the investigation.

    b) Calculate the maximum mass of water lost by the blue crystals.

    c) Explain the reason the tube was heated three times.

    d) Calculate the moles of water in the formula for the blue crystals in this investigation.

    e) Explain why the sample and tube were allowed to cool before each weighing on the balance.

    f) If the sample had not been properly cooled before weighing would this have given a larger or smaller value for the moles of water in the crystal's formula? Justify your answer.

2. Some students like to drink cranberry juice. They are very suspicious that Brand X of cranberry juice is being watered down to reduce the cost of manufacture since it has a watery taste. They have a sample bottle of a different brand that is "pure" cranberry juice.

    a) Given the following apparatus, design an experiment in which the students could test their hypothesis and actually measure the amount of water that Brand X was adding. Not all the apparatus may be needed.

Provide instructions for the students, and show how they could calculate the percentage of water added to cranberry juice as a result of their measurements.

| Colorimeter reading absorbance | 500 mL bottle of Brand X cranberry juice |
|---|---|
| Cuvette (tubes) to fit colorimeter | 150 mL bottle of "pure" cranberry juice |
| 10, 20 and 50 mL pipets | 1000 mL bottle of pure distilled water |
| Several 250 mL beakers | Thermometer, °C |
| Balance weighing up to 150 g | 50 mL buret |

b) When the students tried to measure pure cranberry juice in the colorimeter, the instrument showed a reading of zero as too little light was able to pass through the concentrated juice.

   Would your procedure take account of this problem? If not, suggest how it should be modified. Explain how your modification or your original procedure avoids this problem.

c) The students repeated the measurement three separate times with the same bottle of Brand X. For the % water added, they found 43.2%, 47.5%, and 51.1% water. What is the most likely cause of this variation? Explain what the students should do to report these results, and how they might improve their procedures.

d) How would it affect the result of the experiments if Brand X was using white grape juice that has a pale yellow color to add to the cranberry juice instead of water?

e) Would you get a higher or lower value for the amount of water you calculated that the Brand X had? Justify your conclusion.

f) How could you modify the experiment to allow for the grape juice instead of pure water?

g) Chemists use the quantity "molar absorptivity" to describe how a chemical compound absorbs light in solution. What additional information would you need to know about the "pure" cranberry juice and your colorimeter set-up to be able to calculate the "molar absorptivity" of cranberry juice?

3. Ammonium carbamate, $NH_4CO_2NH_2$, has recently been suggested as a compound to be synthesized as a way to capture $CO_2$ from the environment. The following table provides standard enthalpies of formation

| Substance | $\Delta H_f^\circ$ (kJ/mol) |
|---|---|
| $NH_3(g)$ | −45.9 |
| $CO_2(g)$ | −393.5 |

a) Write the balanced equation for the formation of solid ammonium carbamate from ammonia gas and carbon dioxide gas.

b) Calculate the standard change of enthalpy of formation of solid ammonium carbamate by this reaction, given the enthalpy change for this reaction of −157.5 kJ/mol.

c) When the solid is heated it dissociates back to $NH_3$ and $CO_2$ gases. Considering the $\Delta H_f^\circ$ value you calculated in (b) and the expected entropy change for the dissociation, do you predict this reaction is thermodynamically favored in the forward direction at any temperature? Justify your answer.

d) The dissociation of solid ammonium carbamate to $CO_2(g)$ and $NH_3(g)$ is an equilibrium process. Write the expression for the equilibrium constant for the dissociation reaction.

e) Excess solid ammonium carbamate is placed in a previously evacuated sealed container at 25°C. The total pressure in the container rises and reaches a maximum of 0.136 atm. Calculate the value of the equilibrium constant at this temperature.

f) If the temperature is increased to 50 °C and solid ammonium carbamate is still present do you expect the total pressure in the container to increase, decrease, or remain the same? Justify your answer.

4. Water, $H_2O$, and carbon dioxide, $CO_2$, are two very common substances that have 3 atoms. Yet they have very different properties as shown in the table.

| Substance | Melting point | Boiling point | Dipole moment (D) |
|---|---|---|---|
| $H_2O$ | 0°C | 100°C | 1.85 |
| $CO_2$ | −55.6°C* | −78°C | 0 |

*at > 5 atm pressure = sublimes

a) In the boxes below draw complete Lewis dot structures for each of the two molecules.

| $H_2O$ | $CO_2$ |
|---|---|
| | |

b) In the boxes below draw geometric representations of each of the two molecules and label the approximate bond angles and bond types.

| $H_2O$ | $CO_2$ |
|---|---|
| | |

c) Using your diagrams as a guide explain how the differences in the values of the three properties for water and carbon dioxide can be explained on the basis of the atomic properties, the molecular structures and inter and intra-molecular forces. Be sure to describe BOTH substances in your answer.

5. Metals in the solid state are generally described as having bonding that can be described as an "electron sea."

a) Draw a diagram illustrating a small segment of a metal and its "electron sea."

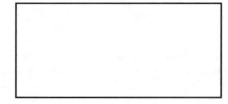

b) In what way are the metal atoms arranged in a solid metal to help establish the electron sea and other properties?

c) Typical metal properties are listed as:

   i) Ductile—can be made into wires

   ii) Lustrous—reflects light and has a shine to it

   iii) Malleable—can be made into thin sheets

   iv) Conducting—has good electrical conductivity

   Describe how each of these four properties can be explained on the basis of the "electron sea" model of metals.

d) An engineer has formed a company to promote the use of sodium wires for high voltage electricity transmission lines since sodium has three times the electrical conductivity per gram compared to copper wires.

   i) Explain why sodium is such a good conductor, using the atomic properties of sodium and the electron sea model.

   ii) Why would sodium NOT be a good choice for this task, despite its conductivity?

6. $PV = nRT$ is a common equation known as the ideal gas equation. It can be derived by using the principles of the kinetic molecular theory (KMT) of gases.

a) What assumptions are made in KMT in order to derive the equation? The graph below shows the value of $PV/RT$ for 1 mole of gas, which should equal 1.0 for noble gases and water as a function of changing pressure.

b) Explain why, in terms of KMT assumptions and intermolecular forces, as the pressure is increased, $H_2O$ vapor and Xe deviate in a negative way from ideal behavior and the other gases deviate in a positive manner.

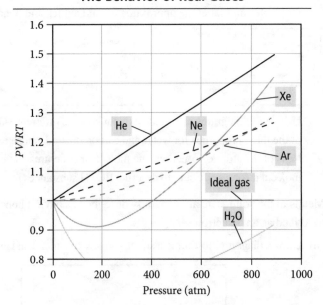

**Figure 1** Real versus ideal behavior for 1 mol of an ideal gas, $PV > RT$ is equal to 1. The combined effects of the volume of gas particles and the interactions among them cause each real gas to deviate from ideal behavior in a slightly different way. These curves were calculated at a temperature of 500 K.

c) Explain why, in terms of KMT assumptions and intermolecular forces, as the pressure gets very high, all the gases show a positive slope (*PV/RT* is increasing in value).

7. Considering the effects of increasing carbon dioxide production as a result of burning fossil fuels, scientists have needed to find a way to estimate surface and deep-ocean temperatures in the past. They can do this by measuring ratios of oxygen and carbon isotopes in such living substances as coral and shells since the rate at which different isotopes react is slightly different and the effect is dependent on temperature. They also measure atmospheric carbon dioxide levels in the past by looking for trapped air bubbles in ice at the Earth's poles.

a) In the past, it seems there is a correlation between $CO_2$ level in the atmosphere and ocean temperatures. Why is ocean temperature very important to understanding carbon dioxide levels in the atmosphere?

b) Explain how the ideas above are related to what happens if you open a room temperature can of soda pop as compared to opening an ice-cold can of soda pop.

The graph below shows the concentration of dissolved oxygen in a lake as function of the temperature.

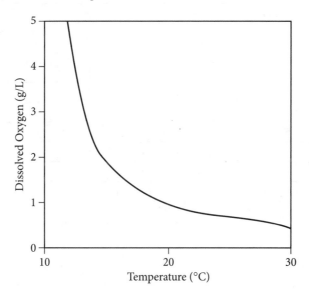

Fish and other living organisms may experience difficulties if the lake temperature rises too much in the summer.

c) What chemical principle does this graph and the phenomena described in parts (a) and (b) have in common? How can this be expressed in an equation? You do **not** need to state the name of the law which the equation represents.

# CHEMISTRY PRACTICE TEST A

## Section I Answer Key

60 Multiple-Choice Questions (Time–90 minutes)

| Question | Key | — | Question | Key | — | Question | Key |
|----------|-----|---|----------|-----|---|----------|-----|
| 1 | D | | 21 | D | | 41 | D |
| 2 | B | | 22 | A | | 42 | C |
| 3 | D | | 23 | C | | 43 | B |
| 4 | A | | 24 | C | | 44 | D |
| 5 | C | | 25 | B | | 45 | A |
| 6 | C | | 26 | D | | 46 | D |
| 7 | A | | 27 | B | | 47 | A |
| 8 | B | | 28 | B | | 48 | C |
| 9 | D | | 29 | B | | 49 | D |
| 10 | B | | 30 | B | | 50 | B |
| 11 | D | | 31 | B | | 51 | C |
| 12 | A | | 32 | C | | 52 | C |
| 13 | C | | 33 | D | | 53 | C |
| 14 | C | | 34 | D | | 54 | B |
| 15 | A | | 35 | B | | 55 | D |
| 16 | A | | 36 | A | | 56 | B |
| 17 | C | | 37 | B | | 57 | C |
| 18 | B | | 38 | C | | 58 | D |
| 19 | B | | 39 | B | | 59 | D |
| 20 | D | | 40 | C | | 60 | D |

# CHEMISTRY PRACTICE TEST A

## Section II Answer Key

7 Constructed-Response Questions (Time–90 minutes)

You may use your calculator for Section II

**Directions:** Questions 1, 2, and 3 are long constructed response questions that should take a student about 20 minutes each to answer. Questions 4, 5, and 6 are short constructed-response questions that should take a student about seven minutes each to answer. You must show all of your work, the steps involved in arriving at your answer, follow the rules for working with significant figures, and include units when appropriate to receive full credit. Your responses to these questions will be scored on the basis of the accuracy and relevance of the information displayed.

1. Students place blue crystals in a test tube and then strongly heat it. The blue crystals are observed to turn to a white powder, and a clear liquid (water) is seen at the mouth of the test tube. The liquid eventually turns to steam (water vapor) as the tube is further heated. Before and after each heating the student allows the tube to cool to room temperature and measures the mass on a sensitive balance. Students were told that the molar mass of the white powder was 159.5.

   The mass data are given in the table below:

   | Sample Information | Mass (gram) |
   |---|---|
   | 1. Test tube empty | 15.25 |
   | 2. Test tube and blue crystals | 20.18 |
   | 3. After first heating—tube and powder | 19.35 |
   | 4. After second heating—tube and crystals | 18.45 |
   | 5. After third heating—tube + crystals | 18.45 |

   a) Calculate the mass of the blue crystals at the start of the investigation.

   Mass 2 − mass 1 = 20.18 − 15.25 grams = 4.93 g

   b) Calculate the maximum mass of water lost by the blue crystals.

   Mass 2 − mass 5 = 20.18 − 18.45 = 1.73 g

   c) Explain the reason the tube was heated three times.

   To ensure all water is removed. (Process called drying to constant weight [mass].)

   d) Calculate the moles of water in the formula for the blue crystals in this investigation.

   Moles of white powder = (mass 5 − mass 1)/molar mass

   = (18.45 − 15.25)/159.5 = 2.006 × $10^{-2}$ mol

   1.73 g water = 1.73/18.0 moles = 9.6 × $10^{-2}$ mol

   Ratio in formula = 9.6/2 approx = 5 moles/formula

e) Explain why the sample and tube were allowed to cool before each weighing on the balance.

Hot objects can create an air updraft affecting the balance.

f) If the sample had not been properly cooled before weighing would this have given a larger or smaller value for the moles of water in the crystal's formula? Justify your answer.

Larger. The air updraft would reduce the apparent mass of the dry powder increasing the moles water lost.

2. Some students like to drink cranberry juice. They are very suspicious that Brand X of cranberry juice is being watered down to reduce the cost of manufacture since it has a watery taste. They have a sample bottle of a different brand that is "pure" cranberry juice.

a) Given the following apparatus, design an experiment in which the students could test their hypothesis and actually measure the amount of water that Brand X was adding. Not all the apparatus may be needed.

Provide instructions for the students, and show how they could calculate the percentage of water added to cranberry juice as a result of their measurements.

| | |
|---|---|
| Colorimeter reading absorbance. | 500 mL bottle of brand X cranberry juice |
| Cuvette (tubes) to fit colorimeter | 150 mL bottle of "pure" cranberry juice |
| 10, 20 and 50 mL pipets | 1000 mL bottle of pure distilled water |
| Several 250 mL beakers | Thermometer, °C |
| Balance weighing up to 150 g | 50 mL buret |

Safety—wear lab coat, goggles.

Step 1. Prepare calibration standards by using pipettes to take 10 mL "pure" juice and add zero, 10, 20 and 50 mL distilled water to each. (A student could also use buret filled with pure(?) juice to add 10 mL to zero, 10, 20, and 50 mL pipetted into beakers)

Step 2. Place samples, in turn, into cuvettes. Place in colorimeter, record absorbances, plot a graph against concentration of standards.

Step 3. Add brand X juice to cuvette. Measure absorbance. Repeat with 3 different samples to get good average.

Step 4. Read values for concentration from standards plot. If less than "pure" then it has been diluted, and can calculate how much percentage.

Note it is a colorimeter, NOT a spectrophotometer, so no spectral scan or setting to wavelength is included.

b) When the students tried to measure pure cranberry juice in the colorimeter, the instrument showed a reading of zero as too little light was able to pass through the concentrated juice.

Would your procedure take account of this problem? If not, suggest how it should be modified. Explain how your modification or your original procedure avoids this problem.

Yes and no. The diluted standards should work on scale, though further dilution might be needed (more than 10 to 60) BUT would need to dilute the brand X samples by a known amount (using same procedure as for "pure"). As long as dilution factors are accurately known, the comparison is valid.

c) The students repeated the measurement 3 separate times with the same bottle of Brand X. For the % water added, they found 43.2%, 47.5%, and 51.1% water. What is the most likely cause of this variation? Explain what the students should do to report these results, and how they might improve their procedures.

1. possibilities: variation from improper mixing of juice; finger prints on cuvettes scattering light; cuvette not clean before each use; or cuvettes washed with water between trials but not dried,; instrument adjustments; changes in light in room (sunlight from window, room lights on or off, etc.)

2. report mean and variation about the mean to show lack of precision.

3. control light conditions, mix juice well before experiment, clean and dry cuvettes before filling; clean cuvettes carefully on outside before placing in colorimeter. Also do repeat of both calibration standards and more than 3 measurements on brand X.

d) How would it affect the result of the experiments if the Brand X was using white grape juice that has a pale yellow color to add to the cranberry juice instead of water?

This will absorb light (or it would not be colored) and therefore change the result compared to the pure juice. The effect will depend on the wave-length dependence/sensitivity of the colorimeter. If students are used to using a spectrophotometer set to a specific wavelength, then they may be puzzled by this!

e) Would you get a higher or lower value for the amount of water you calculated that the Brand X had? Justify your conclusion.

Since the grape juice will absorb some light the brand X will appear to be more concentrated than it really is (in cranberry juice).

f) How could you modify the experiment to allow for the grape juice instead of pure water?

Make up standard comparisons using some "pure" white grape juice in known amounts added to the pure cranberry juice, and proceed similarly. Alternatively, if a spectrophotometer is available, scan cranberry and white grape juice to measure their absorbance spectra and choose a wave-length where the cranberry juice absorbs, but the grape juice does not.

g) Chemists use the quantity "molar absorptivity" to describe how a chemical compound absorbs light in solution. What additional information would you need to know about the "pure" cranberry juice and your colorimeter set-up to be able to calculate the "molar absorptivity" of cranberry juice? Explain how each piece of information you list is used in the calculation.

Would need to know (1) the molar mass of the compound in the cranberry juice that is absorbing the light; (2) the path length of light through the cuvette; (3) the absolute calibration of the read-out of the colorimeter in absorbance units.

3. Ammonium carbamate, $NH_4CO_2NH_2$, has recently been suggested as a compound to be synthesized as a way to capture $CO_2$ from the environment. The following table provides standard enthalpies of formation

| Substance | $\Delta H_f^\circ$ (kJ/mol) |
|---|---|
| $NH_3(g)$ | −45.9 |
| $CO_2(g)$ | −393.5 |

a) Write the balanced equation for the formation of solid ammonium carbamate from ammonia gas and carbon dioxide gas.

$$2NH_3(g) + CO_2(g) \longrightarrow NH_4CO_2NH_2(s)$$

b) Calculate the standard enthalpy of formation of solid ammonium carbamate, using the reported enthalpy change for this reaction of −157.5 kJ/mol.

$$\Delta H_{reax} = \Sigma\, \Delta H_{prod} - \Sigma\, \Delta H_{react}$$

$$\Delta H_{reax} = \Delta H_{form} - ((2 \times -45.9) + (-393.5)) = -157.5 \text{ so}$$

$$\Delta H_{form} = -642.8 \text{ kJ/mol}$$

c) When the solid is heated it dissociates back to $NH_3$ and $CO_2$ gases. Considering the $\Delta H_f$ value you calculated in (b) and the expected entropy change for the dissociation, do you predict this is a spontaneous or non-spontaneous reaction at any temperature? Justify your answer.

$\Delta S$ should be highly positive (solid forming 2 gases increases disorder) $\Delta H$ for decomposition is reverse of formation so is positive.

So sign of $\Delta G = \Delta H - T\Delta S$ will depend on $T$ and magnitude of $\Delta S$. If non-spontaneous at low $T$ ($\Delta G$ is positive), then as $-T\Delta S$ increase with $T\Delta G$ will become negative.

d) The dissociation of solid ammonium carbamate to $CO_2(g)$ and $NH_3(g)$ is an equilibrium process. Write the expression for the equilibrium constant for the dissociation reaction.

$$K_{eq} = ((p_{NH_3})^2 \cdot p_{CO_2})/1$$

[Notes: Solid is not included. [] terms are accepted for p.]

e) Excess solid ammonium carbamate is placed in a previously evacuated sealed container at 25 °C. The total pressure in the container rises and reaches a maximum of 0.136 atm. Calculate the value of the equilibrium constant at this temperature.

Since pure carbamate to start with, $p_{NH_3} = 2\, p_{CO_2}$

Total pressure thus is

$p_{CO2} + p_{NH_3} = p + 2p = 3 p$ so $p = 1/3 \times 0.136 = 0.0453$ atm for $CO_2$
And so $p_{NH_3} = 0.0907$ atm, and
$K_{eq} = (0.0907)^2 \times (0.0453) = 3.73 \times 10^{-3}$

f) If the temperature is increased to 50 °C and solid ammonium carbamate is still present do you expect the total pressure in the container to increase, decrease, or remain the same. Justify your answer.

As the decomposition reaction is endothermic, by Le Chateliers principle, the increase in temperature will increase the forward reaction more than the reverse so more decomposition will take place and the pressure will INCREASE.

4. Water, $H_2O$, and carbon dioxide, $CO_2$, are two very common substances that have 3 atoms. Yet they have very different properties as shown in the table.

| Substance | Melting point | Boiling point | Dipole moment (D) |
|---|---|---|---|
| $H_2O$ | 0 °C | 100 °C | 1.85 |
| $CO_2$ | −55.6 °C* | −78 °C = | 0 |

*at > 5 atm pressure = sublimes

a. In the boxes below draw complete Lewis dot structures for each of the two molecules.

b. In the boxes below draw geometric representations of each of the two molecules and label the approximate bond angles and bond types.

c. Using your diagrams as a guide explain how the differences in the values of the three properties for water and carbon dioxide can be explained on the basis of the atomic properties, the molecular structures and inter and intra-molecular forces. Be sure to describe BOTH substances in your answer.

$H_2O$ has a large dipole moment as it is not symmetrical, each O—H bond has a dipole and they do not cancel. Its boiling and melting points are high because the H atoms on 1 molecule are attracted to the oxygen on another molecule forming an additional "hydrogen bond" between the molecules. These strong intermolecular forces have to be broken for the molecules to separate in the liquid or gas, hence the high b.p and m.p. $CO_2$ has no NET dipole moment as the linear arrangement of the CO bonds which have dipoles cancel each other yielding no NET dipole moment. The BP and MP are low as there are no "hydrogen bonds" and only weak London Dispersion intermolecular forces between the molecules.

5. Metals in the solid state are generally described as having bonding that can be described as an "electron sea."

   a) Draw a diagram illustrating a small segment of a metal and its "electron sea."

   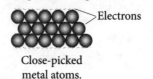

   Close-picked
   metal atoms.

   b) How are the metal atoms arranged in a solid metal to help establish the electron sea, and other properties?

   They are close packed–fitting tightly together so electron orbital overlap can form delocalized orbitals allowing valence electrons easier motion

   c) Typical metal properties are listed as:
   i)   Ductile—can be made into wires
   ii)  Lustrous—reflecting light and having shine
   iii) Malleable—can be made into thin sheets
   iv)  Conductive—have good electrical conductivity

   Describe how each of these four properties can be explained on the basis of the "electron sea" model of metals.
   i)   and (iii) Close packing means atoms can slide easily over one another hence form wires and thin sheets.
   ii)  much light reflection from very even and flat surface of close-packed atoms provides luster (shine)
   iv)  freer motion of electrons provides for high electrical conductivity—has small resistance to flow of electrons

   d) An engineer has formed a company to promote the use of sodium wires for high voltage electricity transmission lines since sodium has three times the electrical conductivity per gram compared to copper wires.
   i)   Explain why sodium is such a good conductor, using the atomic properties of sodium and the electron sea model.
        Sodium is a group I element, so readily gives up an electron or shares it with other sodium atom. It is in period 2 so has a relatively small size that will pack well in a close-packed structure and will have a good electrical conductivity—low resistance to electric current.
   ii)  Why would sodium NOT be a good choice for this task, despite its conductivity?

   Sodium is highly reactive with water and if any water seeped through the wire's coating, they would react violently?

6. $PV = nRT$ is a common equation known as the Ideal Gas equation. It can be derived by using the principles of the Kinetic Molecular theory (KMT) of gases

   a) What assumptions are made in KMT in order to derive the equation?

   $$P = \frac{F}{A}$$

   1. Particles are negligibly small.
   2. Average kinetic energy is proportional to temperature.
   3. Collisions among particles are perfectly elastic.

   The graph below shows the value of $PV/RT$ for 1 mole of gas, which should equal 1.0 for noble gases and water as a function of changing pressure.

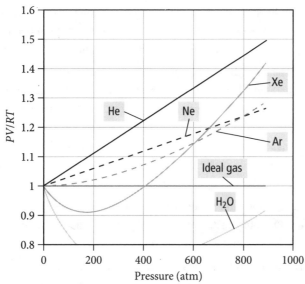

**The Behavior of Real Gases**

**Figure 1** Real versus ideal behavior for 1 mol of an ideal gas, $PV > RT$ is equal to 1. The combined effects of the volume of gas particles and the interactions among them cause each real gas to deviate from ideal behavior in a slightly different way. These curves were calculated at a temperature of 500 K.

   b) Explain why, in terms of KMT assumptions and intermolecular forces, as the pressure is increased, $H_2O$ vapor and Xe deviate in a negative way from ideal behavior and the other gases deviate in a positive manner.

   $H_2O$ and Xe both exhibit higher intermolecular forces between particles. Hydrogen bonding between water molecules creates strong IMFs. Xenon's large electron cloud makes it polarizable and this allows for a large number of and stronger LDFs between xenon atoms creating a strong IMF. This effect starts at quite low pressures to "stick the particles together" so they begin to form liquid clusters and more inelastic collisions so fewer particles are behaving as ideal gases, lowering the pressure and hence giving a negative deviation. The other gases have weaker IMFs but exhibit only positive deviation because of the volume of the particles (assumption [1] above is not valid).

c) Explain why, in terms of KMT assumptions and intermolecular forces, as the pressure get very high, all the gases are showing a positive slope ($PV/RT$ is increasing in value).

All gases have real volume that results in them being less compressible at very high pressures than the ideal gas equation predicts. Assumption 1 is not valid.

7. Considering the effects of increasing carbon dioxide production as a result of burning fossil fuels, scientists have needed to find a way to estimate surface and deep ocean temperatures in the past. They can do this by measuring ratios of oxygen and carbon isotopes in such living substances as coral and shells since the rate at which different isotopes react is slightly different and the effect is dependent on temperature. They also measure atmospheric carbon dioxide levels in the past by looking for trapped air bubbles in ice at the Earth's poles.

a) In the past, it seems there is a correlation between $CO_2$ level in the atmosphere and ocean temperatures. Why is ocean temperature very important to understanding carbon dioxide levels in the atmosphere?

The solubility of any gas in a liquid (aqueous) solution depends on temperature. The oceans comprise the majority of the surface of the Earth and the oceans have a large volume. Because the water in the ocean can absorb, $CO_2$, the extent and the speed to which $CO_2$ dissolves in water makes a great difference to the $CO_2$ concentration in air in contact with the ocean's surface, and hence the air in any region in proximity to the ocean.

Knowing the temperature of the water and the amount of dissolved $CO_2$ in the past, therefore, will give a good indication as to how much $CO_2$ was in the air at that time.

b) Explain how the ideas above are related to what happens if you open a room temperature can of soda pop as compared to opening an ice-cold can of soda pop.

Soda pop has dissolved $CO_2$. The amount of $CO_2$ is larger than the normal pressure of $CO_2$ in the air because the pressure in the can is greater than atmospheric pressure. As temperature rises the amount of $CO_2$ that is <u>in solution</u> goes down, so the pressure of gas in the can goes up as the solution becomes super-saturated with $CO_2$. This causes greater overflow of liquid and more "frothing" as the gas evolves from the liquid at room temperature than it does at ice temperature.

The graph <u>below</u> shows the concentration of dissolved oxygen in a lake as function of the temperature.

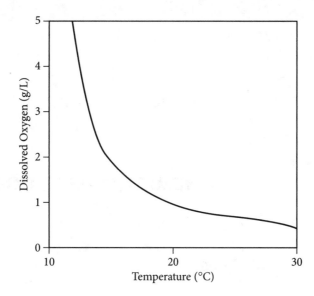

Fish and other living organisms may experience difficulties if the lake temperature rises too much in the summer.

c) What chemical principle do this graph and the phenomena described in parts (a) and (b) have in common? How can this be expressed in an equation. You do **not** need to state the name of the law which the equation represents.

The principle is that when gas dissolves in liquid the amount varies as a function of both the gas pressure and the gas temperature. More gas dissolves as the temperature decreases and/or the pressure increases. The graph exhibits the form (curve) as a function of temperature with the pressure (of $O_2$ in air) remaining constant. $[\text{gas}]_{\text{solution}} = k/T$.

# CHEMISTRY PRACTICE TEST B

Section I    **Multiple-Choice Questions**

(Time–90 minutes)

You May Not Use Your Calculator for Section I

**Note:** For all questions, assume that the temperature is 298 K, the pressure is 1.00 atmosphere, and the solutions are aqueous unless otherwise specified.

**Directions:** Each of the questions or incomplete sentences in Section I are followed by four suggested answers or complete the sentence format. Select the answer that is best in each case and fill in the circle on the answer sheet.

1. Each of the following equations represents a system at equilibrium. In which of the following reactions will a decrease in volume shift the reaction toward the reactants (toward the left)?

    A) $2NO(g) \rightleftharpoons N_2(g) + O_2(g)$
    B) $2NO(g) + O_2(g) \rightleftharpoons 2NO_2(g)$
    C) $2C_2H_4(g) + 2H_2O(g) \rightleftharpoons 2C_2H_6(g) + O_2(g)$
    D) $SO_2(s) + \frac{1}{2}O_2(g) \rightleftharpoons SO_3(g)$

2. A 1.0 molar solution of which of the following salts has the highest pH?

    A) $NaNO_3$
    B) $NH_4Cl$
    C) $Na_2CO_3$
    D) $NaHSO_4$

3. The equilibrium constant for the reaction represented by the following equation is greater than 1.0

    $$H_2PO_4^- + HBO_3^{2-} \rightleftharpoons HPO_4^{2-} + H_2BO_3^-$$

| Acid | $K_{a1}$ |
|---|---|
| $H_3PO_4$ | $7.1 \times 10^{-3}$ |
| $H_3BO_3$ | $5.8 \times 10^{-10}$ |

Which of the following gives the correct relative strengths of the acids and bases in the reaction in terms of a Bronsted-Lowry definition of acids and bases?

| | **Acids** | | **Bases** |
|---|---|---|---|
| (A) | $H_2PO_4^- > H_2BO_3^-$ | and | $HBO_3^{2-} > HPO_4^{2-}$ |
| (B) | $H_2BO_3^- > H_2PO_4^-$ | and | $HBO_3^{2-} > HPO_4^{2-}$ |
| (C) | $H_2PO_4^- > H_2BO_3^-$ | and | $HPO_4^{2-} > HBO_3^{2-}$ |
| (D) | $H_2BO_3^- > H_2PO_4^-$ | and | $HPO_4^{2-} > HBO_3^{2-}$ |

4. Potassium iodide, KI, is an ionic solid. It dissolves in water with an enthalpy of solution that is endothermic. Which of the following best describes the solution process for this system?

A) The value of lattice energy for the ionic solid is more positive (endothermic) than the absolute value of the hydration energy, and the entropy change of the solution process is positive.

B) The enthalpy of the solution process is positive and the entropy change of the solution process is negative.

C) The enthalpy required to separate the solute particles is smaller than the heat required to separate the solvent molecules plus the heat released when the water molecules hydrate the cation and anion, and the entropy change of the solution process is negative.

D) The enthalpy required to separate the solute particles is greater than the heat required to separate the solvent molecules plus the heat released when the water molecules hydrate the cation and anion, and the entropy change of the solution process is positive.

5. A solution is prepared to be initially 0.5 M in NaCl and 1 M in HCl. Which statement best describes this solution?

A) a solution with a pH less than 7 that is not a buffer solution

B) a buffer solution with a pH between 4 and 7

C) a buffer solution with a pH between 7 and 10

D) a solution with a pH greater than 7 that is not a buffer solution

6. Acetic acid is a monoprotic acid, with $K_a = 1.8 \times 10^{-5}$. A solution is prepared to be initially 0.5 M in $CH_3COOH$ and 1 M in $CH_3COONa$. Which statement best describes this solution?

A) a solution with a pH less than 7 that is not a buffer solution

B) a buffer solution with a pH between 4 and 7

C) a buffer solution with a pH between 7 and 10

D) a solution with a pH greater than 7 that is not a buffer solution

## Questions 7–12 pertain to the following information.

Iron and oxygen can combine to form three compounds. Iron(II) oxide, also informally called iron monoxide, is one of the compounds formed. It is a black-colored powder with the chemical formula FeO. The ratio of the mass of iron to mass of oxygen is 3.50 : 1.00. The ratio of the mass of iron to the mass of oxygen for another iron oxide, $Fe_xO_y$, is 2.62 : 1.00. The table below lists the mass of iron and oxygen in one mole of FeO.

|  | FeO | $Fe_xO_y$ |
|---|---|---|
| Mass of Fe | 55.85 g | ? |
| Mass of O | 16.00 g | ? |
| mass Fe : mass O | 3.50 : 1.00 | 2.62 : 1.00 |

7. What is the formula for $Fe_xO_y$?

A) $FeO_2$

B) $Fe_2O_3$

C) $Fe_3O_4$

D) $Fe_4O_5$

8. In the following particulate diagrams a triangle represents an iron atom, a shaded circle represents an oxygen atom and an open circle represents a sulfur atom. When forming $Fe_xO_y$ compounds, which diagrams represent the law of multiple proportions?

Key      △ iron atom      ● oxygen atom      □ sulfur atom

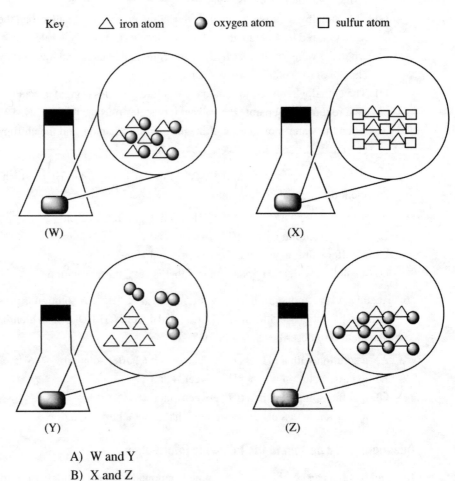

(W)            (X)

(Y)            (Z)

A) W and Y

B) X and Z

C) W and Z

D) W, Y, and Z

9. A student analyzes three samples of compounds containing only iron and oxygen. The results are shown in the table below.

|  | Sample X | Sample Y | Sample Z |
|---|---|---|---|
| Mass Fe | 7.00 g | 7.00 g | 14.00 g |
| Mass O | 2.00 g | 3.00 g | 4.00 g |

Which sample(s) is FeO?

A) X

B) Y

C) X and Y

D) X and Z

10. Compare 10.0 gram samples of the following iron oxides. Which compound contains the most iron?

| Compound | FeO | FeO$_2$ | Fe$_2$O$_3$ | Fe$_3$O$_4$ |
|---|---|---|---|---|
| Molar Mass | 72 | 88 | 160 | 232 |

A) FeO

B) FeO$_2$

C) Fe$_2$O$_3$

D) Fe$_3$O$_4$

11. What is the average mass, in grams, of one atom of iron?

A) less than $1.0 \times 10^{-23}$ g

B) greater than $1.0 \times 10^{-23}$ g but less than $1.0 \times 10^{-20}$ g

C) greater than 0.01 g but less than 100 g

D) greater than 100 g

12. Estimate the number of grams of FeCl$_2$ (molar mass 127) that can form when 10.0 g of FeO (molar mass 72) reacts with excess hydrochloric acid.

FeO + 2HCl $\longrightarrow$ FeCl$_2$ + H$_2$O

A) 5.7

B) 18

C) 25

D) 35

13. The crystal structure of iron(II) oxalate, FeC$_2$O$_4$(s), consists of chains of oxalate-bridged iron atoms, capped by water molecules.

● Oxygen atom    ● Carbon atom    ◢ Iron atom    ○ Hydrogen atom

The geometry around the iron atoms can best be described as

A) square planar

B) trigonal bipyramidal

C) distorted tetrahedron

D) octahedral

**The following information is useful for Question 14.**

FeO can be prepared by heating iron(II) oxalate in a vacuum. A gas mixture consisting of carbon monoxide gas and carbon dioxide gas also forms.

$$FeC_2O_4(s) \rightleftharpoons FeO(s) + CO(g) + CO_2(g)$$

14. How many grams of $FeC_2O_4(s)$ (molar mass 144) are needed to produce a total volume of 2.24 L of gas at 1.00 atm and 273 K, assuming the reaction goes to completion? The gas mixture is collected in a rigid container.

    A) 1.8 g
    B) 3.6 g
    C) 7.2 g
    D) 14.4 g

15. A car tire containing 4.0 liters of air has a measured pressure of 2.0 atmospheres at a temperature of 20.0 °C before the car is driven. When the car has been driven at high speed, the tire temperature is measured to be 50.0 °C. Assuming the volume of the tire is constant at 4.0 liters, which equation correctly estimates the pressure in atmospheres in the tire at 50.0 °C?

    A) $P = 0.82 \times 4.0 \times (50.0 - 20.0)$
    B) $P = 2.0 \times 323 / 293$
    C) $P = 4.0 \times 293 / 323$
    D) $P = 2.0 \times 50.0 / 20.0$

**Questions 16–19 use the following information.**

In a sealed container in the presence of $O_2$ gas, $CO_2$ gas can establish an equilibrium with CO gas.

$$2CO(g) + O_2(g) \rightleftharpoons 2CO_2(g) \qquad \Delta H° = -500 \text{ kJ/mol rxn}$$

16. The partial pressure of $CO(g)$ can be increased by

    A) lowering the temperature and increasing the pressure
    B) increasing the temperature and the pressure
    C) increasing the temperature and lowering the pressure
    D) lowering the temperature and lowering the pressure

17. The partial pressure of $CO(g)$ can be increased by adding the following and waiting for equilibrium to be restored

    A) NaOH(s) to remove $CO_2(g)$
    B) $CO_2(s)$
    C) $O_2(s)$
    D) FeO(s) to form $FeC_2O_4(s)$

18. How much heat is released or absorbed when 0.50 mol of carbon monoxide gas reacts with oxygen gas to form carbon dioxide gas?

    A) 250 kJ is released
    B) 125 kJ is released
    C) 125 kJ is absorbed
    D) 250 kJ is absorbed

19. If $\Delta H_f^\circ$ for $CO_2$ is $-400\,kJ/mol$, estimate $\Delta H_f^\circ$ for CO?

   A) $+150\,kJ/mol$

   B) $-150\,kJ/mol$

   C) $+100\,kJ/mol$

   D) $-100\,kJ/mol$

20. Which of the following is the principal reason for the great difference in properties of carbon dioxide, $CO_2$, and silicon dioxide, $SiO_2$?

   A) carbon atoms have a smaller mass than silicon atoms

   B) carbon is in the first row of the periodic table, silicon is in the second row

   C) carbon atoms have four bonding (valence) electrons, silicon has twelve

   D) carbon readily forms double bonds with oxygen, silicon does not

21. What is the d orbital-filling diagram for the $Fe^{3+}$ ion?

$$\underline{\uparrow\downarrow} \quad \underline{\uparrow\downarrow} \quad \underline{\uparrow} \quad \underline{\phantom{x}} \quad \underline{\phantom{x}} \qquad\qquad \underline{\uparrow\downarrow} \quad \underline{\uparrow} \quad \underline{\uparrow} \quad \underline{\uparrow} \quad \underline{\phantom{x}}$$
$$\text{(A)} \qquad\qquad\qquad\qquad\qquad \text{(B)}$$

$$\underline{\uparrow} \quad \underline{\uparrow} \quad \underline{\uparrow} \quad \underline{\uparrow} \quad \underline{\uparrow} \qquad \underline{\uparrow\downarrow} \quad \underline{\phantom{x}} \quad \underline{\uparrow\downarrow} \quad \underline{\phantom{x}} \quad \underline{\uparrow}$$
$$\text{(C)} \qquad\qquad\qquad\qquad\qquad \text{(D)}$$

22. Oxalate ions can readily react with $Fe^{3+}(aq)$ ions to form iron(III) oxalate ions.

$$Fe^{3+}(aq) + 3\,C_2O_4^{2-}(aq) \rightleftharpoons [Fe(C_2O_4)_3]^{3-}(aq) \qquad K_c = 1.67 \times 10^{20} \text{ at } 25\,°C$$

If 0.0100 M $Fe^{3+}$ is mixed with 1.00 M oxalate ion, estimate the concentration of $Fe^{3+}(aq)$ ions at equilibrium.

   A) less than $1.0 \times 10^{-18}\,M$

   B) between $1.0 \times 10^{-15}\,M$ and $1.0 \times 10^{-8}\,M$

   C) between $1.0 \times 10^{-8}\,M$ and $1.0 \times 10^{-3}\,M$

   D) greater than $1.0 \times 10^{-3}\,M$

23. A solution is prepared by mixing the following:

   10 mL of 0.100 M HCl

   10 mL of 0.100 M $H_2SO_4$

   10 mL of 0.200 M NaOH

   70 mL of pure water

In the following table which column correctly identifies the concentrations of the species present?

| Species | A<br>[X], M | B<br>[X], M | C<br>[X], M | D<br>[X], M |
|---|---|---|---|---|
| $H^+$ (pH) | 3 | 2 | 1 | 2 |
| $Cl^-$ | 0.1 | 0.01 | 0.01 | 0.01 |
| $SO_4^{2-}$ | 0.1 | 0.2 | 0.02 | 0.01 |
| $Na^+$ | 0.2 | 0.1 | 0.02 | 0.02 |

A) Column A

B) Column B

C) Column C

D) Column D

24. Given the following table containing information about some of the elements, which of the following statements is true?

| Element | Atomic radius (pm) | First ionization energy (kJ/mol) |
|---|---|---|
| Li | 152 | 520 |
| Be | 112 | 899 |
| B | 85 | 801 |
| C | 77 | 1086 |
| N | 70 | 1402 |
| O | 73 | 1314 |
| F | 72 | 1681 |
| Ne | 70 | 2081 |

A) Both radius and ionization energy generally increase uniformly across the period, consistent with the shell model of atomic structure.

B) Radius generally increases uniformly, but subshells in the quantum model are needed to explain the inconsistencies in the trend of ionization energies.

C) The trends in radius generally decrease and ionization energy generally increase. Both are as expected based on the nuclear model where atomic electrons are increasingly attracted as the nuclear charge increases.

D) The values of ionization energy for N and O are out of line with the general trend predicted by the shell model because these atoms form unusually strong diatomic molecules ($O_2$ and $N_2$) and influence the measurement of ionization energy.

25. Determine the standard cell potential $(E°)$ for the voltaic cell based on the following reaction.

$$2Cr(s) + 3Fe^{2+}(aq) \rightarrow 3\,Fe(s) + 2Cr^{3+}(aq)$$

| Reduction Half-Reaction | $E°$ |
|---|---|
| $Fe^{2+}(aq) + 2e^- \rightarrow Fe(s)$ | $-0.44$ V |
| $Cr^{3+}(aq) + 3e^- \rightarrow Cr(s)$ | $-0.74$ V |

A) $-0.16$ V

B) $+0.30$ V

C) $+0.83$ V

D) $+2.80$ V

26. In the above electrochemical cell, _____ serves as the anode.

A) Cr

B) Fe

C) $Fe^{2+}$

D) $Cr^{3+}$

**Use the following information to help answer questions 27 and 28.**

Carbon tetrachloride can be formed from the reaction of chlorine gas and $CHCl_3$.

$$CHCl_3(g) + Cl_2(g) \longrightarrow CCl_4(g) + HCl(g)$$

A proposed mechanism for the formation of carbon tetrachloride is

Step 1.  $Cl_2(g) \rightleftharpoons 2Cl(g)$

Step 2.  $Cl(g) + CHCl_3(g) \longrightarrow HCl(g) + CCl_3(g)$ Slow Step (Rate Determining)

Step 3.  $Cl(g) + CCl_3(g) \longrightarrow CCl_4(g)$

27. Identify one or more species serving an an intermediate.

   A) $[Cl_2]$
   B) $[Cl]$
   C) $[CCl_3]$
   D) $[Cl]$ and $[CCl_3]$

28. Given the following particulate diagram of the relative initial amounts of reactants, and the rate law,
   rate = $k[CHCl_3][Cl_2]^{1/2}$,
   identify the particulate diagram representing the initial conditions, which would have the fastest initial reaction.

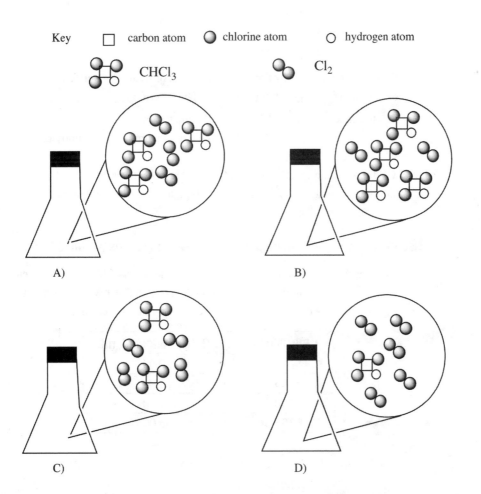

**Questions 29 through 32 pertain to the following information.**

Hydrogen peroxide solution decomposes to oxygen gas and water vapor. As the solution is observed to get warmer, the faster the decomposition occurs.

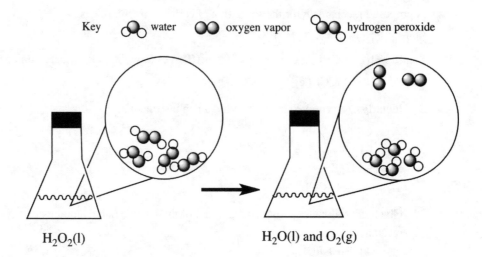

$H_2O_2(l)$                       $H_2O(l)$ and $O_2(g)$

29. What are the signs (+ or −) of ΔH, ΔS, and ΔG for this process?

     A) $\Delta H = +, \Delta S = +, \Delta G = +$

     B) $\Delta H = -, \Delta S = +, \Delta G = -$

     C) $\Delta H = -, \Delta S = -, \Delta G = +$

     D) $\Delta H = +, \Delta S = -, \Delta G = -$

30. How will the tendency of the decomposition of hydrogen peroxide to proceed or not proceed vary with temperature? The reaction is

     A) thermodynamically favored at all temperatures

     B) thermodynamically favored at high temperatures and thermodynamically unfavorable at low temperatures

     C) thermodynamically unfavorable at all temperatures

     D) thermodynamically unfavorable at high temperatures and thermodynamically favored at low temperatures

**Use the following information to help answer Questions 31 and 32.**

A student measured the volume of oxygen gas collected as 1.00 L of hydrogen peroxide decomposed, in the presence of a small amount of $KMnO_4$, as a function of time. The gas was collected at 25.00°C and 1.00 atm of pressure.

| Time, seconds | $O_2(g)$ collected, mL |
|---|---|
| 0.00 | 0.00 |
| 45.0 | 2.00 |
| 90.0 | 4.00 |
| 135.0 | 6.00 |

31. Estimate the average rate of disappearance of hydrogen peroxide in units of M/s in the first 45 seconds.

   A) less than $1.0 \times 10^{-6}$ M/s
   B) greater than $1.0 \times 10^{-6}$ M/s but less than $1.0 \times 10^{-5}$
   C) greater than $1.0 \times 10^{-5}$ M/s but less than $1.0 \times 10^{-4}$
   D) greater than $1.0 \times 10^{-4}$ M/s but less than $1.0 \times 10^{-3}$

32. In a separate experiment, a student started with an initial concentration of 0.800 M hydrogen peroxide and determined the concentration to be 0.100 M after 54.0 minutes. Estimate the half-life for the first-order reaction in units of minutes.

   A) 6.8
   B) 14
   C) 18
   D) 28

33. The VSEPR model predicts the H-O-O bond angle in hydrogen peroxide to be

   A) greater than 60° but less than 90°
   B) less than 109.5° but greater than 90°
   C) greater than 109.5° but less than 110°
   D) less than 120° but greater than 110°

34. Using the table of average bond energies below, estimate the $\Delta H$ for the following reaction.

$$H-C\equiv C-H(g) + H-I(g) \longrightarrow \begin{array}{c} H \\ \diagdown \\ C=C \\ \diagup \\ H \end{array} \begin{array}{c} H \\ \diagup \\ \diagdown \\ I \end{array}$$

| Bond | $C\equiv C$ | $C=C$ | $H-I$ | $C-I$ | $C-H$ |
|------|------|------|------|------|------|
| D (kJ/mol) | 839 | 614 | 299 | 240 | 413 |

   A) −931
   B) −506
   C) −129
   D) +129

35. A sample of gas in a 22.4 L flask has a density of 1.963 grams/L at 1.00 atm and 0.00 °C. Given the following gases, which could it be?

   A) Ne
   B) CO
   C) $CO_2$
   D) Kr

The diagram below represents a ratio of a mixture of gases at the molecule level in a small volume of gas in a sealed container. Oxygen molecules are represented by two joined open circles, helium atoms by grey spheres, and neon atoms by black spheres.

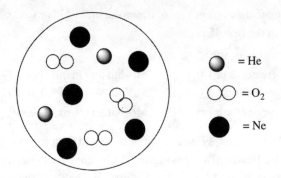

36. If the total pressure of the gases in the sealed container is 450.0 mm Hg, what is the partial pressure of neon?

A) 45.0 mm Hg
B) 90.0 mm Hg
C) 135 mm Hg
D) 225 mm Hg

37. What volume of HCl gas reacts completely with excess zinc metal to produce 2.46 L of $H_2$ gas at 2.00 atm and 400.0 K?

A) 1.23 L
B) 2.46 L
C) 4.92 L
D) 7.38 L

38. If 1.00 mole HBr and HF gases are allowed to effuse through a small hole under identical conditions of pressure and temperature how will the rate of effusion of HF gas compare to HBr gas?

A) twice as fast
B) twice as slow
C) four times as fast
D) four times as slow

39. Which covalent single bond is most polar?

| Element | H | C | N | O |
|---|---|---|---|---|
| Electronegativity | 2.1 | 2.5 | 3.0 | 3.5 |

A) N—H
B) O—H
C) O—C
D) O—N

40. Which of the following compounds is polar?

A) $BeCl_2$
B) $CBr_4$
C) $NF_3$
D) $AlCl_3$

41. Comparing the three bonds C—N, C=N, and C≡N, how does the C—N bond compare to the other two in terms of bond strength and bond length?

   A) strongest shortest

   B) strongest longest

   C) weakest shortest

   D) weakest longest

42. The total number of π bonds in the H—CH=CH—C≡C—C≡N molecule is

   A) 3

   B) 4

   C) 5

   D) 6

43. Which phrase best describes resonance forms of a molecule or ion?

   A) one always corresponds to the observed structure

   B) all the resonance structures are observed in various proportions

   C) the observed structure is an mean of the resonance forms

   D) the same atoms need not be bonded to each other in all resonance forms

44. Figure X represents an electron energy level diagram for the conduction bands and valence bands in a conductor such as copper. Which energy level diagrams represents the electron population when silicon is doped with gallium?

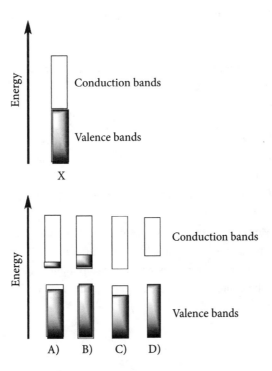

**Questions 45 and 46 use the following information.**

The graph below shows the measurements of carbon dioxide in the atmosphere at the top of a volcano in Hawaii over several years.

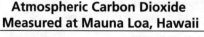

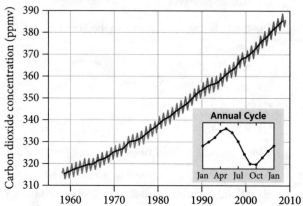

[http://commons.wikimedia.org/wiki/File:Mauna_Loa_Carbon_Dioxide-en.svg]

45. Which of the following best describes the basis for the observed **annual** cycle variation?

    A) The instrument measuring $CO_2$ varies as its temperature changes from summer to winter.

    B) The $CO_2$ transfer between the biosphere and the atmosphere is reversible-in the summer because more plants use it.

    C) More fossil fuel is being used in summer by people on vacation, so more $CO_2$ is produced.

    D) More fossil fuel is being used in winter by people heating homes, so more $CO_2$ is produced.

46. How would you most readily test the hypothesis that you made in question 45?

    A) Find out how much gasoline is used in Hawaii each month and compare to the graph.

    B) Do a survey of heating oil use in the winters in the USA, and compute $CO_2$ produced.

    C) Measure the temperature of the room in which the $CO_2$ measurement instrument is located and plot each month.

    D) Compare these results with a measurement made in the southern hemisphere and compare the annual variation curves.

47. Which particulate diagram below corresponds to the result of mixing aqueous calcium sulfide and aqueous sodium carbonate?

**Solubility Rules:**

| Insoluble compounds contain . . . | Except . . . |
| --- | --- |
| Sulfide ($S^{2-}$) ions | those with alkali metal ions, $Mg^{2+}$, $Ca^{2+}$, $Sr^{2+}$, $Ba^{2+}$ metal ions or $NH_4^+$ |
| Carbonate ($CO_3^{2-}$) ions | those with alkali metal ions or $NH_4^+$ |

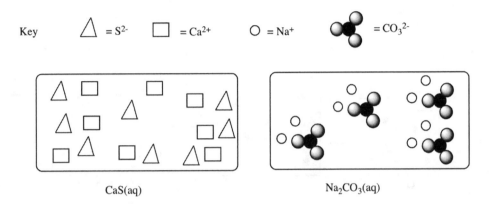

Key    △ = $S^{2-}$    □ = $Ca^{2+}$    ○ = $Na^+$    ⬤ = $CO_3^{2-}$

CaS(aq)                     Na$_2$CO$_3$(aq)

After mixing the two solutions

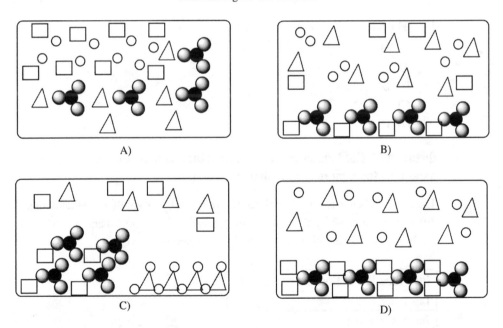

A)                     B)

C)                     D)

48. Which of the descriptions below correctly matches the structure type with its underlying explanation?

A) molecular covalent: interconnected three-dimensional bonds

B) network covalent: alternating lattice throughout solid

C) ionic: individual molecular units within solid

D) metal: delocalized electrons throughout solid

49. A small amount of table salt, NaCl(s), is stirred and completely dissolved in 50.0 mL water. What term best describes the resultant solution?

   A) homogeneous mixture
   B) heterogeneous mixture
   C) compound
   D) pure substance

Diagram (1) represents a 1.0 mL solution of particles at a given concentration. This solution is then diluted to 5.0 mL as represented in Diagram (2). 1.0 mL of this dilute solution was then transferred to each of other boxes.

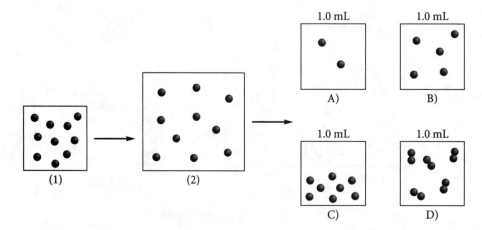

50. Which of the diagrams above represents a particle level representation of a 1.0 mL sample of the diluted solution?

   A) A
   B) B
   C) C
   D) D

## Question 51. Hard water contains more minerals than soft water. Soft water generates foam more readily than hard water.

The diagram below shows the results of five test tubes, initially each containing different water samples, that had 5 drops of soap solution added and then shaken for 30 seconds. In the diagram the shaded area represents foam.

| Test Tube Water Content | Tube |
|---|---|
| Tap water | 1 |
| Tap water + salt | 2 |
| Sea water | 3 |
| Tap water + sodium carbonate | 4 |
| Distilled water | 5 |

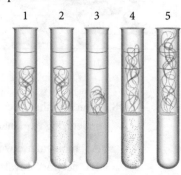

51. Which can be concluded from the results of this experiment?

    A) Sea water is softer than tap water.

    B) Sodium carbonate softens tap water.

    C) Salt softens tap water.

    D) Distilled water is harder than tap water.

## Question 52–54 pertain to the following situation.

When 75.0 mL of 0.100 M $Na_2CO_3(aq)$ and 25.0 mL of 0.200 M $AgNO_3(aq)$ solutions are mixed together in a calorimeter, a white precipitate forms. The initial temperature of both solutions is 25.0°C. The final temperature is 30.0°C. Assume the final volume is 100.0 mL, the density of the solution is 1.08 g/mL, the reaction occurs under constant pressure, and the specific heat of the resultant solution is 4.18 J/g°C.

**Solubility Rules:**

| Soluble Compounds contain . . . | except . . . |
|---|---|
| Alkali metals $(Li^+, Na^+, K^+, Rb^+, Cs^+)$ and $NH_4^+$ | – |
| Nitrate $(NO_3^-)$, acetate $(C_2H_3O_2^-)$ | – |
| Halides $(Cl^-, Br^-, I^-)$ ions | Halides of $Ag^+, Hg_2^{2+}, Pb^{2+}$ |
| Sulfate $(SO_4^{2-})$ ions | Sulfates of $Ag^+, Ca^{2+}, Sr^{2+}, Ba^{2+}, Pb^{2+}$ |
| **Insoluble compounds contain . . .** | **except . . .** |
| Carbonate $(CO_3^{2-})$, phosphate $(PO_4^{3-})$, sulfide $(S^{2-})$ ions | those with alkali metal ions or $NH_4^+$ |
| Hydroxide $(OH^-)$ ions | those with alkali metal ions or $NH_4^+$ or $Ba^{2+}$ |

52. Which of the following represents a complete and balanced equation for the reaction described above?

    $$\underline{\quad}Na_2CO_3(aq) + \underline{\quad}AgNO_3(aq) \longrightarrow \underline{\quad\quad} + \underline{\quad\quad}$$

    Be sure to select the correct phases, i.e., (s), (l), (g), (aq), given for the products

    A) $Na_2CO_3(aq) + AgNO_3(aq) \longrightarrow Ag_2CO_3(s) + NaNO_3(aq)$

    B) $2\,Na_2CO_3(aq) + 2\,AgNO_3(aq) \longrightarrow 2\,AgCO_3(s) + 2\,Na_2NO_3(aq)$

    C) $Na_2CO_3(aq) + 2\,AgNO_3(aq) \longrightarrow Ag_2CO_3(aq) + 2\,NaNO_3(s)$

    D) $Na_2CO_3(aq) + 2\,AgNO_3(aq) \longrightarrow Ag_2CO_3(s) + 2\,NaNO_3(aq)$

53. What is the net **ionic equation** for the reaction that occurs?

    A) $Na^+(aq) + CO_3^{2-}(aq) + Ag^+(aq) + NO_3^-(aq) \longrightarrow Ag^+(s) + CO_3^{2-}(s)$
    $+ Na^+(aq) + NO_3^-(aq)$

    B) $Na^+(aq) + CO_3^{2-}(aq) + 2Ag^+(aq) + 2NO_3^-(aq) \longrightarrow 2Ag^+(s) + CO_3^{2-}(s)$
    $+ 2Na^+(aq) + 2NO_3^-(aq)$

    C) $CO_3^{2-}(aq) + 2Ag^+(aq) \longrightarrow Ag_2CO_3(s)$

    D) $CO_3^{2-}(aq) + Ag^+(aq) \longrightarrow AgCO_3(s)$

54. Which of the following statements is the most appropriate to determine the indicated quantity? In the following equations, q represents heat, n, represents number of moles, c represents the specific heat, and $\Delta T$ represents the change in temperature.

A) For $\Delta H$, $\Delta H_{rxn} = q/n$ where $Na_2CO_3$ is the limiting reagent.

B) For $\Delta H_{rxn}$, $\Delta H_{rxn} = q/n$ where q is determined by $q_{lost} + q_{gain} = 0$.

C) For $q$, $q = mass \times c \times \Delta T$, the mass can be determined by calculating the mass of the water and ignoring the mass of $Na_2CO_3$ and the mass of $AgNO_3$.

D) For $q$, $q = mass \times c \times \Delta T$, the mass can be determined by calculating the mass of $Na_2CO_3$ and mass of $AgNO_3$ and ignoring the mass of the water.

55. Given 0.10 M solutions of the acids listed in the table below, which acid has the lowest pH?

| Acid | $K_a$ |
|---|---|
| $CH_3CHOOH$ | $1.8 \times 10^{-5}$ |
| HCOOH | $1.8 \times 10^{-4}$ |
| HClO | $3.0 \times 10^{-8}$ |
| HF | $6.8 \times 10^{-4}$ |

A) $CH_3CHOOH$
B) HCOOH
C) HClO
D) HF

## Question 56 pertains to the following information.

In an air bag, solid sodium azide, $NaN_3(s)$, decomposes to form sodium metal, $Na(s)$, and nitrogen gas, $N_2(g)$. The heat of reaction is $-57$ kJ/mol. A sensor that detects a crash sets off a small detonator to start the decomposition.

56. Which of the following best describes the reaction?

A) There is a large decrease in temperature so the bag gets cold.
B) There is a large increase in entropy in the reaction.
C) The reaction is non-spontaneous because it has to be started by a detonator.
D) The equilibrium constant value for this reaction must be close to 1.0.

## The answers to Questions 57–60 depend upon the following information.

In a student lab, three colorless solutions were added in turn to four white powders. The student observations were recorded in the following table:

| Powder | Dilute HCl | Pure Water | Dilute NH$_3$ |
|--------|-----------|------------|---------------|
| A | none | none | none |
| B | bubbles, powder dissolves | none | none |
| C | dissolves | dissolves | dissolves |
| D | forms very cloudy white mixture | dissolves | forms cloudy brown mixture |

Note: NONE means observed no change at all

Answer the following questions:

57. Powder A could be which of the following substances?

    A) sodium chloride

    B) calcium carbonate

    C) sugar

    D) barium sulfate

58. The reaction observed with powder B and dilute HCl could most likely be represented by which of the following equations?

    A) $CaCO_3 + 2HCl \longrightarrow Ca^{2+} + 2Cl^- + H_2O + CO_2$

    B) $NaCl + 2HCl \longrightarrow Na^+ + 3Cl^- + H_2$

    C) $2AgNO_3 + 4HCl \longrightarrow 2Ag^+ + 4Cl^- + 2O_2 + 2H_2O + N_2$

    D) $BaSO_4 + 2HCl \longrightarrow Ba^{2+} + 2Cl^- + H_2O + SO_3$

59. If two of the white powders are among the pairs listed below, which two are unable to be distinguished by the tests the student performed?

    A) sodium chloride, silver nitrate

    B) calcium carbonate, barium sulfate

    C) silver nitrate, barium sulfate

    D) sodium chloride, sugar

60. For the two powders that cannot be distinguished by the tests the student performed, which additional test could be done to help distinguish between the two powders?

    A) conductivity of aqueous solution

    B) boiling point of solution in dilute hydrochloric acid

    C) reaction when the two powders are mixed together in water

    D) spectrometry with visible light of aqueous solution

## CHEMISTRY PRACTICE TEST B

Section II    **7 Constructed-Response Questions**

(Time–90 minutes)

You May Use Your Calculator for Section II

**Directions:** Questions 1, 2, and 3 are long constructed-response questions that should take a student about 20 minutes each to answer. Questions 4, 5, and 6 are short constructed-response questions that should take a student about seven minutes each to answer. You must show all of your work, the steps involved in arriving at your answer, follow the rules for working with significant figures, and include units when appropriate to receive full credit. Your responses to these questions will be scored on the basis of the accuracy and relevance of the information displayed.

1.  $^{12}C$ and $^{13}C$ are the stable isotopes of carbon present in sufficient quantities to be readily detected. Hydrogen has three naturally occurring isotopes $^{1}H$ to $^{3}H$. $^{3}H$, known as tritium, is present in only trace amounts and is not easily detected. The following information about the mass and percent abundance of the naturally occurring stable isotopes of carbon and hydrogen are given in the table below.

| Isotope | Mass (amu) | % Abundance | Isotope | Mass (amu) | % Abundance |
|---------|-----------|-------------|---------|-----------|-------------|
| $^{12}C$ | 12.0000 | 98.83 | $^{1}H$ | 1.0078 | 99.99 |
| $^{13}C$ | 13.0034 | 1.070 | $^{2}H$ | 2.0141 | 0.0100 |

a) Calculate the atomic weight (in units of amu) of carbon.

b) Sketch a diagram for a mass spectrum of carbon.

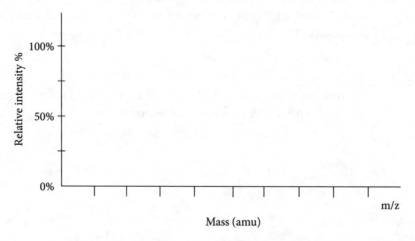

The chemical formula for acetylene (or ethyne –IUPAC nomenclature) is $C_2H_2$. The Lewis diagram for acetylene is

H — C ≡ C — H

c) How many **different stable isotopes** of the acetylene (ethyne) molecule $(C_2H_2)$ exist? How many **stable isotopes** of the acetylene (ethyne) molecule $(C_2H_2)$ have identical masses? Justify your answer and include either a diagram or a written explanation.

d) Which stable isotopes of acetylene are the **least abundant** and the **most abundant** in nature? Explain.

e) An abbreviated diagram of a mass spectrum for the isotopes of acetylene is given below. Most likely, which isotope of acetylene is the highest peak $(m/z = 26)$ due to?

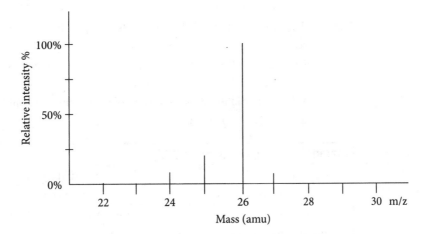

2. Two students performed an acid–base titration experiment in order to determine the concentration solution of NaOH($aq$) using oxalic acid as a primary standard. The students followed most of the proper procedures for doing a titration.

Each student went to a balance and obtained a known mass of solid oxalic acid. The students recorded their mass of oxalic acid in their notebooks, placed the oxalic acid in water and proceeded to titrate the sodium hydroxide solution. Both student placed their data on the board and did their calculations.

**Data–Titration of NaOH($aq$) with Oxalic Acid, $H_2C_2O_4$**

|  | Student A | Student B | Additional Trial (if needed) |
|---|---|---|---|
| Mass of solid oxalic acid | 0.982 g | 0.764 g | 0.853 g |
| Final buret reading NaOH($aq$) | 28.35 mL | 23.13 mL |  |
| Initial buret reading NaOH($aq$) | 0.35 mL | 1.34 mL |  |
| Volume of NaOH solution used in the titration | 28.00 mL | 21.79 mL |  |

Each student calculated the molarity of the sodium hydroxide solution as 0.779 M and decided they did not need to do a second trial since their results were the same. When they reported their molarity to the instructor, the instructor informed the students the data on the board was correct, but their molarity was wrong.

a) Write a balanced chemical equation for the reaction of oxalic acid with sodium hydroxide.

b) The students used 90.0 g/mol as the molar mass of oxalic acid. Use this value to determine how the students calculated the number of moles of oxalic acid present that were completely neutralized by the base.

c) Show how the students calculated their molarity of the sodium hydroxide.

d) The instructor reminded the students to carefully read the label on the reagent bottle of oxalic acid and to record the important Material Safety Data Sheet (MSDS) information for oxalic acid in their notebook. If the true value of the molarity of the sodium hydroxide solution is 0.557 M. What error did the students make? What two things should the students do to improve their experiment?

| Material Safety Data Sheet (MSDS) | |
|---|---|
| MSDS Name | Oxalic acid, dihydrate, reagent ACS |
| Catalog Numbers: | AC423150000, AC423150010 |
| Synonyms: | Ethanedioic acid dihydrate |
| For information in North America, call: | 800-XXXX-01 |
| For emergencies in the US call: | 800-YYYY-02 |

Section 2—Composition, Information on Ingredients

| CAS# | Chemical Name | Percent |
|---|---|---|
| 144-62-7 | Oxalic acid, anhydrous | 0.5 |
| 6153-56-6 | Oxalic acid dihydrate | 99.5 |

e) The instructor asked the students to do an additional titration using their 0.853 g sample of oxalic acid. What volume of sodium hydroxide should the students expect to use in the titration?

3. A student is given the task of determining the identity of four unknown 1.0 M solutions each made with a salt. The solutions are labeled W through Z. The salts in no particular order are

NaCl          NaHCOO          NaCH$_3$COO          NH$_4$Cl

The following table of acid and based dissociation constants is available.

| Formula | Acid or base dissociation constants at 25°C |
|---|---|
| CH$_3$COOH | $K_a = 1.8 \times 10^{-5}$ |
| HCOOH | $K_a = 1.8 \times 10^{-4}$ |
| HCl | $K_a = $ very large |
| NH$_3$ | $K_b = 1.8 \times 10^{-5}$ |

| Formula | Acid or base dissociation constants at 25°C |
|---------|---------------------------------------------|
| NaOH | $K_b$ = very large |
| $H_2O$ | $K_w = 1.008 \times 10^{-14}$ at 25°C     $K_w = 0.681 \times 10^{-14}$ at 20°C |

Upon entering the lab room, the student put on safety goggles, went to the lab bench, standardized the pH meter using a pH = 7 buffer, used a graduate cylinder to measure 30.0 mL samples of each unknown salt solution, and measured the pH of each salt solution. The student recorded the following information in a lab notebook.

| Unknown solution | Measured pH | Identity |
|------------------|-------------|----------|
| W | 5.96 | |
| X | 7.16 | |
| Y | 8.60 | |
| Z | 6.86 | |

a) Identify the salt used to make solutions W and Y and place your answer in the table above.

b) For solutions W and Y, write a balanced chemical equation showing what occurs when the salt interacts with water and establishes an equilibrium, and has a pH.

Salt W

Salt Y

c) For solutions W and Y, calculate the pH expected for the solution.

Solution W

Solution Y

d) Solutions X and Z, are hard to distinguish by pH alone, since the pH of both solution are close. Describe what additional tests can be done to help identify the salts used to make solutions X and Z. Explain.

e) Discuss one ways the student could have improved the procedure in order to obtain more accurate results.

f) Explain how each of the following could lead to an error in the measurement or the calculation of pH. Explain if the measurement or calculation would be higher, lower, or no change.

 i) The deionized water used to make all of the solutions was prepared one week prior to doing the experiment. The bottle was left on a shelf exposed to sunlight and the cap to the bottle of the deionized water was not used, exposing the water to carbon dioxide in the air.

 ii) The student uses the following chemical equation for the sodium acetate solution to determine the concentration of $H_3O^+$ ions in solution and uses this value to calculate pH.

$$CH_3COO^- (aq) + H_2O(l) \rightleftharpoons CH_2COO^{2-} (aq) + H_3O^+ (aq)$$

4. The average person sitting on an airplane exhales about 50.0 mL of gas each breath and exhales about 10 times a minute. Each breath contains about 2.00% carbon dioxide by volume. How many grams of $KO_2(s)$ are needed to remove $CO_2$ from the air in a small passenger jet with 6 people operating for one hour?

$$4KO_2(s) + 2CO_2(g) \longrightarrow 2\,K_2CO_3(s) + 3O_2(g)$$

5. When oxygen gains two electrons it forms the oxide ion, $O^{2-}$. When sulfur gains two electrons it forms the sulfide ion, $S^{2-}$. The electron affinity values for an atom of oxygen gas and an atom of sulfur gas are listed below.

| Group 16 |
| --- |
| O |
| −141 kJ/mol |
| S |
| −200 kJ/mol |

a) Write the equation representing the electron affinity process for an oxygen atom in the gas phase. Is this process exothermic or endothermic? Explain.

b) $\Delta H$ for the second electron affinity to go from $O^-$ to $O^{2-}$ is endothermic. Explain incorporating how Coulombic interactions and or electron configuration play a role in this process.

6. Nitrogen and oxygen can combine to form nitrogen dioxide, $NO_2$, the nitronium ion, $NO_2^+$, or the nitrite ion, $NO_2^-$.

For each of the following:

a) Draw a Lewis structure and include any resonance structures when appropriate.

b) Name the molecular geometry, and arrange in order of increasing bond angle the O—N—O bond angle about the central nitrogen atom for each species. Justify your choice of bond angle.

   i) $NO_2$

   ii) $NO_2^+$

   iii) $NO_2^-$

7. The change in entropy of vaporization, $\Delta S_{vap}$, of a compound can be calculated knowing the boiling point and the change in enthalpy of vaporization of that compound.

| Compound | Name | BP (°C) | $\Delta H_{vap}$ (kJ/mol) | $\Delta S_{vap}$ (J/mol K) |
|---|---|---|---|---|
| $C_4H_{10}O$ | Diethly ether | 34.6 | 26.5 | 86.1 |
| $C_2H_6O$ | Acetone | 56.1 | 29.1 | 88.4 |
| $C_6H_6$ | Benzene | 79.8 | 30.8 | 87.3 |
| $C_2H_5OH$ | Ethanol | 77.8 | 38.6 | ? |
| $H_2O$ | Water | 100.0 | 40.7 | ? |

a) Calculate the values of $\Delta S_{vap}$ for ethanol and water. Compare the calculated values for ethanol and water with the other compounds. Do ethanol and water have $\Delta S_{vap}$ values larger or smaller compared to the $\Delta S_{vap}$ values of the first three compounds?

b) Are the results of your calculation consistent with what you expect taking into account intermolecular forces and the energy involved in the vaporization process? Explain why or why not.

# CHEMISTRY PRACTICE TEST B

## Section I Answer Key

60 Multiple-Choice Questions (Time–90 minutes)

| Question | Key | — | Question | Key | — | Question | Key | |
|----------|-----|---|----------|-----|---|----------|-----|---|
| 1 | D | | 21 | C | | 41 | D | |
| 2 | C | | 22 | B | | 42 | C | |
| 3 | A | | 23 | D | | 43 | C | |
| 4 | A | | 24 | C | | 44 | C | |
| 5 | A | | 25 | B | | 45 | B | |
| 6 | B | | 26 | A | | 46 | D | |
| 7 | C | | 27 | D | | 47 | B | |
| 8 | C | | 28 | B | | 48 | D | |
| 9 | D | | 29 | B | | 49 | A | |
| 10 | A | | 30 | A | | 50 | A | |
| 11 | B | | 31 | B | | 51 | B | |
| 12 | B | | 32 | C | | 52 | D | |
| 13 | D | | 33 | B | | 53 | C | |
| 14 | C | | 34 | C | | 54 | B | |
| 15 | B | | 35 | C | | 55 | D | |
| 16 | C | | 36 | D | | 56 | B | |
| 17 | B | | 37 | C | | 57 | D | |
| 18 | B | | 38 | A | | 58 | A | |
| 19 | B | | 39 | B | | 59 | D | |
| 20 | D | | 40 | C | | 60 | A | |

# CHEMISTRY PRACTICE TEST B

## Answer Key Section II

7 Constructed-Response Questions (Time–90 minutes)

You May Use Your Calculator for Section II

**Directions:** Questions 1, 2, and 3 are long constructed response questions that should take a student about 20 minutes each to answer. Questions 4, 5, and 6 are short constructed-response questions that should take a student about seven minutes each to answer. You must show all of your work, the steps involved in arriving at your answer, follow the rules for working with significant figures, and include units when appropriate to receive full credit. Your responses to these questions will be scored on the basis of the accuracy and relevance of the information displayed.

1. Carbon has fifteen known isotopes, from $^{8}C$ to $^{15}C$. $^{12}C$ and $^{13}C$ are the only stable isotopes present in sufficient quantities to be readily detected. Hydrogen has three naturally occurring isotopes $^{1}H$ to $^{3}H$. $^{3}H$, known as tritium, is present in only trace amounts and is not easily detected. The following information about the mass and percent abundance of the naturally occurring stable isotopes of carbon and hydrogen are given in the table below.

| Isotope | Mass (amu) | % Abundance | Isotope | Mass (amu) | % Abundance |
|---------|------------|-------------|---------|------------|-------------|
| $^{12}C$ | 12.0000 | 98.83 | $^{1}H$ | 1.0078 | 99.99 |
| $^{13}C$ | 13.0034 | 1.070 | $^{2}H$ | 2.0141 | 0.0100 |

   a) Calculate the atomic weight (in units of amu) of carbon.

   12.00 amu (four significant figures)

   b) Sketch a diagram for a mass spectrum of carbon.

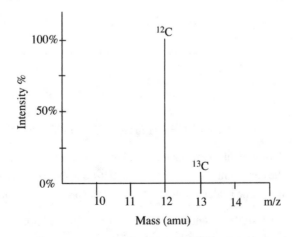

   The chemical formula for acetylene (or ethyne –IUPAC nomenclature) is $C_2H_2$. The Lewis diagram for acetylene is

   H—C≡C—H

c) How many **different stable isotopes** of the acetylene (ethyne) molecule ($C_2H_2$) exist? How many **stable isotopes** of the acetylene (ethyne) molecule ($C_2H_2$) have identical masses? Justify your answer and include either a diagram or a written explanation.

10 possible isotopes. For convenience the mass # are indicated leaving out element symbols.

| | | |
|---|---|---|
| 1-12-12-1   26 | 1-12-13-1   27 | 1-13-13-1   28 |
| 1-12-12-2   27 | 1-12-13-2   28 | 1-13-13-2   29 |
| 2-12-12-2   28 | 2-12-13-1   28 | 2-13-13-2   30 |
| | 2-12-13-2   29 | |

Four isotopes have a mass of 28, two have a mass of 27, two have a mass of 29.

d) Which stable isotopes of acetylene are the **least abundant** and the **most abundant** in nature? Explain.

$^1H$—$^{12}C$≡$^{12}C$—$^1H$ most abundant due to 98.8% carbon-12 and 99.9% hydrogen-1

$^2H$—$^{13}C$≡$^{13}C$—$^2H$ least abundant due to only 1% carbon-13 and 0.1% hydrogen-2

e) An abbreviated diagram of a mass spectrum for the isotopes of acetylene is given below. Most likely, which isotope of acetylene is the highest peak ($m/z = 26$) due to?

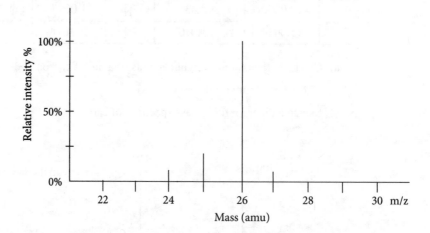

$^1H$—$^{12}C$≡$^{12}C$—$^1H$ mass = 26 and it is the most abundant

2. Two students performed an acid–base titration experiment in order to determine the concentration solution of NaOH($aq$) using oxalic acid as a primary standard. The students followed most of the proper procedures for doing a titration.

Each student went to a balance and obtained a known mass of solid oxalic acid. The students recorded their mass of oxalic acid in their notebooks, placed the oxalic acid in water, and proceeded to titrate the sodium hydroxide solution. Both student placed their data on the board and did their calculations.

**Data–Titration of NaOH(*aq*) with Oxalic Acid, $H_2C_2O_4$**

|  | Student A | Student B | Additional Trial (if needed) |
|---|---|---|---|
| Mass of solid oxalic acid | 0.982 g | 0.764 g | 0.853 g |
| Final buret reading NaOH(*aq*) | 28.35 mL | 23.13 mL | |
| Initial buret reading NaOH(*aq*) | 0.35 mL | 1.34 mL | |
| Volume of NaOH solution used in the titration | 28.00 mL | 21.79 mL | |

Each student calculated the molarity of the sodium hydroxide solution as 0.779 M and decided they did not need to do a second trial since their results were the same. When they reported their molarity to the instructor, the instructor informed the students the data on the board was correct, but their molarity was wrong.

a) Write a completed balanced molecular chemical equation for the reaction of oxalic acid with sodium hydroxide.

$$H_2C_2O_4 + 2NaOH \longrightarrow Na_2C_2O_4 + 2 H_2O$$

b) The students used 90.0 g/mol as the molar mass of oxalic acid. Use this value to determine how the students calculated the number of moles of oxalic acid present that were completely neutralized by the base.

Student A 0.982 g (1 mole / 90.0 g) = 0.0109 mole
Student B 0.764 g (1 mole / 90.0 g) = 0.00849 mole

c) Show how the students calculated their molarity of the sodium hydroxide.

Student A 0.0109 mole acid × (2 mole NaOH / 1 mole acid) = 0.0218 mol NaOH

M = 0.0218 mol NaOH/0.02800 L solution = 0.779 M

Student B 0.00850 mole acid × (2 mole NaOH / 1 mole acid) = 0.0170 mol NaOH

M = 0.0170 mol NaOH / 0.02179 L solution = 0.780 M

d) The instructor reminded the students to carefully read the label on the reagent bottle of oxalic acid and to record the important Material Safety Data Sheet (MSDS) information for oxalic acid in their notebook. If the true value of the molarity of the sodium hydroxide solution is 0.557 M, what error did the students make? What two things should the students do to improve their experiment?

| Material Safety Data Sheet (MSDS) | |
|---|---|
| MSDS Name | Oxalic acid, dihydrate, reagent ACS |
| Catalog Numbers: | AC423150000, AC423150010 |
| Synonyms: | Ethanedioic acid dihydrate |
| For information in North America, call: | 800-XXXX-01 |
| For emergencies in the US call: | 800-YYYY-02 |

Section 2—Composition, Information on Ingredients

| CAS# | Chemical Name | Percent |
|------|---------------|---------|
| 144-62-7 | Oxalic acid, anhydrous | 0.5 |
| 6153-56-6 | Oxalic acid dihydrate | 99.5 |

The students did not take into account the solid acid was a "dihydrate" and contained water. The students used an incorrect molar mass for the oxalic acid. To improve the experiment the students should use the correct molar mass and do three additional titrations.

e) The instructor asked the students to do an additional titration using their 0.853 g sample of oxalic acid. What volume of sodium hydroxide should the students expect to use in the titration?

23.40 mL

3. A student is given the task of determining the identity of four unknown 1.0 M solutions each made with a salt. The solutions are labeled W through Z. The salts in no particular order are

NaCl     NaHCOO     NaCH$_3$COO          NH$_4$Cl

The following solid salts and solutions are available.

pH = 4 buffer solution     pH = 7 buffer solution     pH = 9 buffer solution

1.0 M CH$_3$COOH$(aq)$     1.0 M HCOOH          1.0 M NH$_3$

1.0 M HCl                  1.0 M NaOH           KCH$_3$COO$(s)$

NH$_4$I$(s)$               KCl$(s)$             KHCOO$(s)$

The following table of acid and based dissociation constants is available.

| Formula | Acid or base dissociation constants at 25°C |
|---------|---------------------------------------------|
| CH$_3$COOH | $K_a = 1.8 \times 10^{-5}$ |
| HCOOH | $K_a = 1.8 \times 10^{-4}$ |
| HCl | $K_a = $ very large |
| NH$_3$ | $K_b = 1.8 \times 10^{-5}$ |
| NaOH | $K_b = $ very large |
| H$_2$O | $K_w = 1.008 \times 10^{-14}$ at 25°C   $K_w = 0.681 \times 10^{-14}$ at 20°C |

Upon entering the lab room, the student put on safety goggles, went to the lab bench, standardized the pH meter using a pH = 7 buffer, used a graduate cylinder to measure 30.0 mL samples of each unknown salt solution, and measured the pH of each salt solution. The student recorded the following information in a lab notebook.

| Unknown solution | Measured pH | Identity |
|------------------|-------------|----------|
| W | 5.96 | NH$_4$Cl |
| X | 7.16 | NaCl |
| Y | 8.60 | CH$_3$COONa |
| Z | 6.86 | HCOONa |

a) Identify the salt used to make solutions W and Y and place your answer in the table above.

W is acidic, which corresponds to $NH_4Cl$ $(aq)$

Y is basic which corresponds to $CH_3COONa$ $(aq)$ (see equations below)

b) For solutions W and Y, write a balanced chemical equation showing what occurs when the salt interacts with water, establishes equilibrium, and has a pH.

Salt W $NH_4^+$ $(aq) + H_2O(l)$ $\rightleftharpoons$ $NH_3(aq) + H_3O^+(aq)$

Salt Y $CH_3COO^-(aq) + H_2O(l)$ $\rightleftharpoons$ $CH_3COOH(aq) + OH^-(aq)$

c) For solutions W and Y, calculate the pH expected for the solution. Please tell the students if you are using the 1.0 M cited at the top of the page, or the 0.1 M listed in the materials.

Solution W pH $= 4.63$

Solution Y pH $= 9.37$

d) Solutions X and Z, are hard to distinguish by pH alone. Describe what additional tests can be done to help identify the salts used to make solutions X and Z. Explain.

To 20 drops of each solution add 10 drops of 1.0 M HCOOH. The resultant solution with the HCOONa will produce a buffer and the pH will not change when some HCl is added to it. The NaCl solution with 1.0 M HCOOH will not form a buffer and the pH will change when HCl is added to this solution.

e) Discuss one ways the student could have improved the procedure in order to obtain more accurate results.

Test the solutions with a second calibrated pH meter, this time using a pH = 5 buffer for acidic solutions and a pH = 9 buffer for alkaline solutions.

Boil the deionized water used to make the solutions to expel carbon dioxide. Carbon dioxide dissolved in water will lower the pH.

f) Explain how each of the following could lead to an error in the measurement or the calculation of pH. Explain if the measurement or calculation would be higher, lower, or no change.

i) The deionized water used to make all of the solutions was prepared one week prior to doing the experiment. The bottle was left on a shelf exposed to sunlight and the cap to the bottle of the deionized water was not used, exposing the water to carbon dioxide in the air.

The deionized water will have a lower pH than expected due to dissolved carbon dioxide reacting with a bit of the water to give carbonic acid. If the solution is warmer than 25°C, all of the pH measurements will be higher compared to the calculated pH because the $K_w$ is more than $1.0 \times 10^{-14}$ at temperatures higher than 25°C.

ii) The student uses the following chemical equation for the sodium acetate solution to determine the concentration of $H_3O^+$ ions in solution and uses this value to calculate pH.

$$CH_3COO^-(aq) + H_2O(l) \rightleftharpoons CH_2COO^{2-}(aq) + H_3O^+(aq)$$

The student will calculate an acidic pH when the solution is alkaline.

4. The average person sitting on an airplane exhales about 50.0 mL of gas each breath and exhales about 10 times a minute. Each breath contains about 2.00% carbon dioxide by volume. How many grams of $KO_2(s)$ are needed to remove $CO_2$ from the air in a small passenger jet with 6 people operating for one hour?

$$4KO_2(s) + 2CO_2(g) \longrightarrow 2K_2CO_3(s) + 3O_2(g)$$

22.9 g/hr

5. When oxygen gains two electrons it forms the oxide ion, $O^{2-}$. When sulfur gains two electrons it forms the sulfide ion, $S^{2-}$. The electron affinity values for an atom of oxygen gas and an atom of sulfur gas are listed below.

| Group 16 |
| --- |
| O |
| −141 kJ/mol |
| S |
| −200 kJ/mol |

a) Write the equation representing the electron affinity process for an oxygen atom in the gas phase. Is this process exothermic or endothermic? Explain.

$O + e^- \longrightarrow O^-$ $EA = -141$ kJ/mol. The EA process is exothermic since it involves adding an electron.

b) $\Delta H$ for the second electron affinity to go from $O^-$ to $O^{2-}$ is endothermic. Explain incorporating how Coulombic interaction and/or electron configuration play a role in this process.

Since the ratio of electrons to protons is already greater than one (9:8) in an $O^-$ anion, adding another electron requires an input of energy to overcome the electron-electron repulsion forces.

6. Nitrogen and oxygen can combine to form nitrogen dioxide, $NO_2$, the nitronium ion $NO_2^+$ or the nitrite ion $NO_2^-$.

For each of the following:

a) Draw a Lewis structure and include any resonance structures when appropriate.

b) Name the molecular geometry, and arrange in order of increasing O—N—O bond angle about the central nitrogen atom for each species. Justify your choice of bond angle.

i)   $NO_2$

ii)  $NO_2^+$

iii) $NO_2^-$

$NO_2^-$

$115°$

$NO_2$

$134°$

$NO_2^+$

$180°$

$NO_2^+$ has two regions of electron density around the central atom. It is an $AX_2E_0$ system. The bond angle is $180°$. Adding one electron to achieve the $NO_2$ molecule adds one electron to the nitrogen atom. There are three regions of electron density around the nitrogen atom, however, the one electron is not strong enough to repel the electron in the bond so the bond angle is about $134°$. Adding another electron to achieve the $NO_2^-$ ion, creates three full regions of electron density around the nitrogen atom. The nitrite ion has a bond angle of $115°$. Note, students can arrange the structures in order of increasing bond angle or students can estimate the bond angles: for $NO_2$ they might say "less than 180, but more than 120" or for nitrite "less than 120, but more than 90."

7. The change in entropy of vaporization, $\Delta S_{vap}$, of a compound is the increase in entropy upon vaporization of a liquid. The value of $\Delta S_{vap}$ of a compound can be calculated from the boiling point and the change in enthalpy of vaporization of the compound.

| Compound | Name | BP (°C) | $\Delta H_{vap}$ (kJ/mol) | $\Delta S_{vap}$ (J/mol K) |
|---|---|---|---|---|
| $C_4H_{10}O$ | Diethly ether | 34.6 | 26.5 | 86.1 |
| $C_2H_6O$ | Acetone | 56.1 | 29.1 | 88.4 |
| $C_6H_6$ | Benzene | 79.8 | 30.8 | 87.3 |
| $C_2H_5OH$ | Ethanol | 77.8 | 38.6 | 110 |
| $H_2O$ | Water | 100.0 | 40.7 | 109 |

a) Calculate the values of $\Delta S_{vap}$ for ethanol and water. Compare the calculated values for ethanol and water with the other compounds. Do ethanol and water have $\Delta S_{vap}$ values larger or smaller compared to the $\Delta S_{vap}$ values of the first three compounds?

$\Delta S_{vap}$ for ethanol $= 110\,J/mol\,K$      $\Delta S_{vap}$ for water $= 110\,J/mol\,K$

Ethanol and water have $\Delta S_{vap}$ larger compared to the other compounds listed on the Table.

b) Are the results of your calculation consistent with what you expect taking into account intermolecular forces and the energy involved in the vaporization process? Explain why or why not.

The $\Delta S_{vap}$ of ethanol and water are larger compared to the other compounds because hydrogen bonding in the liquid phase decreases the entropy in the liquid. Strong hydrogen bonding causes the molecules to "stick" together, therefore, there is less movement of molecules. When the molecules in the liquid have enough energy to escape as a gas, the gas particles are far enough away where hydrogen bonding does not occur as frequently. Furthermore, the gas particles are moving much faster, therefore there is a good deal more entropy. Thus the change in entropy from the liquid phase to the gas phase is large. The results are consistent with the calculations.